Instructor's Manual
to accompany

CONCEPTUAL
Physics
SEVENTH EDITION

City College of San Francisco

HarperCollinsCollegePublishers

Acknowledgments

I dedicate this manual to the memory of Ronald E. Lindemann, one of the most wonderful human beings I have known. Brilliant Ron was a resource to many people. I was favored to be one of them, for ideas he contributed to earlier editions are sprinkled all through *Conceptual Physics*. He died in 1990 of heart failure in his sleep at the young age of 37.

For many ideas new to this 7th edition of this manual, I am especially thankful to my friends Charlie Spiegel and Marshall Ellenstein. Thanks also go to Kenneth Genezer and Graham Robertson, Calilfornia State Univeristy and California Academy of Mathematics and Science, both at Dominguez Hills.

For several new ideas to embellish lecture topics I credit newspaper columnist Cecil Adams and his delightful book, *The Straight Dope*, published by the Chicago Review Press. For ideas from the previous edition, carried over to this edition, I am grateful to William J. Beaty, Peter Crooker, Charlie Hibbard, John Hubisz, Dack Lee, Chelcie Liu, Chester Vause, and many others.

For assistance in putting this all together I am grateful to Meidor Hu.

Instructor's Manual to accompany **CONCEPTUAL PHYSICS**, *Seventh Edition*

Copyright © 1993 by Paul G. Hewitt

ISBN 0-673-54146-0

95 5 4 3 2

Contents

CONCEPTUAL Physics

The purpose of this manual is to help you combat the all-too-common notion that a course in physics is a punishing chore, and to dispel the idea that a course in physics has to be a course in applied mathematics. Your students will see that the many equations of physics are something other than recipes for plugging in numerical data — they will see that equations are guides to thinking, that tell which ideas in their environment relate to which, and in what way. Encountering conceptual physics should be a delightful surprise for your students. They should leave your course with a more positive attitude of what our cherished discipline is about.

Introduction

People feel good about themselves when they exceed self expectations. School is sometimes a place where we fall below expectations — not only self expectations, but the expectations of teachers, family, and the overall community. Physics courses have been notorious in this regard.

Too often, physics has the reputation of being the "killer course" — the course that diminishes average-ability students, who may drop or take an incomplete, and spread the word about how tough it is. Or they hear about it and simply avoid it in the first place. But we physics teachers have a secret: We know that the concepts of physics for the most part are much more comprehensible than the public expects. And when that secret is shared with students in a nonintimitating way that prompts them to discover they are learning more than they thought they could, they feel wonderful — about us, about physics, but more important, about *themselves*. Because they are not bogged down with time-consuming mathematical exercises of "the most threatening kind — word problems," they instead get a deeper and wider overview of physics that can be their most enlightening and positive school experience.

This manual describes a way to teach physics conceptually. It helps tie physics to the student's personal experience in the everyday world, so your students learn to see physics not as a classroom or laboratory activity, but as a part of everyday living. People with a conceptual understanding of physics are more alive to the world, just as a botanist taking a stroll through a wooded park is more alive than most of us to the trees, plants, flora, and the life that teems in them. The richness of life is not only seeing the world with wide open eyes, but knowing what to look for. This puts you in a very nice role — being one who points out the relationships of things in the world about us. You are in a good position to add meaning to your student's lives.

The appeal of the conceptual approach for nonscience students is obvious. Because conceptual physics has no "mathematical road blocks" and little or no prerequisites, it is a rare chance for the nonscience student to learn solid science in a hard-core science course. I say rare chance, because nonscience students do not have the opportunity to study science as science students have to study the humanities. Any student, science or humanities, can take an intermediate course in literature, poetry, or history at any time and in any order. But in no way can a humanities student take an intermediate physics or chemistry course without first having a foundation in elementary physics and mathematics. Science has a *vertical structure* , as noted by the prerequisites. So we see that it is much easier for a science student to become well rounded in the humanities than for a humanities student to become well rounded in science. Hence the importance of this conceptual course.

2

The rest of my remarks here concern science majors. I maintain that science students who use this book in their first physics course are even greater benefactors than nonscience students. Not because it is an "easy" introduction or even because it gets them excited about physics, but because it *nurtures that gut-level conceptual understanding that is the missing essential in so many science and engineering students* — who like their would-be poet counterparts, have mistaken being able to recite poetry for understanding it.

I feel strongly that the ideas of physics should be understood conceptually before they are used as a base for applied mathematics. We are all acquainted with students who can crank out the answers to many problems by virtue of little-understood formulas and a knack for algebraic manipulation — students who even in graduate school are able to do well in written exams (which are most always exercises in problem solving), but who do poorly in oral exams (which are most always conceptual). Is this a surprising outcome for students who have never had a good exposure to the concepts and ideas of physics that weren't at the same time paired with the techniques of mathematical problem solving? To many of these people, physics *is* applied mathematics — so much so, that a physics course without mathematical problem solving seems a contradiction! Conceptual understanding in every physics course they ever encountered took a back seat to problem-solving techniques. The name of the game in every physics course has been PROBLEM SOLVING. Students are solving problems involving the manipulation of twigs and branches when they lack a conceptual understanding of the trunk and base of the tree from which the branches stem.

We all know that the beauty of physics is its elegant mathematical structure. If you want to teach mathematics to your students, a physics course is the way to go. This is because the mathematics is applied to actual things. But if you want to teach *physics* to your students, put the niceties of mathematical problem solving in the back seat for a semester and teach physics conceptually. You'll provide your students, especially your mathematical whizzes, a look at physics they may otherwise miss. First understanding the concepts on a conceptual level is an essential foundation for a serious further study of physics. Provide your students with a good look at the overall forest before they make measurements of any single tree — place comprehension comfortably before calculation.

My recommendation is to offer Conceptual Physics to science majors during their first semester of school, before they take the calculus-based introductory course. The outcome is predictable: greater enrollments in other physics courses and a greater proportion of physics majors. I further recommend that the same course be offered to nonscience majors, with no distinction made between those who call themselves science majors and those who call themselves nonscience majors. This mixture will help you to stay on a conceptual track in your lectures, and help your students dispel the myth that science and nonscience students are fundamentally different people.

The challenge is yours. Let's get to work!

On Class Lectures

Many students are confused if the lecture seems remote from the chapter being studied, and bored if the lecture is a verbatim presentation of it. A successful lecturer avoids both of these extremes, holding to the assigned chapter, but providing additional examples and explanations — depending on the reaction of students — emphasizing concepts that were missed in reading. You may find that your students are an excellent source of new analogies and examples to supplement those in the text. A productive class assignment is:

> Choose one (or more) of the concepts presented in the reading assignment and cite any illustrative analogies or examples that *you* can think of.

This exercise not only prompts your students to relate physics to their own experiences, but adds to your future teaching material.

Equations are important in a conceptual course — not as a recipe for plugging in numerical values, but as a guide to thinking. The equation tells the student what variables to consider in treating an idea. How much an object accelerates, for example, depends not only on the net force, but on mass as well. The formula $a = F/m$ reminds one to consider both quantities. Does gravitation depend on an object's speed? Consideration of $F \sim mM/d^2$ shows that it doesn't, and so forth. The problem sets at the ends of many chapters involve computations that help to illustrate concepts rather than challenge your students' mathematical abilities. Their numbers are few to avoid overload.

A note of caution: Please, please, do not overwhelm your students with excessive written homework! (Remember those courses you took as a student where you were so busy with the chapter-end material that you didn't get into the chapter material itself?) The exercises are numerous only to provide you a wide selection to consider. Depending on your style of teaching, you may find that posing and answering exercises in class is an effective way to develop physics concepts. A successful course may place either very much or very little emphasis on the exercises.

In lecture I think that before moving on to new material it is important to provide the student with a self check after important ideas and concepts are presented. I do this by posing the following, after presenting an idea and supporting it with examples: "If you understand this — if you really do — then you can answer the following question." Then I pose the question slowly and clearly, usually in multiple-choice form or such that a short answer is called for, and ask the class to make a response — usually written. Then I ask them to look at their neighbors' papers, and depending on the importance of the question, I ask them to briefly discuss it with their neighbors (at the beginning of the course I add that if their neighbors aren't helpful, to sit somewhere else next time). Several of this type questions in a lecture brings the students into an active role, no matter how large the lecture section. It also clears misconceptions before they are carried along into new material. I call such questions, CHECK QUESTIONS, in the suggested lectures on the following pages of this manual. The check-question procedure may also be used to *introduce* ideas. A discussion of the question, the answer, and some of the misconceptions associated with it, will get more attention than the same idea presented as a statement of fact. And one of the neat features of asking for neighbor participation is that it gives you pause to reflect on your delivery.

I strongly recommend lecture notes. Ater teaching conceptual physics for more than 20 years I still bring a note to every lecture. They're quite abbreviated, much more than my earlier ones, as the sample on the right shows. This is the first of three lectures on Chapter 4, the suggested lecture on pages 34 - 41. It is simply a check list that I glance at when students are going through a check-your-neighbor routine. Such notes insure I don't forget main points, and a mark or two will let me know next time what I missed or where I stopped.

Getting students to come to class prepared is a perennial problem. A simple idea for combatting this is the practice of Suk R. Hwang of the University of Hawaii at Hilo, who has been teaching Conceptual Physics for several years. To get students to read the assigned material before coming to class, he first did as most of us do: "preach" about the value of coming to class prepared. During the last two years he has gone an important step further, with what he reports are significantly greater results. He simply rewards the reading behavior he wants. He does this by beginning each class by handing out a sheet of paper with one or two questions that highlight the chapter to be treated. Before lecturing on gravity, for example, the students will take one or two minutes to respond to "State Newton's law of gravity in both words and equation form." Suk collects the sheets and then begins his lecture. The whole process takes less than five minutes. He assigns a grade to the sheets, with brief comments, and returns them. But the grades do not count at all to the final course grade. He is out front with his class when he tells them that the only purpose of the practice is to increase the probability of coming to class having first read the assigned reading material. Suk claims that because students abhor returning blank sheets, or dislike not being able to correctly answer the simple questions, they DO the reading assignment. Evidently a well-answered paper, even though it doesn't count to the final grade, is sufficient reward for the student. Since hearing of Suk's success, I now do the same — but intermittently because of my large classes. It works! Suk's practice is in keeping with what we all know: the best ideas are often the simplest.

Sample NEXT-TIME QUESTIONS pages are shown on the facing page. These can be photocopied and used on display boards to capture attention and create discussion. They can also be made into OHP transparencies to be used as a brain teaser for homework and for class discussion. So conclude your lessons with them in class as ties to the next class meeting, or post them in the hallway for all to ponder. Many first appeared as *Figuring Physics* in *The Physics Teacher*, the magazine of the American Association of Physics Teachers (AAPT).

The student book PRACTICING PHYSICS can serve as a tutor on the side. At CCSF it is carried in the student book store as "recommended but not required" and used by about one-third of my students. I post answered pages in the glass case at appropriate times. A sample is shown on page 7.

The Conceptual Physics package of text and ancillaries lend themselves to teaching by way of the 3-stage LEARNING CYCLE, developed by Robert Karplus.

EXPLORATION— giving all students a commn set of experiences that provide opportunities for student discussion. Activities are mainly in the *Laboratory Manual*.
CONCEPT DEVELOPMENT — lectures, textbook reading, doing worksheets from *Practicing Physics*, and class discussions.
APPLICATION — doing end-of-chapter Exercises and Problems, Next-Time Questions, and experiments from the *Laboratory Manual*.

5

Use of the learning cycle does not do away with presentation of information by the instructor, but simply delays such presentation until the students have, experienced the phenomena. Before hearing a lecture on Archimedes' Principle, for example, students first get their hands wet by dunking objects in containers of water to experience displacement, buoyancy, floating and sinking. When the lecture follows recent first-hand experience, there are more hooks for catching information. Well-designed learning-cycle activities should take no longer than more traditional approaches. The difference comes in using laboratory activities before classroom activities rather than after.

Many of the suggested lectures in this manual will require more than one class period, depending on your pace of instruction and what you choose to add or omit. The lectures of each instructor, of course, must be developed to fit his or her style of teaching. My suggested lectures may or may not be useful to you. If you're new to teaching conceptual physics and your lecture tendency is to lean on chalk-board derivations, you may find them quite useful, and a means of jumping off and developing your own non-computational way of teaching.

Videotapes of my classroom lectures are described on page 6.

Please bring to my attention any errors you find in this manual, in the test bank, or in the text. I welcome correspondence suggesting improvements in the presentation of physics, and I answer mail [One San Antonio Place, Apt 2D, San Francisco, 94133]. Good luck in your course!

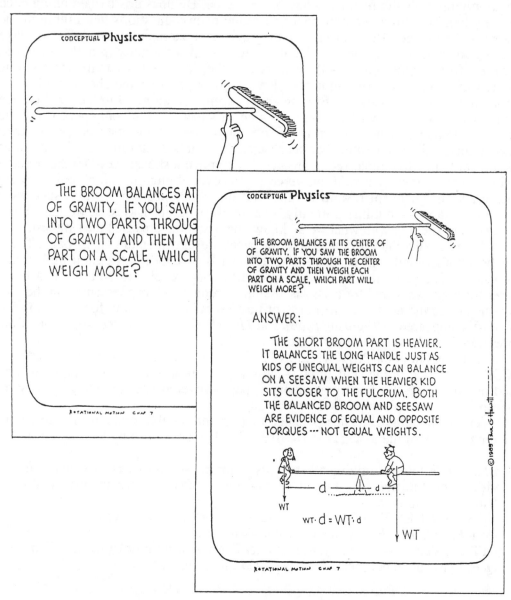

NEW ANCILLARY PACKAGE FOR THE 7th EDITION

In addition to this Instructor's Manual, there are the NEXT-TIME QUESTIONS book, printed TEST BANK, and TESTMASTER test-generating software for IBM-PC or Macintosh computers. All these items make up the Hewitt Easy Lecture Program (HELP). A notebook to hold the printed items is available to adopters of the text. Also available to adopters are 100 transparencies of selected figures from the text that will be useful to those who use an overhead projector in their presentations. Ancillaries available for student purchase include the new LABORATORY MANUAL by Paul Robinson and the worksheet booklet, PRACTICING PHYSICS. To obtain any of these ancillaries, contact your HarperCollins representative or reginal sales office.

NEXT-TIME QUESTIONS: These are now in book form, on 8-1/2 x 11 standard pages. If you use an overhead projector, you can make transparencies from them to display at the end of your lectures. Or you can simply post them as is for your students as homework, or as food for thought. Each question has a cartoon and is hand lettered. On the back side of each question is an answer sheet, with the question reduced and repeated. Display each at the appropriate time. There are next-time-questions for every chapter.

TESTMASTER AND THE TEST BANK: The Test Bank for the 7th edition has been upgraded with more than 1600 revised multiple-choice questions. They are rated by three levels of difficulty as well as by emphasis on mathematical or conceptual understanding. The Test Bank now includes the illustrated double-multiple choice questions that were provided in the Instructor's Manual for earlier editions. New to this edition is the TestMaster software for creating tests. The TestMaster program available for either IBM-PC or Macintosh, provides options to scramble questions, print different versions of a test, edit questions and answers, or add to and modify existing question files. It contains all of the items provided in the printed Test Bank. This unique program is extremely simple to use, even for people inexperienced with computers. Documentation for the test-generating software and a description of how it works is contained in an accompanying booklet.

VIDEOTAPES: A number of VHS videotapes relevant to Conceptual Physics have been produced over the past several years. Tapes from my classroom lectures at CCSF in the spring of 1984 include the 60-minute *Teaching Conceptual Physics*, which documents how I teach physics conceptually, and the 55-minute *Lecture Demonstrations in Conceptual Physics,* which is more classroom footage with emphasis on demonstrations (most of which are in the "Suggested Lectures" in this manual). Another tape is a 45-minute general-interest opening lecture, *The Fusion Torch and Ripe Tomatoes.* Still another tape is *Relativistic Time Dilation*, a 15-minute animated film made by Steve Smith and myself back in 1976. Also while in Hawaii, I prepared Physics for Phun for Hawaiin Public Television, a 30-minute videotape of 29 short physics demonstrations, featuring topics in mechanics, fluids, heat, and light.

A more recent video lecture series of 34 tapes *Conceptual Physics Alive!* features my classroom lectures while teaching Conceptual Physics at the University of Hawaii in 1989-1990. Contact your HarperCollins sales representative for information on obtaining videotapes.

LABORATORY MANUAL: New to this edition is a laboratory and activities manual, written by Paul Robinson. It is rich with simple activities to precede the coverage of course material, as well as experiments that are a follow through to course material. An instructor's manual for the laboratory manual is also available.

PRACTICING PHYSICS: This booklet of 33 worksheets to help students develop concepts is very different from traditional workbooks that are seen as drugery by students. A reduced sample worksheet is shown here. These are insightful and interesting activities that prompt your students to engage their minds and DO physics. They play the role of a tutor when you post worksheet solutions at appropriate times (like the posting of Next-Time Questions). Work-sheet solutions are included in the back of this Instructor's Manual. The booklets are low priced so they can be offered as a suggested supplement to the text in your student bookstore.

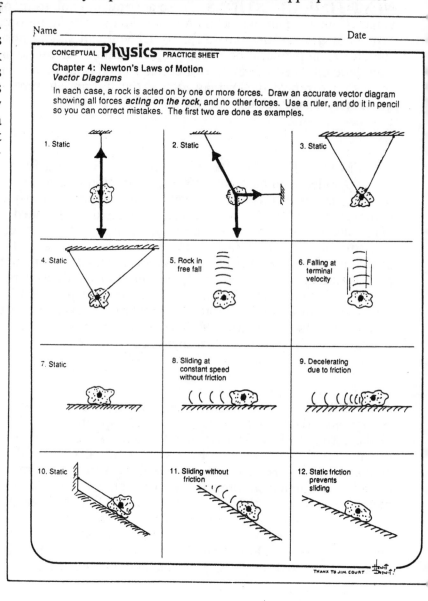

Flexibility of Material for Various Course Designs

Very few one-semester and virtually no one-quarter courses will include all the material presented in the text. The wide variety of chapters provides a selection of course topics to suit the tastes of individual instructors. Most begin their course with mechanics, and treat other topics in the order presented in the text. Some will go immediately from mechanics to relativity. Others will begin with the atom and properties of matter before treating mechanics, while others will begin with sound, then go to light, and then to electricity and magnetism. Others who wish to emphasize modern physics will skim through Chapters 10, 18, 29 and 30, to then get into Parts 7 and 8. Some will cover many chapters thereby giving students the widest possible exposure of physics, while others will set the plow deeper and treat fewer chapters.

The following breakdown of parts and chapters is intended to assist you in selecting a chapter sequence and course design most suited to your objectives and teaching style. You should find that the chapters of this edition are better suited to stand on their own.

PART 1: MECHANICS Central to any treatment of mechanics is Chapter 4 (*Newton's Laws of Motion*). At least a brief overview of Chapter 2 (*Linear Motion*) is prerequisite to Chapter 4. And with a brief overview of Chapters 2 and 4, any of the other chapters in Part I can stand on their own. Only Chapters 2, 4, and 8 have a historical flavor. You may wish to begin with Chapter 2 and go immediately to Chapter 4. If a short mechanics treatment is to emphasize satellite motion you may precede Chapter 9 (*Satellite Motion*) with Chapter 3 (*Nonlinear Motion*). Note in the text order that projectile motion follows linear motion, and momentum conservation follows Newton's 3rd law. I recommend that all the chapters of Part I be treated in the order presented. To amplify the treatment of vectors in Chapter 3, consider Appendix III. Consider concluding your treatment of mechanics with Appendix IV, *Exponential Growth and Doubling Time*. (Or it can follow Chapter 17, *Thermodynamics*, Part 3.)

PART 2: PROPERTIES OF MATTER The very briefest treatment of matter should be of Chapter 10, which is background for nearly all the chapters to follow in the text. Chapters 11, 12 and 13 are not prerequisites to chapters that follow. Part 2, with the exception of the brief treatment of kinetic and potential energies in the Bernoulli's principle section of Chapter 13 may be taught before, or without, Part 1. With the exception noted, Part 1 is not prerequisite to Part 2.

PART 3: HEAT Except for the idea of kinetic energy, potential energy, and energy conservation from Part 1, the material in these chapters is not prerequisite to the chapters that follow, nor are Parts 1 and 2 prerequisites to Part 3.

PART 4: SOUND Material from these chapters (forced vibrations, resonance, transverse and standing waves, interference) serves as a useful background for Chapters 25, 28 and 30. Parts 1 - 3 are not prerequisites to Part 4.

PART 5: ELECTRICITY AND MAGNETISM Part 1 is prerequisite to Part 5. Also helpful are Chapters 10, 14, and 18. The chapters of Part 5 build from electrostatics and magnetism to electromagnetic induction— which serve as a background for the nature of light.

PART 6: LIGHT Parts 4 and 5 provide useful background to Part 6. If you haven't covered Part 4, then be sure to discuss simple waves and demonstrate resonance. If you haven't covered Part 5, then be sure to discuss and demonstrate electromagnetic induction if you plan to treat the nature of light. The very briefest treatment of light can cover Chapters 25 - 27. A very brief treatment of lenses is in Chapter 27. A modern treatment of light should include Chapters 29 and 30.

PART 7: ATOMIC AND NUCLEAR PHYSICS Chapter 10 provides a good background for Part 7. Chapter 32 is prerequisite to Chapter 33. Otherwise, Part 7 can stand on its own.

PART 8: RELATIVITY This part can stand on its own and will nicely follow immediately from Part 1, if the ideas of the Doppler effect and wave frequency are treated in lecture. A thorough treatment of only Parts 1 and 8 should make a good quarter-length course.

IN YOUR TEACHING, BETTER TO BE A GUIDE ON THE SIDE THAN A SAGE ON THE STAGE !

CHALKBOARD ILLUSTRATION TECHNIQUES

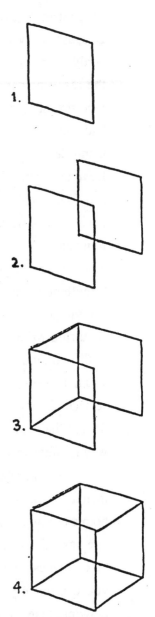

1.

2.

3.

4.

I vividly remember as a student how annoyed I was with a professor who couldn't draw a simple cube in his lectures. He'd make an attempt, step back and look at it, wipe part of it from the board and patch it here and there with no improvement whatever, continue wiping and patching and finally settle for a "cube" with non-parallel sides. I thought, "He's forever overloading us with homework assignments that take up entire weekends and he won't take a few minutes of his own time to learn how to draw a simple cube." The professor probably never did learn to draw a cube and may still be bumbling at the board at cube-drawing time. If he were as inept in some physics topic during lecture he'd feel quite compelled to clean up his act in short order. But not so with "art." I think many instructors feel they are "scientists, not artists," and therefore have no responsibility to improve the "art" that is part of their lectures, or is avoided in their lectures. Unfortunately, they likely overestimate the effort required to draw well, and underestimate the value of drawing well. Only a small amount of practice is all that is required.

A step-by-step method for drawing a cube is shown at the right. The important thing is keeping the vertical lines vertical, and the other two sets of lines parallel to one another. Simply draw a "square" tilted for perspective, draw its twin slightly displaced, then connect the two with four parallel lines. For a finishing touch, wipe away part of the lines to indicate which lines are behind.

When my friend and colleague Dave Wall joined the physics faculty at CCSF about 15 years ago, he sat in on my conceptual physics class and was most impressed with my chalkboard illustrations — not that they well especially well drawn, but that they were drawn quickly. (Before getting into physics, I was a professional signpainter and silkscreen printer, and an amateur cartoonist, so I brought a talent for chalkboard illustrations with me into the teaching profession.) Dave told me that he wished he had a talent for drawing that he could bring to his lectures. He wanted very much to be a good classroom lecturer, for

WIPE AWAY BACKGROUND
LINES WITH FINGER !

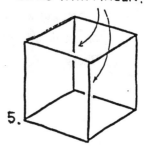

5.

he knew that instructors who are good in class have altogether more satisfying careers than instructors who somehow don't connect with their classes. He was more than willing to put whatever effort was required to improve his instruction, so when I told him I'd give him a couple of lessons in drawing, he was estatic. I asked him to first select cartoons in comic strips from the Sunday newspaper that he would most like to be able to draw. So he brought in Andy Capp. I had Dave copy Andy Capp on the chalkboard. Why copy? Because Andy Capp's creator spent many years developing the few lines that show how Andy Capp walks — the posture, the position of the legs and feet, the arms and hands, all the result of not only a great talent, but years of embellishment. Better to start with a rendition of Andy Capp and have the "lines right" than to begin at ground zero. When Dave had some semblance of Andy Capp on the board, I asked him to copy his own drawing, using less lines. Then the same again until he had something better. So my advice to Dave and to all of you is to begin by *copying* the work of the professionals. Then after you can do that, add your own touch of "originality." Dave was bolstered by the surprise that he could draw after all, and from that semester on, has been and is a very proficient chalkboard illustrator.

Stick figures are easiest to draw. Excellent stick figures by Eric Rogers are shown in his classic text, "Physics For The Inquiring Mind," Princeton University Press, 1960. If you learn to draw a few of these, you'll be doing yourself and your students a service. You can go one step further and use double lines for a full figure, as shown. Either way is effective.

The number of basic drawings that I do in my classes is surprisingly small — less than a dozen. Variations on a few basic drawings results in many drawings. For example, both a person running along the street and a person pitching a ball, with minor changes, are one basic drawing. This is shown on the following pages, on the step-by-step illustrations that I suggest you copy a few times on a chalkboard. Take your time with them and after you can make your own renditions, then work on speed. If after much practice your drawings take too long to draw, try stick figures, for effectiveness depends not on how well your drawings look, but on the quickness with which you draw them. You're highly successful when you can casually draw an illustration at about the pace you write a formula on the board. So give these a try, then try copying your favorite comic strip figures. Good Energy!

Draw Me ... *Step by step!*

1. 2. 3. 4. 5. 6. 7. 8.

$T = ?$

13

Draw Me ... Step by step!

1.

2.

3.

4.

5.

6.

7.

8.

9.

10.

Draw Me ... Step by step!

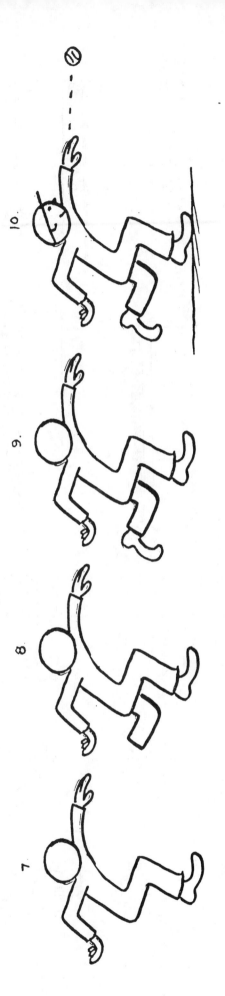

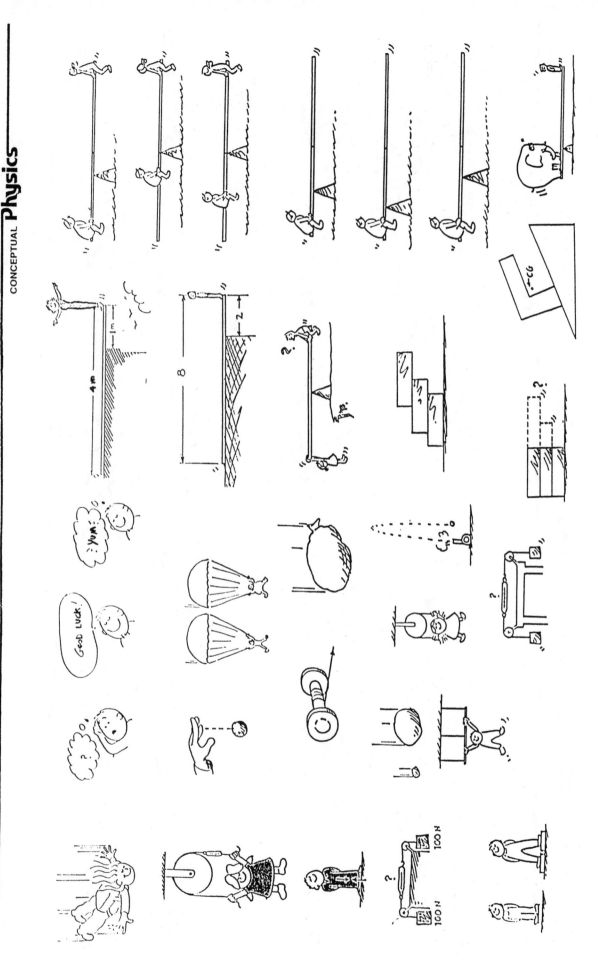

Odds & Ends -- *Paste ons for exams, etc.*

CONCEPTUAL **Physics**

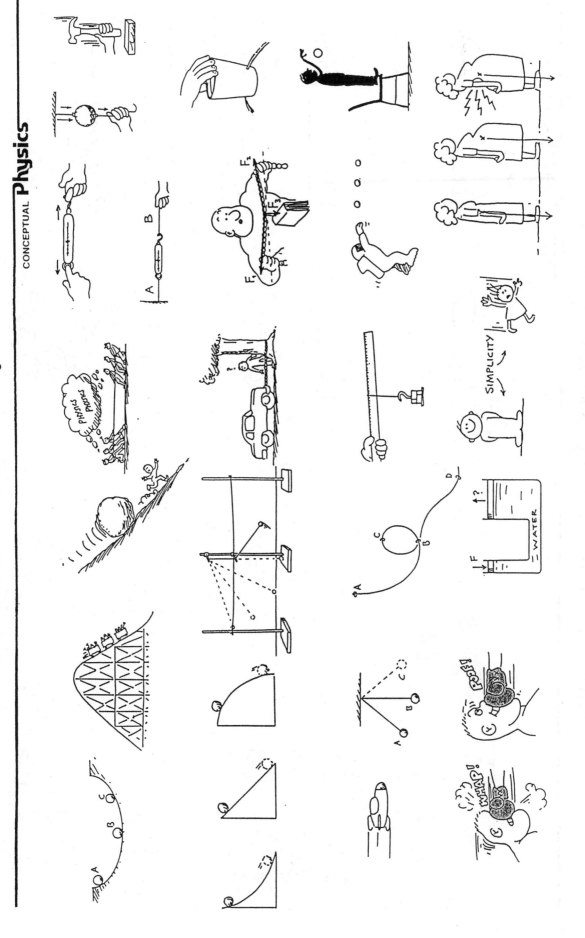

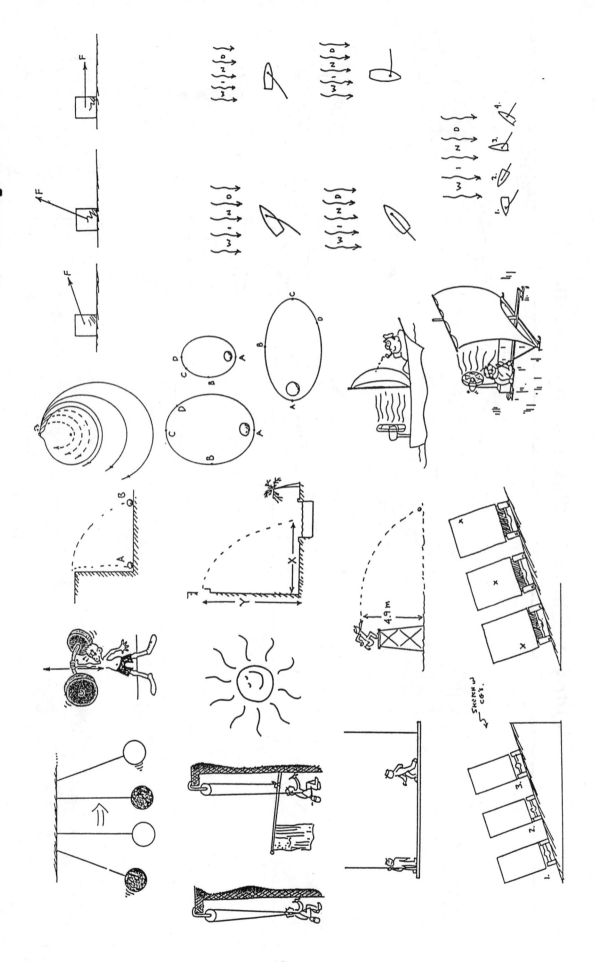

Odds & Ends --- Paste ons for exams, etc.

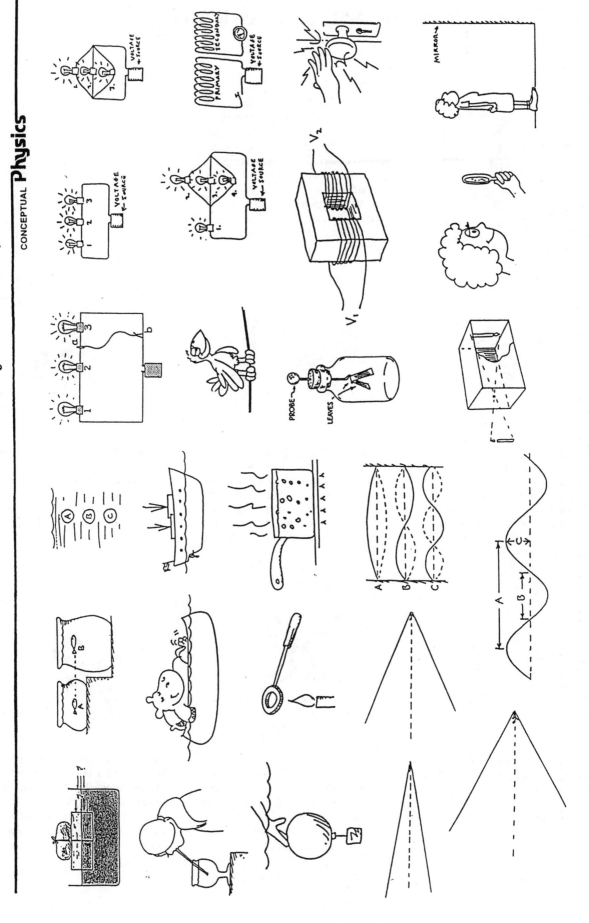

A Do-it-Yourself Recipe for a Simple Electric Motor

The finished motor shown to the left can be built with the following commonplace tools and materials: eight thumbtacks, three 2-inch paper clips, two 3½-inch nails, needle-nosed pliers, electrical or adhesive tape, a wooden board about five inches square, about seven feet of No. 20 insulated copper wire, and a knife to scrape the ends with. Two 1½-volt dry cells provide an adequate power supply.

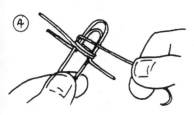

Step 1. The first step in making the motor is straightening the smaller loop of one of the paper clips, and then twisting it so that it stands upright at right angles to the larger loop. Then use the pliers to bend a tiny loop in the upright end. Do the same with a second paper clip.

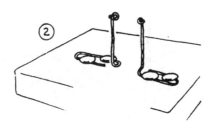

Step 2. Next, attach the paper clips to the board with tacks as shown. The upright ends of the clips should be about an inch apart. The tacks should be loose enough for final adjustment later. These clips are the supports for the axle of the motor's rotor.

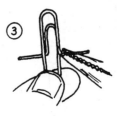

Step 3. Next make the rotor. With pliers, bend the ends of the third paper clip perpendicular to the clip's midpoint as shown. The ends, which will serve as the rotor's axle, should each be about a half-inch long.

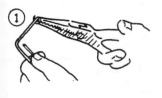

Step 4. Leaving one inch free, wrap the copper wire tightly around the rotor clip, working out from the middle. Wind the turns of wire closely together, but not so tightly that the clip is bent out of shape.

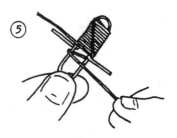

Step 5. Wrap about 20 coils out toward the end of the rotor clip. Then take the wire back to the center and wrap—in the same direction—an equal number of turns around the other half. These coils will make the clip an electromagnet.

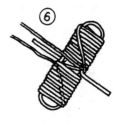

Step 6. When the copper wire has been wound around the second half of the rotor clip as shown, it is brought back to the center of the clip. The ends of the wire will serve as the rotor's *commutator*, which reverses its current with each rotation.

Courtesy of Time-Life, Inc.

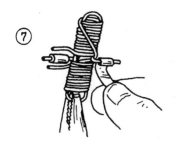

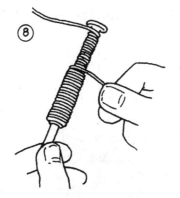

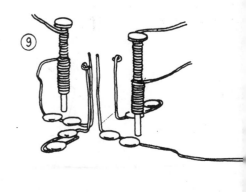

Step 7. The next step is to cut the ends of the wire so that they are slightly shorter than the projecting end of the clip. Then scrape the coating off the ends of the wires making sure to expose the bare copper.

Then take two strips of electrical or adhesive tape—each about $\frac{1}{4}$ inch wide and 2 inches long—and wrap them around the axle next to the clip as shown. This tape keeps the rotor-clip axle in the paper-clip supports. The center of gravity of the finished rotor should be along the axle so that it will twirl without wobbling.

Step 8. Make two stationary electromagnets by wrapping each nail with wire, leaving about 9 inches of wire free close to the head. Wind the wire evenly for about $2\frac{1}{2}$ inches down from the top, then about half-way back up again. Both nails should be wound in the same direction.

Leave about 6 inches of wire sticking out from the middle of each nail and cut it. Each nail should now have a 9-inch and a 6-inch tail. Scrape about $\frac{3}{4}$ inch of insulation from the end of each tail, exposing the bare copper.

Step 9. Hammer the nails into the board just far enough apart to make room for the rotor. Tack the 6-inch tail from one nail to the board. Lead it to within $\frac{1}{4}$ inch of either support and bend it up so its tip is slightly higher than the support. Do the same with an unattached 12-inch length of wire. These form the *brushes*. About $\frac{3}{4}$ inch of insulation should be thoroughly scraped from each end of the 12-inch length of wire. Now all loose ends of wire are scraped free of insulation.

Step 10. Fit the axle of the rotor into the loops of each support so that the rotor's commutators, when twirling, will make contact with the brushes. Twist the end of the 6-inch tail from the second nail around the 9-inch wire from the first nail. The 9-inch wire from the second nail will connect with the dry-cell terminal. Link the free end of the 12-inch wire to the opposite dry-cell terminal and the circuit is complete.

It is important to make final adjustments so that the rotor will spin freely. As the rotor spins, both commutators should touch the brushes simultaneously. Only then will current be established in the entire circuit, making the rotor and nails electromagnets. Each time the rotor makes a half-turn, the direction of current in the rotor alternates, changing its magnetic-field polarity. It may be necessary to give the rotor a gentle nudge for the motor to operate, just as you sometimes have to do with some types of electric shavers.

Utilizing the fact that like magnetic poles repel each other and unlike poles attract, can you explain the operation of this motor?

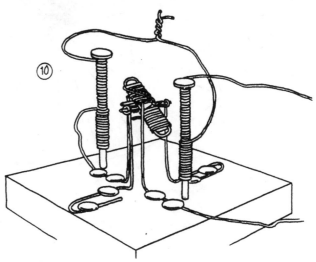

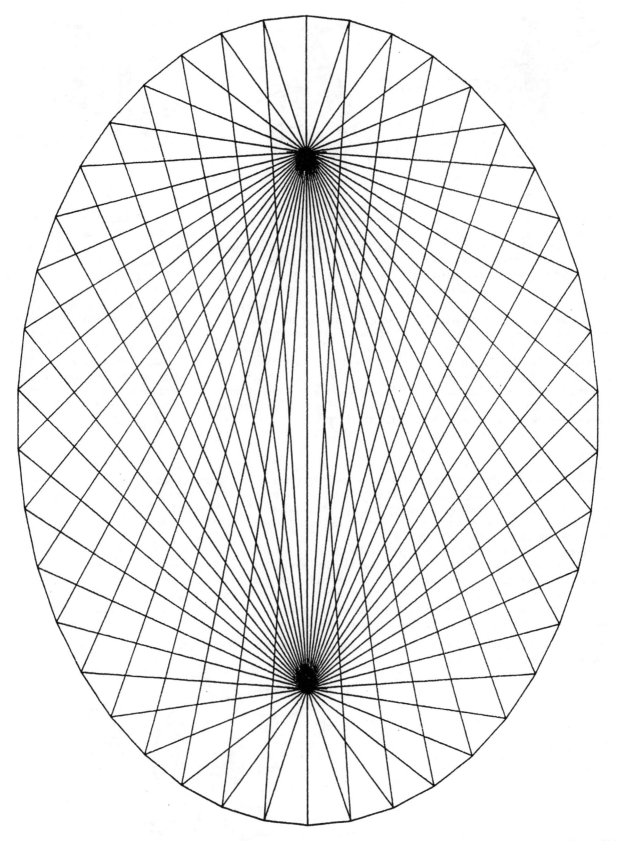

Ronald E. Lindemann (1953 — 1990)

22

1

About Science

Much of this introductory chapter, like most introductions, can be regarded as a personal essay by the author. While most physics instructors may choose to discuss somewhat different topics in a somewhat different way, the comments made here may prove to be useful as a background for further comments of your own.

New to this edition is the early role of measurements of the earth, moon and sun by Erathosthenes and Aristarchus. This high-interest treatment should be a good kickoff for your course. More on this is found in the excellent book *Physics for the Inquiring Mind*, by Eric Rogers, originally published in 1960 by Princeton University Press.

New to this edition also is the **Laboratory Manual**, with a variety of activities and experiments for the 8 parts of this text. There are two activities for getting started that complement Chapter 1.

It is important to emphasize throughout your course that **science is a human endeavor**. It is a human activity that answers questions of human interest. It is done by and for humans.

You may consider elaborating on the idea about the possible *wrongness* **versus** **rightness** of ideas; an idea that characterizes science. This is generally misunderstood, for it is not generally a criterion in other disciplines. State that it is the prerogative of science, in contrast to the speculative procedures of philosophy and metaphysics, to embrace only ideas that can be tested and to disregard the rest. Ideas that can't be tested are not necessarily wrong — they are simply useless insofar as advancement in scientific knowledge is concerned. Ideas must be verifiable by other scientists. In this way science tends to be self-correcting.

Expand on the idea that **honesty in science** is not only a matter of public interest, but is a matter of self interest. Any scientist who misrepresents or fudges data, or is caught lying about scientific information, is ostracized by the scientific community. There are no second chances. The high standards for acceptable performance in science, unfortunately, do not extend to other fields that are as important to the human condition. For example, consider the standards of performance required of politicians.

Distinguish between *hypothesis, theory, fact,* and *concept.* Point out that theory and hypothesis are not the same. A **theory** applies to a synthesis of a large body of information. The criterion of a theory is not whether it is true or untrue, but rather whether it is useful or nonuseful. A theory is useful even though the ultimate causes of the phenomena it encompasses are unknown. For example, we accept the theory of gravitation as a useful synthesis of available knowledge that relates to the mutual attraction of bodies. The theory can be refined, or with new information it can take on a new direction. It is important to acknowledge the common misunderstanding of what a scientific theory is, as revealed by those who say, "But it is not a fact; it is *only* a theory." Many people have the mistaken notion that a theory is tentative or speculative, while a fact is absolute.

Impress upon your class that a **fact** is not immutable and absolute, but is generally a close agreement by competent observers of a series of obseravtions of the same phenomena. The observations must be testable. Since the activity of science is the determination of the most probable, there are no absolutes. Facts that were held to be absolute in the past are seen altogether differently in the light of present-day knowledge.

By **concept**, we mean the intellectual framework that is part of a theory. We speak of the concept of time, the concept of energy, or the concept of a force field. Time is related to motion in space and is the substance of the Theory of Special Relativity. We find that energy exists in tiny grains, or quanta, which is a central concept in the Quantum Theory. An important concept in Newton's Theory of Universal Gravitation is the idea of a force field that surrounds a material body. A concept envelops the overriding idea that underlies various phenomena. Thus, when we think "conceptually" we envelop a generalized way of looking at things.

Prediction in science is different from prediction in other areas. In the everyday sense, one speaks of predicting what has not yet occurred, like whether or not it will rain next weekend. In science, however, prediction is not so much about what *will* happen, but about what *is* happening and is not yet noticed, like what the properties of a hypothetical particle are and are not. A scientist predicts what can and cannot happen, rather than what will or will not happen.

Science and technology — In discussions of science and technology and their side effects, a useful statement is: *You can never do just one thing.* This is similar to "there is never just one force" in discussions of Newton's third law.

Science and religion — do the two contradict each other — must one choose between them? These questions are foremost among many students, yet physics texts usually sidestep such questions, for religion is very personal for so many people. I hope the very brief treatment in the text presents a satisfactory answer to these questions. Your feedback on this matter will be appreciated.

With regard to science courses and liberal arts courses, there is a central factor that makes it difficult for liberal arts students to delve into science courses the way that science students can delve into liberal arts courses — and that's the **vertical nature of science courses.** They build upon each other, as noted by their prerequisites. A science student can take an intermediate course in literature, poetry, or history at any time, and in any order. But in no way can a humanities student take an intermediate physics or chemistry course without first having a foundation in elementary physics and mathematics. Hence the importance of this conceptual course.

Except for the measurements by early Greek scientists, I do not lecture about Chapter 1 material, and instead assign it as reading. It can be omitted without interfering with the following chapters.

2

Linear Motion

This chapter begins mechanics with a brief historical treatment of motion as classified by Aristotle and studied by Galileo. It serves mainly to make the distinction between speed, velocity, and acceleration, which is a point of confusion for many students. The emphasis of accelerated motion is on falling objects. An extended treatment of motion analysis is in Appendix II.

If you are new to teaching with the non-computational approach, this chapter may prove challenging. It should be sufficient, however, to make the distinction clear between speed, velocity, and acceleration, plant the seeds for the idea of inertia, and move quickly to Chapter 3. (I most often spend only *one* class lecture on this chapter, and never more than two class periods — most of that outlined below.) Too much treatment of motion analysis can be counter productive to stimulating an early student interest in physics.

If you do go further with this chapter, and you have a TV monitor that can freeze single frames in class or lab, do as Jim Goodwin at Cal State College at Stanislaus does, and make use of the fact that two images, not one, are on display at any instant. Each image of alternate horizontal sweeps is time separated by 1/30 second, so the "blur" you see for a dropping ball, or for anything moving, provides good data for determining speed. Simply note from the screen the displacement between the image as seen on alternate sweeps, scale to actual length and divide by 1/30 second!

The first page of the **Practicing Physics** book of worksheets treats the distinction between velocity acquired and distance fallen for free fall via a freely-falling speedometer-odometer. Students *do* learn from these, in class or out of class, so whether you have your students buy their own from your bookstore or you photocopy select pages for class distribution, get these sheets to your students.

The textbook does not describe motion by graphs. Per chance that is your style, be sure to consider the lab that features the sonic ranger, *Blind as a Bat*, in the

Laboratory Manual. This is conceptual graphing at its best, and if not done as a lab experiment, can be demonstrated as part of your lecture.

This chapter is prerequisite to the following chapters on mechanics.

SUGGESTED LECTURE PRESENTATION

Start by acknowledging a sensible way to begin the course is with simple concepts and then gradually build to more complicated concepts as the course progresses — but you're not going to do it that way. A description of motion will be more quantitative than later material, and will begin your course. This should relieve some anxiety to students who have read Chapter 2 and found it intimidating. Although kinematics can be a difficult field to cover, your plow setting will not go too deep. Your first question: What means of motion has done more to change the way cities are built than any other? Answer: The elevator!

Explain the importance of motion as it pertains to the other areas of physics — state that such things as air resistance, buoyancy, spin, and the shape of a moving object are important considerations in the study of motion — but beneath all these are some very simple relationships that might otherwise be masked by these considerations, and that these *relationships* are what Chapter 2 and your lecture are about. Add that by completely neglecting the effects of air resistance not only exposes the simple relationships, but is a reasonable assumption for heavy and compact (dense) objects traveling at moderate speeds; i.e., one would notice no difference between the rates of fall of a heavy rock dropped from the class-room ceiling to the floor below, when falling through either air or a complete vacuum. For a feather and heavy objects moving at high speeds, air resistance does become important, and will be treated in Chapter 4.

> DEMONSTRATION: Here's a simple and nice one: Drop a sheet of paper and a book, side by side. Of course the book falls faster, due to its greater weight compared to air resistance. (Interestingly, the air resistance is greater for the faster-falling book — an idea you'll return to in Chapter 4.) Now place the paper against the lower surface of the raised horizontally held book and when you drop them, nobody is surprised to see they fall together. The book has pushed the paper with it. Now repeat with the paper on *top* of the book and ask for predictions and neighbor discussion. Then surprise most of your class by showing that the paper falls as fast as the book! (Or you may choose to tease your class and *not* show what happens — ask them to try it on their own after class.) The book will "plow through the air" leaving an air-resistance free path for the paper to follow! Now with your class sufficiently impressed you move onward!

Speed, Velocity, and Acceleration   Define speed, writing its equation in longhand form on the board while giving examples — automobile speedometers, etc. Similarly define velocity, then acceleration. State there are three controls in an automobile that make the auto accelerate. Ask for them (accelerator, brakes, and steering wheel). State how one lurches in a vehicle that is undergoing acceleration, especially for circular motion, and state why the definition of velocity includes direction to make the definition of acceleration all-encompassing. Talk of how without lurching one cannot sense motion, giving examples of coin flipping in a high-speed aircraft versus doing the same when the same aircraft is at rest on the runway.

Give numerical examples of acceleration in units of kilometers/hour per second to establish the idea of acceleration. Be sure that your students are working on the examples with you. For example, ask them to find the acceleration of a car that goes from rest to 100 km/hr in 10 seconds. It is important that you not use examples involving seconds twice until they taste success with the easier kilometers/hour per second examples. Have them check their work with their neighbors as you go along. Only after they get the hang of it, introduce meters/second/second in your examples to develop a sense for the units m/s².

Falling Objects If you round 9.8 m/s² to 10 m/s² in your lecture, you'll more easily establish the velocity and distance relationships. Later you can then move to the more precise 9.8 m/s², in accord with the following chapters.

> CHECK QUESTION: If an object is dropped from an initial position of rest from the top of a cliff, how *fast* will it be traveling at the end of one second? (You might add, "Write the answer on your note paper." And then, "Look at your neighbor's paper — if your neighbor doesn't have the right answer, reach over and help him or her — talk about it." And then possibly, "If your neighbor isn't very cooperative, sit somewhere else next time!")

After explaining the answer a few seconds later when class discussion dies down, repeat the process asking for the speed at the end of 2 seconds, and then for 10 seconds. This leads you into stating the relationship $v = gt$, which by now you can express in shorthand notation. After any questions, discussion, and examples, state that you are going to pose a different question — not asking for how *fast*, but for how *far*. Ask how far the object falls in one second.

Ask for a written response and then ask if the students could explain to their neighbors *why* the distance is only 5 m rather than 10 m. After they've discussed this for almost a minute or so, ask "If you maintain a speed of 60 km/hr for one hour, how far do you go?" — then, "If you maintain a speed of 10 m/s for one second, how far do you go?" Important point: You'll appreciably improve your instruction if you allow some thinking time after you ask a question. Not doing so is the folly of most instructors I have encountered. Then continue, "Then why is the answer to the first question not 10 meters?" After a suitable time, stress the idea of *average* velocity and the relation $d = vt$.

Show the general case by deriving on the board $d = 1/2\, gt^2$. (I tell my students that the derivation is a sidelight to the course — something that will be the crux of a follow-up physics course. In any event, the derivation is not something that I expect of them, but is to show that $d = 1/2\, gt^2$ is a reasoned statement that doesn't just pop up from nowhere.)

> CHECK QUESTION: How far will a freely falling object that is released from rest, fall in 2 seconds? In 10 seconds? (When your class is comfortable with this, then ask how far in 1/2 second.)

To avoid information overload, I restrict all numerical examples of free fall to cases that begin at rest. Why? Because it's simpler that way. (I prefer my students understand simple physics than be confused about not-so-simple physics!) I do go this far with them.

> CHECK QUESTION: Consider a rifle fired straight downward from a high-altitude balloon. If the muzzle velocity is 100 m/s and air resistance can be neglected, what is the *acceleration* of the bullet after one second? (If most of your class say that its g, you're on!)

What I do *not* do is ask for the time of fall for a freely-falling object, given the distance. Why? Unless the distance given is the familiar 5 meters, algebraic manipulation is called for. If one of my teaching objectives were to teach algebra, this would be a nice place to do it. But I don't have time for presenting this stumbling block and then teaching how to overcome it. I'd rather put my energy *and theirs* into straight physics!

Thus far you've considered motion that is either horizontal or vertical. You won't get into motion along inclined planes here, except to cite an interesting example. We all know it is easier to gain speed in a vehicle if it is moving downhill. And it is easier to lose speed in a vehicle if it moves uphill. This is true whether the vehicle is a car or an airplane. We all know that airport runways are level, and we further know that much fuel is consumed by aircraft during their runs along the runways — taking off or coming to a stop while landing. Question for discussion: Why not build runways on a slight slope so that during takeoff planes ride slightly downhill, and during landing ride slightly uphill? It seems that considerable savings in fuel could be accomplished by slightly elevated central air terminals!

NEXT-TIME QUESTION: Via overhead transparency, if desired. Shown below are reduced pages from the Next-Time Questions book. The pages are a full 8-1/2 x 11, just right for overhead transparencies. At least one of these Next-Time Questions each answer on the back is available for every chapter in the text. Because of space limitations, Next-Time Questions are not shown for other chapters in this manual.

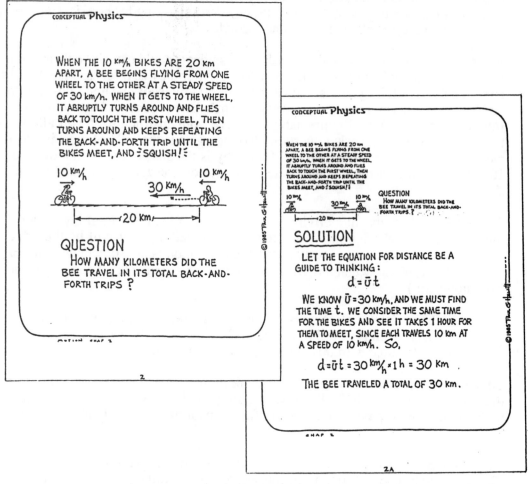

[State the usefulness of handling the "Bikes and the Bee" problem with the formula $d = vt$; that the problem is difficult if one doesn't consider the time involved, yet manageable if one does consider time. Whether or not one thinks about time should not be a matter of cleverness or good insight, but a matter of letting the formula dictate the variables to consider in handling an idea. The v is given, but the time t is not. The formula instructs you to consider time. Formulas are important in guiding our thinking about things.]

3

Nonlinear Motion

Motion is Relative
Velocity — A Vector Quantity
Projectile Motion
Fast-Moving Projectiles — Satellites
Circular Motion

This chapter logically follows Chapter 2 by combining horizontal and vertical motion. (Nevertheless, you may wish to postpone this chapter and couple it with Chapters 8 and 9.) This chapter also introduces vectors, and to avoid early confusion and information overload, treats only velocity vectors. You can dig deeper into vectors at any time by getting into the more general treatment in Appendix III. When projectiles move fast enough for the earth's curvature to make a difference, you're at the doorstep of satellite motion. Only circular orbits are treated and a follow-up more detailed treatment of both circular and elliptical orbits occurs in the separate chapter on satellites, Chapter 9, following the chapter on gravity.

Regarding 45° as the maximum range for projectiles, keep in mind that this is only true when air resistance can be neglected, and when the launching speed is the same at all angles concerned. Tilt a water hose up 45° and sure enough, for short distances where air resistance is nil, it attains maximum range. The same is true for a slowly-bunted baseball. But for a high-speed ball, air drag is a factor and maximum range occurs for angles between 39° and 42°. For very high speeds where the lesser air resistance of high altitudes is a consideration, angles greater than 45° produce maximum range. During World War I, for example, the German cannon "Big Bertha" fired shells 11.5 km high and attained maximum range at 52°. Air resistance is one factor; launching speed is another. When one throws a heavy object, like a shotput, its launching speed is less for higher angles simply because some of the launching force must be used to overcome its weight. (You can throw a heavy boulder a lot faster horizontally than you can straight up.) Shotputs are usually launched at angles slightly less than 40°. The fact that they are launched higher than ground level decreases the angle as well. Note that this is considered in the answer to Exercise 8.

The interesting fact that projectiles launched at a particular angle have the same range if launched at the complementary angle is stated without proof on page 45, and is shown in Figure 3.15. This fact is shown by the range formula, $R = (2v^2 \sin\phi \cos\phi)/g$. Since the sine of an angle is the cosine of the complement of that angle, replacing the angle with its complement will give the same range. So the range is the same whether aiming at ø or at (90° - ø). Maximum range occurs at a projection angle of 45°, where sine and cosine are equal.

For your personal information and at the risk of contributing to "information overload" with your students, there is a simple rule for estimating how much less than 45° to project when the landing spot is below the launching elevation, like downhill. Simply subtract half the angle of the "incline" from 45°. For example, if the landing spot is 10° below the launch point, project at (45° - 5°) 40° for maximum horizontal displacement. If the landing spot is above the launching point, say uphill, then add half the

ment. If the landing spot is above the launching point, say uphill, then add half the angle of "incline" above the launch point to 45°. So if your projectile is to land uphill by 10°, launch it at 50°. This rule holds for maximum horizontal distance from launch point to landing point when air resistance is not important. This and other interesting tidbits about the projectile motion of baseballs, footballs, and frisbees, can be found in the delightful book, Sport Science, by Peter J. Brancazio (Simon & Schuster, 1984).

Regarding the path of objects dropped from an airplane (Exercise 6): We've all seen those World War II photos of bombs dropping beneath B-17s and the like. Some of those photos show a vertical path for the dropping bombs. No can be! Air resistance acting on the bombs is not overcome by propellors or jet engines as is the case for the airplane, so they fall behind the vertical path they would otherwise follow. The photos we see are slightly tipped (note that the airplane travels at the same angle slightly upward).

This chapter is represented by three exercises in the student book, **Practicing Physics**. One is on vectors, and two nicely reinforce the physics of Figure 3.11.

The lab experiment *On Target* in the **Laboratory Manual** is a particularly nice wrap up of this chapter.

The following suggested lecture will probably span at least two class periods.

SUGGESTED LECTURE PRESENTATION

Vectors Begin by stating that if one were to be sitting next to a physicist on a long bus ride, and the physicist were attempting to explain some physical idea on the back of an envelope, that it is highly probable that the physicist would make extensive use of little arrows. These little arrows, that illustrate size and direction, are part of a physicist's language. They are vectors. Then explain how vectors make the ground speed of an airplane flying in the wind easier to understand — flying with the wind, against the wind, and then cross wind. Avoid information overload by avoiding cases that aren't parallel or at right angles to the wind. Your purpose at this stage is to acquaint your students with vectors, not push them past their level of comprehension.

Roll a ball off the edge of your lecture table and call attention to the curve it follows. The ball is a projectile. Discuss the idea of the "downwardness" of gravity, and how there is no "horizontalness" to it, and therefore no horizontal influence on the projectile. Draw the far left illustration of Figure 3.9 on the board, *with vectors*. Call attention to the same-size vectors to show constant velocity. Then consider merely dropping the ball off the edge of the table, and the right side of Figure 3.9. Draw progressively longer vectors starting from the top down. Then superpose your two drawings and add vectors. You're going an extra step beyond the textbook treatment.

Independence of Horizontal and Vertical Motion   Pose the situation of the horizontally-held gun and the shooter who drops a bullet at the same time he pulls the trigger, and ask which bullet hits the ground first.

> DEMONSTRATION: Show the independence of horizontal and vertical motion with a spring-gun apparatus that will shoot a ball horizontally while at the same time dropping another that falls vertically. Follow this up with the popular "monkey-and hunter" demonstration.

Point to some target at the far side of your classroom and ask your class to imagine you are going to project a rock to the target via a slingshot. Ask if you should aim at the target, above it, or below it. Easy stuff. Then ask your class to suppose it takes 1 second for the rock to reach the target. If you aim directly at the target, it will fall be-

30

neath and miss. How far beneath the target would the rock hit (supposing the floor weren't in the way)? Have your students check with their neighbors on this one. Then ask how far above should you aim to hit the target. Do a neighbor check on this one. Now you're ready to discuss Figure 3.11 on page 43.

Point out that the relationship of the curved path of Figure 3.11 and the vertical distance fallen, $d = 5t^2$, of the previous chapter. Stress that the projectile is falling beneath the straight line it would otherwise follow. This idea is important for later understanding of satellite motion.

Discuss Figure 3.18 and ask for the pitching speed if the ball travelled 30 m instead of 20 m. (Note the vertical height is 4.9 m. If you use any height that does not correspond to an integral number of seconds, you're diverting your focus from physics to algebra.) More important is considering greater horizontal distances — great enough for the curvature of the earth to make a difference in arriving at the answer. Its easy to see that the time the projectile is in the air increases when the earth curves beneath the trajectory.

Satellite Motion   Sketch "Newton's Mountain" and consider the longer and longer time intervals for greater and greater horizontal speeds. Ask if there is a "pitching speed" or cannonball velocity large enough so the time in the air is forever. Not literally "in the air", which is why the cannon is atop a mountain that extends above the atmosphere. The an-swer of course is yes. Fired fast enough the cannonball will fall around the world rather than into it. You're into satellite motion.

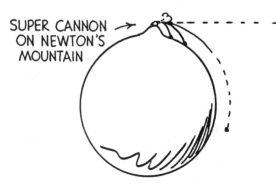

Calculating Satellite Speed An effective skit that can have your class calculating the speed necessary for close earth orbit is as follows: Call attention to the curvature of the earth, Figure 3.20. Consider a horizontal laser standing about a meter above the ground with its beam shining over a level desert. The beam is straight but the desert floor curves 4.9 m over an 8000 m or 8 km tangent, which you sketch on your chalk-board (or overhead projector). Stress this is not to scale:

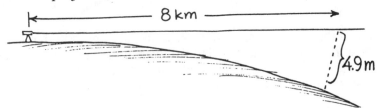

Now erase the laser and sketch in a super cannon positioned so it points along the laser line. Consider a cannonball fired at say, 2 km/s, and ask how far downrange will it be at the end of one second. A neighbor check should yield an answer of 2 km, which you indicate with an "X". But it doesn't really get to the "X", you say, for it falls beneath the "X" because of gravity. How far? 4.9 m if the sand weren't in the way. Ask if 2 km/s is sufficient for orbiting the earth. Clearly not, for the cannonball strikes the ground. If the cannonball is not to hit the ground, we'd have to dig a trench first, as you show on your sketch, which now looks like this:

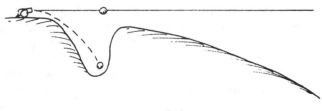

Continue by considering a greater muzzle velocity, say 4 km/s, so the cannonball travels 4 km in one second. Ask if this is fast enough to attain an earth orbit. Student response should indicate that they realize that the cannonball will hit the ground before 1 second is up. Then repeat the previous line of reasoning, again having to dig a trench, and your sketch looks like this:

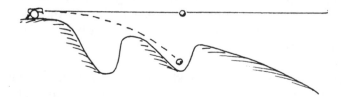

Continue by considering a greater muzzle velocity — great enough so the the cannonball travels 6 km in 1 second. this is 6 km/s. Ask if this is fast enough not to hit the ground (or equivalently, if it is fast enough for earth orbit!) Then repeat the previous line of reasoning, again having to dig a trench. Now your sketch looks like this:

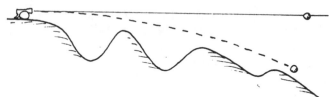

You're almost there: Continue by considering a muzzle velocity great enough so the cannonball travels 8 km in one second. (Don't state the velocity is 8 km/s here as you'll diminish your punch line.) Repeat your previous reasoning and note that this time you don't have to dig a trench! After a pause, and with a tone of importance, ask the class with what speed must the cannonball have to orbit the earth. Done properly, you have led your class into a "derivation" of orbital speed about the earth with no equations or algebra.

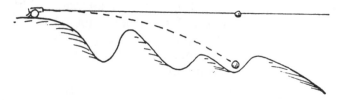

Acknowledge that the gravitational force is less on satellites in higher orbits so they do not need to go so fast. This is acknowledged later in the book in the footnote on text page 167. (Since $v = \sqrt{GM/d}$, a satellite at 4 times the earth's radius needs to travel only half as fast, 4 km/s.)

You can wind up your brief treatment of satellite motion and catch its essense via the following skit: Ask your students to pretend they are encountered by a bright youngster, too young to have much knowledge of physics and mathematics, but who nevertheless asks why satellites seem to defy gravity and stay in orbit. You ask what answer could correctly satisfy the curiosity of the kid, then pose the following dialogue between the kid and the students in your class (you're effectively suggesting how the student might interact with the bright kid). Ask the kid to observe and then describe what you do, as you hold a rock at arm's length and then simply drop it. The kid replies, "You dropped the rock and it fell to the ground below," to which you respond, "Very good — now what happens this time?", as you move your hand horizontally and again drop the rock. The kid observes and then says, "The rock dropped again, but because your hand was moving it followed a curved path and fell farther away." You continue, "Very good — now again —" as you throw the rock still farther. The kid replies, "I note that as your hand moves faster, the path follows a wider curve." You're elated at this response, and you ask the kid, "How far away will

32

the rock hit the ground if its curved path matches the curved surface of the earth?" The kid at first appears very puzzled, but then beams, "Oh — I get it! The stone doesn't hit at all — its in earth orbit" Then you interrupt your dialogue and ask the class, "Do YOU get it?" Then back to the kid who asks, "But isn't it really more complicated than that?", to which the answer is NO. The essential idea of satellite motion IS that simple. State that you'll return to satellite motion in Chapter 9 — nice stuff.

Circular Motion   You may wish to postpone lecturing about circular motion until you treat rotational mechanics, Chapter 7. In a treatment of circular motion at this stage, it is enough to make the distinction between tangential speed (linear speed) and rotational speed. Only for a rigid rotating system such as a solid turntable or a stiff spoke does $v = r\omega$ apply — the greater the distance from the axis of rotation, the greater the linear speed. Don't be surprised to find students applying this relationship to a non-rigid system, such as a system of planets. They are confused about Mercury, which is relatively fast in its orbit about the sun, and Pluto, which is very slow. Horses running around a circular track obey $v = r\omega$ only if they are constrained, like joined by a giant nonflexible spoke. If this possible misconception is not corrected, it will cause trouble in Chapter 7 when rotational motion is treated in more detail.

> CHECK QUESTION: A phonograph record rotates at a constant RPM (the speeds of which have more to do with marketing than physics, by the way). Two music pieces of equal times are on a record, one at the beginning of the record (outside), and the other at the end of the record (inside). Which piece is wider in the radial direction on the record? [The inside piece is wider, since the same length of track must wind around the record more times.]

Side point: Today's toilet tissue rolls are smaller in diameter than rolls of toilet tissue years ago. Since more tissue makes a complete circle on the outer part of the roll, decreasing the diameter only slightly means appreciably less tissue per roll.

While we're on the subject of circles, you might ask why manhole covers are round. The answer is so some moron type doesn't drop them accidentally into the manhole. If they were square, they could be tipped up on edge and dropped through the hole on the diagonal. Similarly with ovals. But a circular hole will defy the most determined efforts in this regard. Of course there is a lip around the inside of the manhole that the cover rests on, making the diameter of the hole somewhat less than the diameter of the cover.

4

Newton's Laws of Motion

Acceleration, inertia, and falling objects as introduced in Chapter 2, are further developed in this chapter. In the treatment of Newton's 1st law the distinction between mass and weight is emphasized, but very little attention is given to units of measurement. (Because I think time spent on this is better spent on physics concepts.) A brief treatment of units and systems of measurement is provided in Appendix I.

It is useful to represent magnitudes with numerical quantities from time to time. An option that sometimes better makes the point is the exagerrated symbol technique that is shown on pages 64 and 70 and later in following chapters.

This chapter is central to the study of mechanics. It is reinforced with 5 exercises from the student workbook, **Practicing Physics**. You may or may not be interested in the new Practice-Book treatment of *free-body diagrams* — a must if you emphasize problem solving.

There are 3 activities to choose from and 1 experiment in the **Laboratory Manual** to complement this chapter.

You may find that the following suggested lecture may span 3 or 4 class periods.

SUGGESTED LECTURE PRESENTATION

Newton's 1st Law Begin by pointing to an object in the room and stating that if it started moving, one would reasonably look for a cause for its motion. We would say that a force of some kind was responsible, and that would seem reasonable. Tie this idea to the notion of force maintaining motion as Aristotle saw it. State that a cannonball remains at rest in the cannon until a force is applied, and that the force of expanding gases drives the ball out of the barrel when it is fired. (I have a 10-cm-diameter solid steel sphere, actually a huge ball bearing, that I use in this lecture. Use one. or a bowling ball, if available.) But what keeps the cannonball moving when the gases no longer act on it? This leads you into a discussion of inertia. In the everyday sense, inertia refers to a habit or a rut. In physics it's another word for laziness, or the resistance to change as far as the state of motion of an object is concerned. I roll the ball along the lecture table to show its tendency to keep rolling. Inertia was first introduced with Galileo's inclined plane experiments in Chapter 2.

DEMONSTRATION: Show that inertia refers also to objects at rest with the classic *tablecloth-and-dishes demonstration*. [Be sure to pull the tablecloth slightly downward so there is no upward component of force on the dishes!] I precede this demo with a simpler version, a simple block of wood on a piece of cloth — but with a twist. I ask what the block will do when I suddenly whip the cloth toward me. After a neighbor check, I surprise the class when they see that the block has been stapled to the cloth! This illustrates Newton's zeroth law — be skeptical. Then I follow up with the classic tablecloth demo. Don't think the classic demo is too corny, for your students will really love it.

(Of course when we show a demonstration to illustrate a particular concept, there is almost always more than one concept involved. The tablecloth demo is no exception, which also illustrates impulse and momentum (Chapter 5 stuff) The plates experience two impulses; one that first involves the friction between the cloth and dishes, which moves them slightly toward you. It is brief and very little momentum builds up. Once the dishes are no longer on the cloth, a second impulse occurs due to friction between the dishes and table, which acts in a direction away from you and prevents the dishes from sliding toward you. This brief impulse brings the dishes to rest. Done quickly, the brief displacement of the dishes is hardly noticed. Is inertia really at work here? Yes, for if there were no friction in the demo, the dishes would strictly remain at rest.

DEMONSTRATION: Continuing with inertia, do as Jim Szeszol does and fashion a wire coat hanger into an m shape as shown. Two globs of clay are stuck to each end. Balance it on your head, with one glob in front of your face. State you wish to view the other blob and ask how you can do so without touching the apparatus. Then simply turn around an look at it. It's like the bowl of soup you turn only to find the soup stays put. Inertia in action! (Of course, like the tablecloth demo, there is more physics here than inertia; this demo can also be used to illustrate rotational inertia and the conservation of angular momentum.)

A useful way to impart the idea of mass and inertia is to place two objects, say a pencil and a piece of chalk, in the hands of a student and ask for a judgement of which is heavier. The student will likely respond by shaking them, one in each hand. Point out that in so doing the student is really comparing their inertias, and is making use of the intuitive knowledge that weight and inertia are directly proportional to each other.

To distinguish between mass and weight compare the efforts of pushing horizontally on a block of slipery ice on a frozen pond versus lifting it. Or consider the weightlessness of a massive anvil in outer space and how it would be difficult to shake, weight or not weight. And if moving toward you, it would be harmful to be in its way because of its great tendency to remain in motion. The following demo (often used to illustrate impulse and momentum) makes the distinction nicely:

DEMONSTRATION: Hang a massive ball by a string and show that the to string breaks when the bottom is pulled with gradually more force, but the bottom string breaks when the string is jerked. Ask which of these cases illustrates weight. [Interestingly enough, its the weight of the ball that makes for the greater tension in the top string.] Then ask which of these cases illustrates inertia. [When jerked, the tendency of the ball to resist the sudden downward acceleration, its inertia, is responsible for the lower string breaking.] This is the best demo I know of for showing the different effects of weight and mass.

DEMONSTATION: An unforgettable follow-up to the previous demo is lying on your back and having an assistant place a blacksmith's anvil on your stomach and then striking it rather hard with a sledge hammer. The principles here are the same as the ball and string demo. Both the inertia of the ball and the inertial of the anvil resist the changes in motion they would otherwise undergo. So the string doesn't break, and your body is not squashed. (Be sure that your assistant is good with the hammer. When I began teaching I used to trust students to the task. In my fourth year the student who volunteered was extra nervous in front of the class and missed the anvil entirely — but not me. The hammer smashed into my hand breaking two fingers. I was lucky I was not harmed more.).

Relate the idea of tightening a hammer head, Figure 4.1, with the bones of the human spine, and how as a result of jostling all day, we are a bit shorter at night. Ask your students to find a place in their homes that they can't quite reach before going to bed — a place that is one or two centimeters higher than their reach. Then tell them to try again when they awake the next morning. Unforgettable, for you are likely instructing them to discover something about themselves they were not aware of!

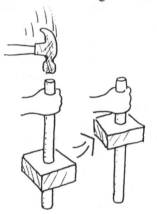

DEMONSTRATION: Follow the hammer bit with a broom handle or wooden dowel that fits rather snuggly in a hole through a few-kilogram wooden block. When held as shown, they stay together due to friction. Strike the top of the dowel with a hammer and viola, the block climbs the handle! The block tends to stay put while the handle suddenly moves downward. More inertia in action.

DEMONSTRATION: Do as Marshall Ellenstein does and place a metal hoop atop a narrow jar. On top of the hoop balance a piece of chalk. Then whisk the hoop away and the chalk falls neatly into the narrow opening. The key here is grabbing the hoop on the inside, on the side farthest from your sweep. This elongates the hoop horizontally and the part that supports the chalk drops from beneath the chalk. (If you grab the hoop on the near side, the elongation will be vertical and pop the chalk up into the air!)

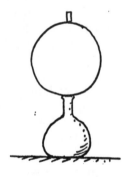

CHECK QUESTIONS: Pose the other two questions of Figure 4.1, p.55. Discuss other examples of things at rest remaining so, and things in motion remaining in motion along straight-line paths. Jump up — then ask why the wall does not smash into you as the earth rotates under you while you're in the air. Then ask about moving objects that do not follow straight-line paths, or objects that speed up or slow down, and you have led into Newton's 2nd law.

Newton's 2nd Law Briefly review the idea of acceleration and its definition, and state that it is produced by an imposed force. Write this as a ~ F and give examples of doubling the force and the resulting doubling of the acceleration, etc. Introduce the idea of net force, with appropriate examples — like applying twice the force to a stalled car gives it twice as much acceleration — three times the force, three times the acceleration.

Shift to *static* examples, where the net force is zero as evidenced by zero acceleration. Hold an object at rest in your hand, say a 1-kg mass that weighs 9.8 N, and ask what is the net force on the object. Be sure they distinguish between the 9.8 N gravitational force on the object and the zero net force on it — as evidenced by its zero acceleration. Then suspend the same object from a spring scale and show the 9.8-N reading. The scale is pulling up on the object, with just as much force as the earth is pulling down on it. Pretend to step on a bathroom scale. Ask how much gravity is pulling on you. This is evident by the scale reading. Then ask what the net force is that acts on you. This is evident by your absence of acceleration. Consider two scales, one foot on each, and ask how each scale would read. Then ask how the scales would read if you shifted your weight more on one than the other. Ask is there is a rule to guide the answers to these questions. Before answering, go into the following skit.

Signpainter Skit: Draw on the board the sketch to the left below, which shows two painters on a painting rig suspended by two ropes. Step 1: If both painters have the same weight and each stands next to a rope, the supporting force in the ropes will be equal. If spring scales, one on each rope, were used, the forces in the ropes would be

evident. Ask what the scale reading in each rope would be in this case. [The answer is each rope will support the weight of one man + half the weight of the rig — both scales will show equal readings.] Step 2: Suppose one painter walks toward the other as shown in the sketch at the right, which you draw on the chalkboard (or show via overhead projector).Will the reading in the left rope increase? Will the reading in the right rope decrease? Grand question: Will the reading in the left rope increase exactly as much as the tension in the right rope decreases? And if so, how does either rope "know" about the change in the other rope? After neighbor discussion, be sure to emphasize that the answers to these questions lie in the framework of Newton's second law, $a = F_{net}/m$. Since there is no acceleration, the net force must be zero, which means the upward support forces supplied by the ropes must add up to the downward force of gravity on the two men and the rig. So a decrease in one rope must necessarily be met with a corresponding increase in the other. (This example is dear to my heart. When I was a signpainter and before I had any training in physics, my sign-painting buddy, Burl Grey, posed this question to me. He didn't know the answer, nor did I. That was because neither he nor I had a model for analyzing the problem. We didn't know about Newton's second law, and therefore didn't think in terms of zero acceleration and a corresponding zero net force. How different one's thinking is when one has or does not have a model to guide it. If Burl and I had been mystical in our thinking, we might have been more concerned with how each rope "knows" about the condition of the other. This is the approach that intrigues many people with a nonscientific view of the world.)

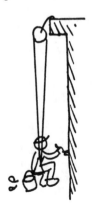

SKIT: Harry the painter swings year after year from his bossun's chair. He weighs 500 N and the rope, unknown to Harry, has a breaking point of 300 N. Ask the class if the rope should break when attached as shown to the left. One day Harry is painting near a flagpole and to be different, he ties the free end of the rope to the flagpole instead of to his chair. Why was this Harry's last day on the job?

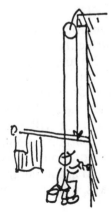

NonacceleratedMotion   Continue to cases of zero acceleration and zero net force for moving things. Drag a block at constant velocity across your lecture table. Acknowledge friction, and how the force of friction must exactly counter your pulling force. Show the pulling force with a spring balance.

> CHECK QUESTION: (similar to the one on page 63 in the text) Suppose in a high-flying airplane the captain announces over the cabin public address system that the plane is flying at a constant 900 km/h and the thrust of the engines is a constant 80,000 newtons. What is the acceleration of the airplane? [Answer: Zero, because velocity is constant.] What is the combined force of air resistance that acts all over the plane's outside surface? [Answer: 80,000 N. If it were less, the plane would speed up; if it were more, the plane would slow down.]

Friction   Continue your activity of pulling the block across the table with a spring balance Show what happens when you pull harder. Your students see that when the pulling force is greater than the friction force, there is a net force greater than zero, as evidenced by the observed acceleration. Show different constant speeds across the table with the same applied force, which shows that friction is not dependent on speed. Distinguish between static and sliding friction, and show how a greater force is needed to get the block moving from a rest position. Show all this as you discuss these ideas. Cite the example in the book about skidding with locked brakes in a car [where the distance of skid for sliding friction is greater than static friction, where lower braking application results in non-sliding tires and shorter sliding distance]. Discuss the new Automatic braking systems (ABS) now available on cars.

After you have adequately discussed friction and the idea of net force, pose the following (Be careful that your class may not be ready for this, in which case you may confuse rather than enlighten):

> CHECK QUESTION: If one were able to produce and maintain a constant net force of only 1 newton on the Queen Mary ocean liner, what would be its maximum speed? [Give multiple choices for an answer: a) 0 m/s; b) 1 m/s; c) less than 1 m/s; d) about 10 m/s; e) almost the speed of light!] In the following discussion, the key concept is net force. Point out the enormous applied forces necessary to overcome the enormous water resistance at high speeds, to yield a net force of 1 newton; and the meaning of acceleration — that every succeeding second the ship moves a bit faster than the second before. This would go on seemingly without limit, except for relativistic effects which result in (e) being the correct answer.

Falling Objects   Point out that although Galileo introduced the idea of inertia, discussed the role of forces, and defined acceleration, he never tied these ideas together as Newton did in his second law. Although Galileo is credited as the first to demonstrate that in the absence of air resistance, falling objects fall with equal accelerations, he was not able to say why this is so. The answer is given by Newton's 2nd law.

> SKIT: Hold a heavy object like a kilogram weight and a piece of chalk with outstretched hands, ready to drop them. Ask your class which will strike the ground first if you drop them simultaneously. They know. Ask them to imagine you ask the same of a bright youngster, who responds by asking to handle the two objects before giving an answer. Pretend you are the kid judging the lifting of the two objects. "The metal object is heavier than the chalk, which means there is more gravity force acting on it, which means it will accelerate to the ground before the chalk does." Write the kids argument in symbol notation on the board. $a \sim F$. Then go through the motions of asking the same of another child, who responds with a good argument that takes inertia rather than weight into account. This kid says, after shaking the metal and chalk back and forth in his or her hands,

"The piece of metal is more massive than the chalk, which means it has more inertia than the chalk, which means it will be harder to get moving than the chalk. So the chalk will race to the ground first, while the inertia of the metal causes it to lag behind." Write this kid's argument with, a ~1/m. State that the beauty of science is that such speculations can be ascertained by experiment. Drop the weight and the chalk to show that however sound each child's argument seemed to be, the results do not support either. Then bring both arguments together with a ~F/m, Newton's 2nd Law.

Relate your skit to the case of falling bricks, Figure 4.13, and the falling boulder and feather, Figure 4.14. Once these concepts are clear, ask how the bricks would slide on a frictionless inclined plane, then illustrate with examples such as the time required for a fully loaded roller coaster and an empty roller coaster to make a complete run. In the absence of friction effects, the times are the same. Cite the case of a Cadillac limousine and Volkswagen rolling down a hill in the absence of friction. By now you are fielding questions having to do with air resistance and friction. (Avoid getting into the buoyancy of falling objects — information overload.)

DEMONSTRATION: After you have made clear the cases with no friction, then make a transition to practical examples that involve friction — leading off with the dropping of sheets of paper, one crumpled and one flat. Point out that the masses and weights are the same, and the only variable is air resistance. Bring in the idea of net force again, asking what the net force is when the paper falls at constant speed. (If you left the Chapter 2 demo of the falling book with piece of paper on top of it hanging, reintroduce it here.)

CHECK QUESTIONS: What is the acceleration of a feather that "floats" slowly to the ground? What is the net force acting on the feather? If the feather weighs one-hundredth newton, how much air resistance acts upward against it?

These questions lead into a discussion of the parachutists in Figure 4.16. When the decrease of acceleration that builds up to terminal velocity is clear, return to the point earlier about the Cadillac and Volkswagen rolling down an incline, only this time in the presence of air resistance. Then ask whether or not it would be advantageous to have a heavy cart or a light cart in a soap-box-derby race. Ask which would reach the finish line first if they were dropped through the air from a high-flying balloon. Then consider the carts on an inclined plane.

For your information, the terminal velocity of a falling baseball is about 150 km/h (95 mi/h), and for a falling ping pong ball about 32 km/h (20 mi/h).

Newton's 3rd Law Begin by reaching out to the class and stating, "I can't touch you, without you touching me in return — I can't nudge this chair without the chair in turn nudging me — I can't exert a force on a body without that body in turn exerting a force on me — In all these cases of contact there is a *single* interaction between *two* things— contact requires a *pair* of forces, whether they be slight nudges or great impacts, between *two* things. We're talking, of course, about Newton's 3rd Law of motion. Then state the law and support it with examples.

A good one is to extend your hand and show the class that you can bend your fingers upward only very little. Show that if you push with your other hand, and thereby apply a force to them, or have a student do the same, they will bend appreciably more. Then walk over to the wall and show that the inanimate wall does the same (as you push against the wall). State that everybody will acknowledge that you are pushing on the wall, but only a few realize the fundamental fact that the wall is simultaneously pushing on you also — as evidenced by your bent fingers!

State that this is just one of the fundamental physical laws that completely escape the notice of most people, even though it's staring them right in the face. We look without always seeing. State that much of this course is to point out the obvious that is all around us.

Call attention to Figures 4.19 (impact between balls) and 4.20 (A on B, B on A, etc.) and discuss.

> CHECK QUESTION: Identify the action and reaction forces for the case of a bat striking the ball.

Discuss walking on the floor in terms of the single interaction between you and the floor, and the pair of action and reaction forces that comprise this interaction. Contrast this to walking on frictionless ice, where no interaction occurs. Ask how one could get off a pond of frictionless ice. Make the answer easy by saying one has a massive brick in hand. By throwing the brick there is an interaction between the thrower and the brick. The reaction to the force on the brick, the recoiling force, sends one to shore. Or without such a convenient brick, one has clothing. Or if no clothing, one has air in the lungs. One could blow air in jet fashion. Exhale with the mouth facing away from shore, but be sure to inhale with the mouth facing toward shore.

> CHECK QUESTION: Identify the force that pushes a car along the road. [Interestingly enough, the force that pushes cars is provided by the road. Why? The tires push on the road, action, and the road pushes on the tires, reaction. So roads push cars along. A somewhat different viewpoint!]

Most people say that the moon is attracted to the earth by gravity. Ask most people if the earth is also attracted to the moon, and if so, which pulls harder, the earth or the moon? You'll get mixed answers. Physicists think differently than most people on this topic: rather than saying the moon is attracted to the earth by gravity, a physicist would say there is an attractive force between the earth and the moon. There is an important difference here.

Asking if the moon pulls as hard on the earth as the earth pulls on the moon is similar to asking if the distance between New York and Los Angeles is the same as the distance between Los Angeles and New York. Rather than thinking in terms of two distances, we think of a single distance *between* New York and Los Angeles. Likewise there is a single gravitational interaction between the earth and the moon.

Support this point by showing your outstretched hand where you have a stretched rubber band between your thumb and forefinger. Ask which is pulling with the greater force, the thumb or the finger. Or, as you increase the stretch, which is being pulled with more force toward the other — the thumb toward the finger or the finger toward the thumb. After neighbor discussion, stress the single interaction between things that pull on each other. The earth and the moon are each pulling on each other. Their pulls on each other comprise a single interaction. This point of view makes a moot point of deciding which exerts the greater force, the moon

on the earth or the earth on the moon, or the ball on the bat or the bat on the ball, et cetera. Pass a box of rubber bands to your class and have them do it.

Discuss the firing of a bullet from a rifle, as treated in the chapter. I illlustrate Newton's 3rd Law with a skit about a man who is given one last wish before being shot, who states that his crime demands more punishment than being struck by a tiny bullet, who wishes instead that the mass of the bullet match the magnitude of his crime (being rational in a rigid totalitarian society), that the mass of the bullet be much much more massive than the gun from which it is fired — and that his antagonist pull the trigger!

The recoil from rifle fire is what underlies rocket propulsion. Users of previous edition may notice that analogous Figures 4.25 and 4.26 of the recoiling machine gun and propelled rocket that illustrate the third law, formerly illustrated momentum conservation in Chapter 5. Of course, the third law and momentum conservation have the same examples.

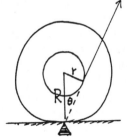

Drop a sheet of paper and then punch it in midair. State that the heavyweight champion of the world couldn't hit the paper with a force equaling the weight of his arm — that he can't exert any greater force on the paper than the paper can exert on him.

Philosophically we know that if you try to do one thing, something else happens as a result. So we say you can never do only one thing. In this chapter we similarly see that you can never have only one force.

NEXT-TIME QUESTION: Home Project 4 — Show this before the class with the string from the spool directed over the top of the spool. The spool, not surprisingly, rolls in the direction of the pull. Ask which way it would roll if the string were directed from the bottom of the spool (as shown in the sketch accompanying Home Project 4).

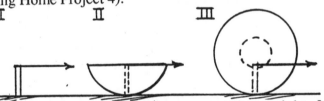

Step I. On the board sketch a wooden peg standing upright. Make an arrow at the top of the peg as shown, which represents a string being pulled toward the right. Ask the class which way the peg will topple.

Step II. Sketch two "wings" on both sides of the peg so that it will roll rather than topple. Ask the class which way it will roll when pulled.

Step III. Sketch a "cap" on the top, effectively sketching a side view of the spool. Again question the class.

If you pull the string upward, there is a point where it doesn't roll at all, but slides, and beyond that elevation the spool will roll in the opposite direction. The explanation for this involves torques, perhaps too early to treat now. Interestingly enough, the critical angle for this is when the string extends to the point of spool contact with the table, as the sketch shows. Then there is no torque.

41

5

Momentum

This chapter begins by picking up where chapter 4 leaves off. Newton's 2nd and 3rd Laws lead directly to momentum and its conservation. We emphasize the impulse-momentum relationship with applications to many examples which have been selected to catch the students' interest. In presenting your own, the exaggerated symbol technique as shown in Figures 5.3, 5.4, 5.5, and 5.8 is suggested. Draw a comparison between momentum conservation and Newton's 3rd Law in explaining examples such as rocket propulsion. You might point out that either of these is fundamental — i.e., momentum conservation may be regarded as a consequence of Newton's 3rd Law, or equally, Newton's 3rd Law may be regarded as a consequence of momentum conservation.

The increased impulse that occurs for bouncing collisions is treated very briefly and is expanded in the next chapter. Angular momentum is postponed to chapter 7.

Interesting fact: The time of contact for a tennis ball on a racquet is about 5 milliseconds, whether or not a player "follows-through." The idea that follow-through in tennis, baseball, or golf appreciably increases the duration of contact is not supported by recent studies. Follow-through guides one's behavior in applying maximum force to supply the impulse.

The popular swinging balls apparatus shown in the sketch is popular for demonstrating momentum conservation. But any thorough analysis of it ought to be postponed to the next chapter when energy is treated. This is because the question is often raised,"Why cannot two balls be raised and allowed to swing into the array, and one ball emerge with twice the speed?" Be careful.  Momentum would indeed be conserved if this were the case. But the case with different numbers of balls emerging never happens. Why? Because energy would not be conserved. For the two-balls-one-ball case, the KE after would be twice as much as the KE before impact. KE is proportional to the square of the speed, and the conservation of both momentum and KE cannot occur unless the numbers of balls for collision and ejection are the same. Consider postponing this demo until the next chapter.

A system is not only isolated in space, but in time also. When we say that momentum is conserved when one pool ball strikes the other, we mean that momentum is conserved during the brief duration of interaction when outside forces can be neglected. After the interaction, friction quite soon brings both balls to a halt. So when we isolate a system for purposes of analysis, we isolate both in space and in time.

You may want to assign an "Egg Drop" experiment. Students design and construct a case to hold an egg that can and will be dropped from a three-or-four story building without breaking. The design cannot include means to increase air resistance, so all cases should strike the ground with about the same speed. By requiring the masses of all cases to be the same, the impulses of all will be the same upon impact. The force of impact, of course, should be minimized by maximizing the time of impact. This project is one that stirs considerable interest, both for your students and others who are not (yet?) taking your class.

There are no exercises in **Practicing Physics** nor lab activities or experiments in the **Laboratory Manual** for this chapter.

This chapter is important in its own right, and serves as a foundation for the concept of energy in the next chapter.

SUGGESTED LECTURE PRESENTATION

Momentum Begin by stating that there is something different between a Mack truck and a roller skate — they each have a different inertia. And that there is still something different about a moving Mack truck and a moving roller skate — they have different momenta. Define and discuss momentum as inertia in motion.

> CHECK QUESTION: After stating that a Mack truck will always have more inertia than an ordinary roller skate, ask if a Mack truck will always have more momentum than a roller skate.

Cite the case of the supertanker shown in Figure 5.1, and why such huge ships normally cut off their power when they are 25 or so kilometers from port. Because of their huge momentum (due mostly to their huge mass), about 25 kilometers of water resistance are needed to bring them to a halt.

Impulse and Momentum Derive the impulse-momentum relationship. In Chapter 2 you defined acceleration as $a = \Delta v/t$ (really Δt, but you likely used t as the "time interval"). Then later in Chapter 4 you defined acceleration in terms of the force needed, $a = F/m$. Now simply equate; $a = a$, or $F/m = \Delta v/t$, with simple rearrangement you have, $Ft = \Delta mv$. (as in the footnote, page 81.)

Then choose your examples in careful sequence: First, those where the object is to increase momentum — pulling a sling shot or arrow in a bow all the way back, the effect of a long cannon for maximum range, driving a golf ball. Second, those examples where small forces are the object when decreasing momentum — pulling your hand backward when catching a ball, driving into a haystack versus a concrete wall, falling on a surface with give versus a rigid surface. Then lastly, those examples where the object is to obtain large forces when decreasing momentum — karate.

Point of confusion: In boxing, one "follows through" whereas in karate one "pulls back". But this is not so — a karate expert does not pull back upon striking his target. He strikes in such a way that his hand is made to bounce back, yielding up to twice the impulse to his target (just as a ball bouncing off a wall delivers nearly twice the impulse to the wall than if it stuck to the wall).

CHECK QUESTION: Why is falling on a wooden floor in a roller rink less dangerous than falling on the concrete pavement? [Superficial answer: Because the wooden floor has more "give." Emphasize that this is the beginning of a fuller answer—one that is prompted if the question is reworded as follows:] Why is falling on a floor with more give less dangerous than falling on a floor with less give? [Answer: Because the floor with more give allows a greater time for the impulse that reduces the momentum of fall to zero. A greater time for Δ momentum means less force.]

The loose coupling between railroad cars (Exercise 10) makes a good lecture topic. Discuss the importance of loose coupling in bringing a long train initially at rest up to speed, and its importance in braking the train as well. (I compare this to taking school load in proper sequence, rather than all at once where for sure one's wheels would simply spin.)

Conservation of Momentum   Distinguish between external and internal forces and lead into the conservation of momentum. Show from the impulse-momentum equation that no change in momentum can occur in the absence of an external net force.

DEMONSTRATION: Show momentum conservation with an air-track performance.

Defining Your System   Momentum is not conserved in a system that experiences an external net force. Consider a cue ball that makes a head-on collision with an 8-ball at rest. If the system is taken to be only the 8-ball at rest, then we isolate it with a dotted border around it, sketch I. So long as no outside force acts on it, there will be no impulse on it and no change in its momentum. But when the cue ball strikes it, there is an outside force and an impulse on it. Its momentum changes as it speeds away with the speed of the incident cue ball. Or take the system to be the cue ball, sketch II. Initially it has momentum mv. Then it strikes the 8-ball and its momentum undergoes a change. The reaction force by the 8-ball brings it to a halt. Now consider the system of both balls, sketch III. Before collision the momentum is that of the moving cue ball. When the balls strike, no outside force acts, for the interaction is between the balls, both parts of the same system. So no impulse acts on the system and no change in momentum of the system occurs. In this case momentum is converved. It is the same before and after the collision. Again, the momentum of a system is conserved only when no external impulse is exerted on the system.

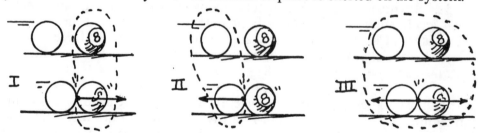

Consider a dropped rock in freefall. If the system is taken to be the rock, sketch IV, then momentum is not conserved as it falls because an external force acts on the system (its vector is seen to penetrate the dotted border of the system). This external force, gravity, produces an impulse on the rock that changes its momentum. If the system is instead considered to be the rock + the entire world, sketch V, then the interaction between the rock

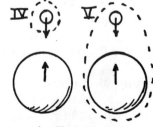

and the earth is internal to the system (there is no penetrating vector). For this larger system, momentum is conserved. Momentum is always conserved if you make your system big enough. The momentum of the universe is without change.

The numerical examples of lunchtime for the fish, new to this edition, should clarify the vector nature of momentum — particularly for the case of the fishes approaching each other. Going over this should be helpful.

Bouncing Discuss bouncing and how Lester Pelton made a fortune from applying some simple physics to the old paddle wheels.

Consider the demo of swinging the dart against the wooden block to show the effect of bouncing. This is treated in the text in Figure 6.16, page 108, of the next chapter. (The models in the figure are Dave Vasquez, who videotaped my classroom lectures in 1984, and Helen Yan, who lettered the artwork in the text and most of the Next-Time Questions.) A weak point of this demonstration is the fact that if the dart securely sticks to the block, then the center of gravity of the block is changed to favor non tipping. This weak point is neatly circumvented by the following demo by Rich Langer of Beaumont High School in St. Louis, MO, which considers sliding rather than tipping.

DEMONSTRATION: Toy dart gun and computer-disc box. Tape some toothpicks to only one side of the box, so a suction-cup dart won't stick to it. First fire the dart against the smooth side of the box. The dart sticks and the box slides an observed distance across the table. Then repeat, but with the box turned around so the dart sticks to the toothpick side. When the dart hits is doesn't stick but instead bounces. Note the appreciably greater distance the box slides!

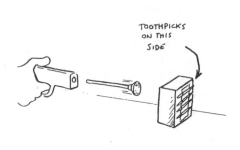

TOOTHPICKS ON THIS SIDE

Exercises 21, 22 and 23 may need your elaboration if you wish to go this deep in your lecture. Simply removing the sail, as Exercise 23 suggests, is the option used by propellor-driven aircraft. Consider suddenly producing a sail in the airstream produced by the propellor of an airplane. The result would be a loss of thrust, and if bouncing of the air occurred, there would be a reverse thrust on the craft. This is precisely what happens in the case of jet planes landing on the runway. Metal "sails" move into place behind the engine in the path of the ejected exhaust, which cause the exhaust to reverse direction. The resulting reverse thrust appreciably slows the aircraft.

On the matter of slowing aircraft on the runway, the question is begged: Why not have the runway sloped, so that during takeoff the plane accelerates slightly downhill, and in landing runs slightly uphill? (I recall seeing this suggestion in the newspaper some months ago. Sounds good.)

Vectors If you wish to expand on vectors in your course, you may want to assign Appendix III at this point. The sailboat is excellent for illustrating the usefulness of vectors. An interesting demonstration is the model "sailboat", which you can easily build yourself with a small block of wood and a piece of aluminum. Cut slots in a piece of 2 x 4 inch wooden block as shown, and mount it on a small cart (or ideally, on an air track). A ft² piece of aluminum serves as a sail, and wind from a hand-held fan is directed against the sail in various directions. Most impressive, of course, is holding the fan in front, but off to the side a bit, so that the boat will sail into the wind. Later in the course, when discussing Bernoulli's principle, the sailboat may again be demonstrated with a curved sail. The difference in speeds is quite noticeable.

The function of the keel on a sailboat is a trouble spot for many students, so you can sidestep this and consider an iceboat instead. Its easy to see that the runners cut into the ice and don't slip sideways like a sailboat can.

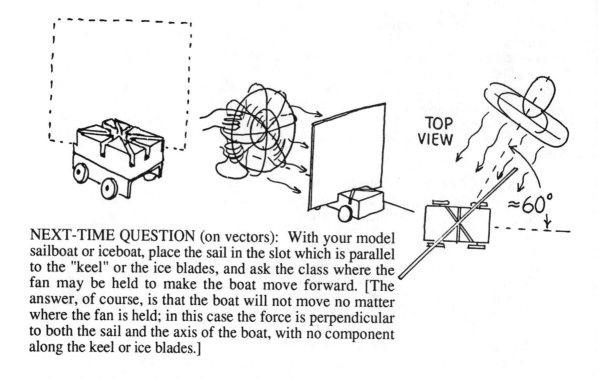

NEXT-TIME QUESTION (on vectors): With your model sailboat or iceboat, place the sail in the slot which is parallel to the "keel" or the ice blades, and ask the class where the fan may be held to make the boat move forward. [The answer, of course, is that the boat will not move no matter where the fan is held; in this case the force is perpendicular to both the sail and the axis of the boat, with no component along the keel or ice blades.]

6
Energy

This is an important chapter. The concept of energy is central to physics and is discussed in its various forms throughout the remainder of the text. The previous chapter is prerequisite to at least the section "Comparison Between Kinetic Energy and Momentum." The last section of the chapter, "Energy for Life," can be expanded upon in lecture.

The section "Comparison of Kinetic Energy and Momentum," pages 106—109, should be skipped if you are presenting a short treatment of mechanics. Although it is important to students who will take a follow-up physics course, it is likely not useful enough to belabor with non-science students.

The bed of nails demonstration Figure 6.17 has been around for many years. Gerald L. Hodgson of Kansas City Kansas Community College has been sandwiching himself between beds of nails in class for more than a decade. [This demo is shown in the opening title shots of the videotape series, *Conceptual Physics Alive!*]

For neat energy-of-automobile physics, see the Oct. 88 issue of *The Physics Teacher*.

This chapter is represented in **Practicing Physics**, with a page on *Energy conservation*.

There is an activity on energy and power and an experiment on leverage and mechanical advantage in the **Laboratory Manual** to complement this chapter.

A nice discussion to kick off a treatment of energy is presented by Feynman in the beginning of his Chapter 4, *The Feynman Lectures On Physics* (Addison-Wesley, 1963).

SUGGESTED LECTURE PRESENTATION

Begin by standing on a chair against a wall with an extended heavy pendulum bob held at the tip of your nose. Say nothing. Release the bob and let it swing out, then back to your nose. Don't flinch. Then comment on your confidence in physical laws and lead into a distinction between potential and kinetic energy. That is, point out that where the bob is moving fastest, it is lowest, and where it is highest, it doesn't move at all. The bob transforms energy of motion to energy of position in cyclic fashion. Allow the pendulum to swing to and fro while you're talking. Its motion decays. Why? Then point out the transformation of energy from the moving bob to the molecules of air that are encountered, and to the molecules in the bending string or wire at the pivot point. The energy of the pendulum will end up as heat energy. I quip that on a very hot day, somebody, somewhere, is swinging a giant pendulum to and fro.

Work Define work and compare it to impulse of the previous chapter. In both cases, the effect of exerting a force on something depends on how long the force acts. In the previous chapter, how long was meant as time, and we spoke of impulse. In this chapter, how long is meant as distance, and we speak of work. Cite the examples of the drawn sling shot and the long barrelled cannon, where the added length produces greater speed. We described this greater speed in terms of greater momentum: Now we describe this greater speed in terms of greater energy — that is, greater KE.

Distinguish between the energy one expends in doing things, and the work that is actually done on something. Reiterate the caption of Figure 6.2, that no work is done *on the wall*. Emphasize that when work is done *on* something, that something undergoes a change — either in position (ΔPE), or in motion (ΔKE).

Potential Energy Return to your pendulum: With the pendulum at equilibrium show how the force necessary to pull it sideways (which varies with the angle made by the string) is very small com-pared to the force necessary to lift it vertically (its weight). Point out that for equal elevations, the arced path is correspondingly longer than the vertical path — with the result that the product of the applied force and distance traveled — the work done — is the same for both cases. (Without overdoing it, this is a good place to let your students know about integral calculus — how calculus is required to add up the work segments that continuously increase in a non-linear way.) Then discuss the work needed to elevate the ball in Figure 6.5.

> CHECK QUESTIONS: Does a car hoisted for lubrication in a service station have PE? How much work will raise it car twice as high? Three times as high? How much more PE will it have in these cases?

Kinetic Energy Relate force x distance = Δ KE to examples of pushing a car, and then to braking a car as treated in the text. You may do Exercise 9 (about skidding distance as a function of speed) at this point.

You may or may not at this point preview future material by relating the idea of the KE of molecules and the idea of temperature. State that molecules in a substance having the same temperature have the same average KE. If the masses of the molecules are the same, then it follows that the speeds of the molecules are the same. But what if the masses are different, for example in a sample of gas made up of light and heavy molecules at the same temperature? Which molecules would move faster? (If you shook a container of billiard balls mixed with ping pong balls so that both kinds of balls had the same kinetic energy, which would move faster in the container?) (If an elephant and a mouse run with the same kinetic energy, which is to say both will do the same amount of work if they bump into the door of a barn, can you say which of the two is running faster?) You might consider the demonstration of inhaling helium and talking at this point — particularly if you are not including the chapters on sound in your course design. Relate the higher temper due to the faster moving helium molecules to the higher temper in a bugle when faster moving air is blown through it.

Energy Conservation Discuss Figures 6.6 through 6.9 and then return to your pendulum. Explain how the kinetic energy and hence, the speed of the bob at the bottom of its swing is equal to the speed it would have if dropped vertically through the same height.

> CHECK QUESTION: Refer to Figure 6.5 in "inclines" a and b: how does the speed of the ball compare at ground level when released from equal elevations? [It is impressive that the speeds will be the same. The lesser acceleration down the sloped ramp is compensated by a longer time. But return to the situation and ask how the *times* to reach the bottom compare and be prepared for an incorrect response, "The same!" Quip and ask if the colors and temperatures will also be the same. Straightfoward physics can be confusing enough!]

If you wish to treat the solution to Exercise 20 as part of your lecture, you'll be underscoring the great usefulness of the energy concept in dealing with motion. You can also state that one of the reasons you didn't spend too much time working out numerical examples and posing problems on the material back in Chapter 2 is that physicists usually treat these ideas in the context of energy.

> DEMONSTRATION: Do a mini version of Figure 6.17 and place a heavy object on your forearm and hand, and strike it very hard with a hammer with your other hand. (If you wish to explain this in detail for science majors in your class, cite the roles of both energy and momentum, and compare the brief impulses of both your demonstration and that of the ball hanging by the string back in Figure 4.1.)

> DEMONSTRATION: Preview electricity and magnetism and bring out the horseshoe magnet hand-cranked generator that lights up the lamp. Have student volunteers attest to the fact that more work is needed to turn the crank when the lamp is connected than when it is not. Then relate this to Exercise 13.

I follow through on the fuel economy bit (remember we used to say "mileage" in the pre-SI days?) with escalators in a department store. Even though the escalator is in operation, more electrical energy is consumed when you add to its load. The motor "knows" when you get on and when you get off. It does work to pull you up to the next floor. So strictly speaking, you'll save electrical energy if you walk up the stairs rather than ride the escalator. And as for riding the escalator down, do so and feel good about it, for friction aside, you'll be doing work *on* the escalator, relieving the work the motor does, and you'll be saving electrical energy. Pushed to the idealistic extreme, at least, this is really be the case!

Go over the check question on page 106 of the text — very important. (I pose the same question on my exams, which to the student is the *definition* of what's important!) If the car in question is a compact, a better figure for the drag force at 55 mph is about 500 N. With this force to overcome, ideal fuel economy would be 80 km per liter. As a side point, gas economy is increased when tires are inflated to maximum pressures, where less flattening of the tire occurs as it turns. The very important point of this exercise is the upper limit possible.

I extend this idea of an upper limit to the supposed notion that certain gadgets attached to automobile engines will give phenomenal performance — so much in fact, that the oil companies have gobbled up the patents and are keeping them off the market. Charlatans stand ready to benefit from this public perception, and offer the public a chance to invest in their energy producing machines. They prey on people who are ignorant of or do not understand the message of the energy conservation law. You can't get something for nothing. You can't even break even, because of the inevitable transformation of available energy to heat.

Efficiency It should be enough that your students become acquainted with the idea of efficiency, so I don't recommend setting the plow setting too deep for this topic. The key idea to impart is that of useful energy. To say that an incandescent lamp is 10% efficient is to say that only 10% of the energy input is converted to the useful form of light. All the rest goes to heat. But even the light energy converts to heat upon absorption. So all the energy input to an incandescent lamp is converted to heat. This means that it is a 100% efficient *heater* (but not a 100% device for emitting light)!

NEXT-TIME QUESTION: Exercise 31, when you've shown the swinging ball apparatus in class.

7

Rotational Motion

This chapter extends the translational ideas of Chapter 4 to rotation. A space habitat theme is briefly treated which opens the door to the myriad of interesting physics applications in a rotating frame of reference.

The classic oldie but goodie PSSC film, "Frames of Reference" goes nicely with this chapter. For good ideas read "Which Way is up" Al Bartlett TPT 10,429 (1972); "Up in the Lab and in Literature" D. Easton TPT 22, (100) 1984, and the book "Sport Science" by Peter Brancazio (Simon & Shuster, 1984). Brancazio's book is an excellent source of physics applications, with emphasis on the human body.

A nice extension of HP 4 of two fingers sliding to the center of a balanced meter stick, is doing the same to a horizontally balanced plate on your 3 fingers. Bring your fingers together as the plate remains in balance!

This chapter can be skipped or skimmed if a short treatment of mechanics is desired.

There are two exercises, *Torques*, which treats center of gravity in "mobile building," and *Centripetal Force* in **Practicing Physics**.

The activity *Torque Feeler* in the **Laboratory Manual** is especially worthwhile — even in a lecture setting. There are two other activities and two experiments to complement this chapter.

The suggested lecture should take two or three class periods.

SUGGESTED LECTURE PRESENTATION

Recall from Chapter 3 the difference between rotational and linear speed — the examples of riding at different radial positions on a merry-go-round, or the different speeds of different parts of a phonograph record. A couple of coins on a record player, one close to the axis and the other near the edge, dramatically show the greater speed of the outer one. Cite the motion of "tail-end Charlie" at the skating rink.

Rotational Inertia   Compare the idea of inertia and its role in linear motion to rotational inertia (moment of inertia) in rotational motion. The difference between the two involves the role of *distance* from a rotational axis. The greater the distance of mass concentration, the greater the resistance to rotation. Discuss the role of the pole for the tightrope walker in Figure 7.2. A novice tightrope walker might begin with the ends of the pole in supporting slots, similar to the training wheels on a beginner's bicycle. If the pole has adequate rotational inertia, the slots mainly provide psychological comfort as well as actual safety. Just as the training wheels could be safely removed without the rider's knowledge, the slots could be safely removed without the walker's knowledge.

Show how a longer pendulum has a greater period and relate this to the different strides of long and short legged people. Imitate these strides yourself — or at least with your fingers walking across the desk.

> DEMONSTRATION: This is a good one. Have two 1 meter pipes, one with two lead plugs in the center, the other with plugs in each end. They appear identical. Weigh both to show the same weight. Give one to a student (with plugs in ends) and ask her to rotate it about its center (like in Figure 7.1). Have another student do the same with the pipe that has the plugs in the middle. Then have them switch. Good fun. Then ask for speculations as to why one was noticeably more difficult to rotate than the other.

> DEMONSTRATION: As in the check question on page 118, have students try to balance on a finger a long stick with a massive lead weight at one end. Try it first with the weight at the finger tip, then with the weight at the top. Or you can use a broom, or long-handled hammer. Relate this to the ease with which a circus performer balances a pole full of people doing acrobatics, and cite how much more difficult it would be for the performer to balance an empty pole!

Relate this demonstration and the continued adjustments you have to execute to keep the object balanced to the similar adjustments that must be made in keeping a rocket vertical when it is first fired. Amazing.

> DEMONSTRATION: Fasten a mass to the end of a meter-stick. A blob of clay works fine. Set it on end on your lecture table, along with another meter stick with no attached mass. When you let go of the sticks, they'll topple to the table top. Ask which stick will reach the table top first. [The plain stick wins due to the greater rotational inertia of the clay-top stick. There is more to this than simply greater rotational inertia, for torque is increased as well. If the clay is located at the middle of the stick, the effects of greater torque and greater rotational inertia balance each other and both sticks fall together.]

Discuss the variety of rotational inertias shown in Figure 7.3. Stress the formulas are for comparison, and point out why the same formula applies to the pendulum and the hoop (all the mass of each is at the same distance from the rotational axis). State how reasonable the smaller value for a solid disk is, given that much of its mass is close to the rotational axis.

> DEMONSTRATION: Place a hoop and disk at the top of an incline and ask which will have the greater acceleration down the incline. Do not release the hoop and disk until students have discussed this with their neighbors. Try other shapes after your class makes reasoned estimates.

Ask why a football is set spinning when it is thrown. Show also for minimum air resistance and maximum range that a 2nd spin is imparted about another axis; a very slow spin that finds the nose of the ball always aligned with its trajectory. Relate this to the spiral grooves cut in the bores of guns.

Center of Mass and Torque Depart a bit from the order of the chapter and begin a discussion of center of mass before treating torque. Do this by tossing a small metal ball across the room, stating it follows a smooth curved path — a parabola. Then pick up an irregularly shaped piece of wood, perhaps an L-shape, and state that if this were thrown across the room it would not follow a smooth path, that it would wobble all over the place — but a special place, the place we are going to discuss today — the center of mass, or center of gravity. Illustrate your definition with figures of different shapes, first those where the center of mass lies within the object and then to shapes where the center of mass lies outside the objects.

CHECK QUESTION: Where is the center of mass of a donut?

Ask you students if they "have" a CG. Acknowledge that the CG in men is generally higher than in women (1% - 2%), mainly because women tend to be proportionally smaller in the upper body, and heavier in the pelvis. On the average it lies about 6 inches above the crotch, a bit below the bellybutton. Interestingly enough, the reason for the bellybutton being where it is relates to CG. A fetus turning in its mother's womb would rotate about its CG, the likely place for its umbilical cord. When we bend over, of course, the CG extends beyond the physical body.

Place an L-shaped body on the table and show how it topples — because its center of mass lies outside a point of support. Sketch this on the board. Then stand against a wall and ask if it is possible for one to bend over and touch their toes without toppling forward. Attempt to do so. Sketch this next to the L-shape as shown. By now your chalkboard looks like the following:

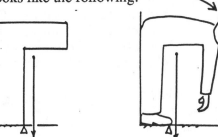

Discuss a remedy for such toppling, like longer shoes or the wearing of snowshoes or skiis. Sketch a pair of skiis on the feet of the person in your drawing. Seem to change the subject and ask why a pregnant woman often gets back pains. Sketch a woman before and after getting pregnant, showing how the CG shifts forward — beyond a point of support for the same posture. (Those familiar with the 4th Edition may remember that this was featured in the text via a photo of my friend Jackie Spears who was several months pregnant and wearing skiis. Jackie and husband Dean Zollman have since written *The Fascination of Physics*, published by Benjamin Commings, 1985. This whole idea goes over much better in lecture than as reading material, so is not found in this edition. So now

53

you can introduce it as a fresh idea in class.) Make a third sketch showing how a woman can adjust her posture so that her CG is above the support base bounded by her feet, sketching lastly, the "marks of pain." Ask the class how she could prevent these pains, and if someone in class doesn't volunteer the idea of wearing skiis, do so yourself and sketch skiis on her feet in the second drawing.

Lead your class into an alternate solution, that of carrying a pole on her shoulder, near the end of which is a load. Erase the skiis and sketch in the pole and load as shown. Acknowledge the objection that she would have to increase the mass of the load as the months go by, and ask what else can be done. Someone should volunteer that she need only move the load closer to the end, which in effect shifts the overall CG in a favorable direction. This routine is effective and sparks much class interest. However, you must be very careful that you don't offend your students, particularly your female students. Whenever you single out any "minority (?)" you run the risk of offending members of that minority group or those sensitive to the feelings of members of that group. We instructors, whether male or female ourselves, are for the most part conscious of this and therefore make our examples as general as possible — mixing "shes" and "hes" whenever these pronouns come up. But in the case of a person becoming pregnant, its a definite "she." Any classroom laughter that your presentation elicits should be, after all, directed to the situation and not particularly toward the woman. In any event, we are in sad shape when we cannot laugh at ourselves occasionally.

Return to your chalkboard sketches of L-shaped objects and relate their tipping to the torques that exist. Point out the lever arms in the sketches.

CHECK QUESTION: An L-shaped object with CG marked by the X rests on a hill as shown. Draw this on your paper and mark it appropriately to determine whether the object will topple or not.

Comment: Be prepared for some students to sketch in the "vertical" line through the CG perpendicular to the slope as shown.

WRONG!

A simple example of this is to balance a pipe (smoking kind) on your hand when held at an angle.

Cite examples involving the CG in animals and people — how the long tails of monkeys enable them to lean forward without losing balance — and how people lean backwards when carrying a heavy load at their chests, and how the coolie method with the load distributed in two parts suspended at the ends of a pole supported in the middle is a better way.

You may note that missing from this edition is the figure of the pigeon with the caption that stated that a pigeon jerks its head back and forth with each step and thereby keeps its center of gravity always above the supporting foot. Although this is true, the primary reason for the pigeon's behavior seems to have more to do with its vision. Forward movements for a creature with side-mounted eyes result in parallax shifts — apparent motion of near objects relative to distant objects. The retina of the pigeon works much better with completely stationary images. So for better vision the pigeon keeps its head at rest while it steps forward. It jerks its head forward for the next step and so on. Creatures with eyes mounted in the front of the head have no such parallax problem. Why don't horses similarly jerk their heads when they walk?

Also missing from the 7th Edition is the cartoon at the right. In page makeup there simply was no room for it.

Ask why a ball rolls down a hill (Exercise 16). State that "because of gravity" is an incomplete answer. Gravity would have it slide down the hill. The fact it rolls, or rotates, is evidence of an unbalanced torque. Sketch this on your chalkboard.

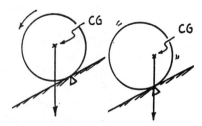

DEMONSTRATION: Show how a "loaded disk" rolls *up* an inclined plane. After class speculation, show how the disk remains at rest on the incline. Modify your chalkboard sketch to show how both the CG with respect to the support point is altered, and the absence of a lever arm and therefore the absence of a torque.

Discuss wrenches and clarify moment arm distances. Cite how a steering wheel is simply a modified wrench, and why trucks and heavy vehicles that do not have power steering use large diameter steering wheels.

DEMONSTRATION: Attempt to stand from a seated position without putting your feet under the chair. Explain with center of gravity and torques.

See Saws Extend rotation to see-saws, like in Figures 7.7 and 7.8.

DEMONSTRATION: Do as Cindy Dube at Farmington High School in Conneticut does and make a candle see saw. Trim with the wick exposed at both ends, and balance the candle by a needle through the center. Rest the ends of the needle on a pair of drinking glasses. Light both ends of the candle. As the wax drips, the CG shifts, causing the candle to oscillate.

Explain how participants on a see-saw can vary the net torque by not only sliding back and forth, but by leaning. In this way the location of their CGs and hence the lever arm distance is changed. Discuss the boy playing by himself in the park (Exercise 15), and how he is able to rotate up and down by leaning toward and away from the fulcrum.

DEMONSTRATION: Place a heavy plank on your lecture table so that it overhangs. Walk out on the overhanging part and ask why you don't topple. Relate this to the solitary see-saw example.

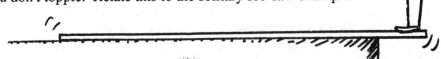

Here's a neat application of CG that is not in the text. If you gently shake a basket of berries, the larger berries will make their way to the top. In so doing the CG is lowered by the more compact smaller berries settling to the bottom. You can demonstrate this with a ping pong ball at the bottom of a container of dried beans, peas, or smaller objects. When the container is shaken, the Ping-Pong ball surfaces, lowering the CG of the system. This idea can be extended to the ping pong ball in a glass of water. The CG of the system is lowest when the Ping-Pong ball floats. Push it under the surface and the CG is raised. If you do the same with something more dense than water, the CG is lowest when it is at the bottom.

Centripetal force   Whirl an object tied to the end of a string overhead and ask if there is an outward or an inward force exerted on the whirling object. Explain how no outward or centrifugal force acts on the whirling object (the only outward directed force is the reaction force *on the string*, but not on the object). Emphase also that centripetal force is not a force in its own right, like gravity, but is the name for any force that pulls an object into a curved path.

> DEMONSTRATION: Swing a bucket of water in a vertical circle and show that the water doesn't spill (when centripetal force is at least equal to the weight of the water). All your students have heard of this demon-stration, but only a few have actually seen it done. (I underestimated this demo for too many years!)

Centrifugal Force in a Rotating Frame   The concept of centrifugal force is useful when viewed from a rotating frame of reference. Then it seems as real as gravity to an occupant — like inside a rotating space habitat. State how it differs from a real force in that there is no agent such as mass. The magnetic force on a magnet, for example, is caused by the presence of another magnet; the force on a charge is caused by the presence of another charge. Whereas a real force is an interaction between one body and another, there is no reaction counterpart to centrifugal force. Distinguish centrifugal force from the action-reaction pairs of forces at the feet of an astronaut in a rotating habitat.

Discuss rotating space habitats. Show how *g* varies with the radial distance from the hub, and with the rotational rate of the structure. The earth has been the cradle of humankind; but humans do not live in the cradle forever. We will likely leave our cradle and inhabit structures of our own building; structures that will serve as lifeboats for the planet earth. Their prospect is exciting. (Read oldie-but-goodies Gerard O'Neill's "The High Frontier", or Harry Stine's "The Third Industrial Revolution" — fascinating books.)

Angular Momentum   Just as inertia and rotational inertia differed by a radial distance, and just as force and torque also differed by a radial distance, so momentum and angular momentum differ by a radial distance. Relate linear momentum to angular momentum for the case of a small mass at a relatively large radial distance — the object you swung overhead.

For the more general case, angular momentum is simple the product of rotational inertia I and angular velocity w. This is indicated in Figure 7.41.

> DEMONSTRATION: With weights in your hand, rotate on a platform as shown in Figure 7.41.

> DEMONSTRATION: Show the operation of a gyroscope — either a model or a rotating bicycle wheel as my late son James demonstrates in Figure 7.39.

NEXT-TIME QUESTIONS: Which will roll with the greater acceleration down an incline, a can of solid food or a can of non-viscous liquid? Double credit for a good explanation of what is seen. [The can of liquid will undergo appreciably more acceleration because the liquid is not made to rotate with the rotating can. It in effect "slides" rather than rolls down the incline (it should be established that an object will slide a lot faster down an incline than it will roll, providing friction is nil for sliding, and adequate for rolling). Fine, one might say, then if the liquid doesn't rotate, the can ought to behave as an empty can, with the larger rotational inertia of a "hoop" and lag behind. This brings up an interesting point: The issue is not which can has the greater rotational inertia, but which has the greater rotational inertia compared to its mass [note the *compared to its mass* qualifier in Figure 7.6.] The liquid content has appreciably more mass than the can that contains it; hence the non-rolling liquid serves to increase the mass of the can without contributing to its rotational inertia. It gives the can of liquid a relatively small rotational inertia compared to its mass.

Exercises 32 through 34: When answering these, demonstrate again on the rotating platform, holding the weights over your head to simulate earth washing toward the equator, melting ice caps spreading toward the equator by lowering your hands in an outstretched position to simulate earth and water flowing toward the equator. To simulate the effects of skyscraper construction, hold the weights short of fully stretched, then extend your arms full-length.

8

Gravity

This chapter begins and ends on an astronomical theme, and makes use of the historical approach. It is prerequisite to the following chapter on satellite motion.

Be sure to acquaint yourself with the delightful book *The Attractive Universe*, by E.G. Valens and Berenice Abbott (World, 1969). Good material!

This chapter offers a good place to reiterate the idea of a scientific theory, and comment on the all-too common and mistaken idea that because something has the status of scientific theory, it is somehow short of being valid. This view is evident in those who say, "But its *only* a theory." Bring the essence of the first footnote on page 143 into your discussion.

Kepler's 3rd law follows logically from Newton's law of gravitation. Equate the force of gravity between planet m and the sun M to the centripetal force on m. Then,

$GmM/r^2 = mv^2/r = m(2\pi r/T)^2/r$

where the speed of the planet is simply its circular distance $2\pi r$ per period T. Cancel and collect terms,

$GM/4\pi^2 = r^3/T^2$

This is Kepler's 3rd law, for $GM/4\pi^2$ is a constant.

The idea of the force field is introduced in this chapter and is a good background for the electric field treated later in Chapter 21. The gravitational field here is applied to regions outside as well as inside the earth.

On page 153 the text states without explanation that the gravitational field increases linearly with radial distance inside a planet of uniform density. Figure 8.19 shows that the field increases linearly from zero at its center to maximum at the surface. This is also without explanation. The text states that "perhaps your instructor will provide the explanation." Here it is: We know that the gravitational force F between a particle m and a spherical mass M, when m is outside M is simply $F = GmM/d^2$. But when m is inside a uniform density solid sphere of mass M, the force on m is due only to the mass M' contained within the sphere of radius $r < R$, represented by the dotted line in

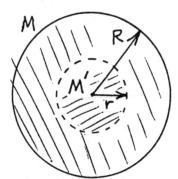

the figure. Contributions from the shell $> r$ cancel out (established on pages 153 and 154 and Figure 8.20, and again for the analogous case of the electric field in Figure 21.19, page 386). So, $F = GmM'/r^2$. From the ratio of M'/M, you can show that $M' = Mr^3/R^3$. [that is, $M'/M = V'/V = (^4/_3 \pi r^3)/(^4/_3 \pi R^3) = r^3/R^3$.] Substitute M' in Newton's equation for gravitation and we get $F = GmMr/R^3$. All terms on the right are constant except r. So $F = kr$; force is linearly proportional to radial distance when $r < R$.

Interestingly enough, the condition for simple harmonic motion is that the restoring force be proportional to displacement, $F = kr$ — hence the simple harmonic motion of one who falls in the tunnel through the earth. (Hence also the simple harmonic motion of one who slides without friction to and fro along any straight line tunnel through any part of the earth. The displacement is then the component $r \sin ø$.) The period of simple harmonic motion, $T = 2\pi\sqrt{R^3/GM}$ is the same as that of a satellite in close circular orbit about the earth. Note that it is independent of the length of the tunnel. See more detail in a text such as Tipler's *Physics For Scientists and Engineers*.

You can compare the pull of the moon that is exerted on you with the pull exerted by more local masses, via the gravitational equation. Consider the ratio of the mass of the moon to its distance squared:

$$7.4 \times 10^{22} kg/(4 \times 10^5 km)^2 = 5 \times 10^{12} kg/km^2$$

This is a sizable ratio, one that buildings in your vicinity cannot match (city buildings of greatest mass are typically on the order of 10^6 or 10^7 kilograms). However, if you stand 1 kilometer away from the foot of a mountain of mass 5×10^{12} kilograms (about the mass of Mt. Kilimanjaro), then the pull of the mountain and the pull of the moon are about the same on you. Interestingly enough, with no friction you would tend to gravitate from your spot toward the mountain — but you experience no tendency at all to gravitate from your spot toward the moon! That's because the spot you stand on undergoes the same gravitational acceleration toward the moon as you do. Both you and the whole earth are accelerating toward the moon. Whatever the lunar force on you, it has no tendency to pull you off a weighing scale — which is the essence of Exercises 17 and 18.

A brief treatment of black holes is included in this chapter. The idea that light is influenced by a gravitational field isn't treated until Chapter 35, so may merit further explanation. You'll probably want to acknowledge that light bends in a gravitational field as does a thrown baseball. We say light travels in straight lines much for the same reason that some people say that a high-speed bullet doesn't curve downward in the first part of its trajectory. Over short distances the bullet doesn't appear to drop only because of the high speed and short time involved. Likewise with light, which we don't notice because of the high speed and therefore vast distance involved compared to the brief time it is in the strong part of the earth's gravitational field. Note the treatment of this idea in Figure 35.8 on page 679.

Gravitational force is treated on one page in **Practicing Physics**.

If you have a computer and the Laserpoint program *Trial and Error*, the activity by the same name in the **Laboratory Manual** is a dandy.

While the information in this chapter is useful as a background for Chapter 35 (general relativity) and Chapter 20 (the inverse-square law, and the analogy between a gravitational and electric field) it may be skipped without complicating the treatment of other material. This is an interesting chapter, for the material is interesting in itself, is interesting historically, and is closely related to areas of space science that are currently in the public eye.

SUGGESTED LECTURE PRESENTATION

Begin by briefly discussing the simple codes and patterns that underlie the complex things around us, whether musical compositions or DNA molecules, and then briefly describe the harmonious motion of the solar system, the Milky Way and other galaxies in the universe — stating that the shapes of the planets, stars, and galaxies, and their motions are all governed by an extremely simple code, or if you will, a pattern. Then write the gravitational equation on the board. Give examples of bodies pulling on each other to convey a clear idea of what the symbols in the equation mean and how they relate. State that Newton's equation was deduced from Kepler's laws.

Kepler's Laws Briefly discuss Kepler's laws. Sketch an elliptical path of a planet about the sun as in Figure 8.1. Show how the equal areas law means that the planet travels slowest when farthest from the sun, and fastest when closest. State that Kepler had no idea why this was so. Walk to the side of your room and toss a piece of chalk upward at a slight angle so the class can see the parabolic path it traces. Ask where the chalk is moving slowest? Fastest? Why is it moving slowest at the top? [Because it has been traveling against gravity all the way up!] Why is it moving fastest when it is thrown and when it is caught? [It's moving fastest when it is caught because it has been traveling in the direction of gravity all the way down!] Speculate how amazed Kepler would have been if the same questions were asked him, and related to the speeds of the planets around the sun — slowest where they have been traveling against the gravity of the sun, and fastest where they have been falling back toward the sun. Kepler would have been amazed to see the physics of a body tossed upward is essentially the physics of satellite motion! Kepler lacked this simple model to guide his thinking. What simple models of tomorrow do we lack today, that finds us presently blind to the common sense of tomorrow?

Inverse-Square Law Discuss the inverse square law and go over Figures 8.4 and 8.6 or their equivalents with candlelight or radioactivity.

Plot to scale an inverse-square curve on the board, showing the steepness of the curve — 1/4, 1/9, and 1/16, for twice, three times, and four times the separation distance occur rather "suddenly." This is shown in Figure 8.6. (You'll return to this curve when you explain tides.)

> CHECK QUESTIONS: How is the gravitational force between a pair of planets altered when one of the planets is twice as massive? When both are twice as massive? When they are twice as far apart? When they are three times as far apart? Ten times as far apart?

Weight and Weightlessness Discuss weightlessness and relate it to the queasy feeling your students experience when in a car that goes too fast over the top of a hill. State that this feeling is what an astronaut is confronted with all the time in orbit! Ask how many of your class would still welcome the opportunity to take a field trip to Cape Canaveral and take a ride aboard the shuttle. What an exciting prospect!

Discuss the fate of Skylab when its orbit decayed and it "scraped its feet" in the atmosphere in 1978. I show the NASA film "Zero G" every semester, for it not only is fascinating in its shots of astronaut acrobatics in the orbiting lab, but recaps Newton's laws as they apply to interesting situations. The film shows the good sense of humor of the astronauts. A must!

Discuss the differences in a baseball game on the moon, and your favorite gravity-related topics.

Tides Begin your treatment of tides by asking the class to consider the consequences of someone pulling your coat. If they pulled only on the sleeve, for example, it would tear. But if every part of your coat were pulled equally, it and you would accelerate — but it wouldn't tear. It tears when one part is pulled harder than another — or it tears because of a *difference* in forces acting on the coat. In a similar way, the spherical earth is "torn" into an elliptical shape by differences in gravitational forces by the moon and sun.

Misconceptions About the Moon
This is an appropriate place for you to dispel two popular misconceptions about the moon. One is that since one side of the moon's face is "frozen" to the earth, it doesn't spin like a top about its polar axis; and two, that the crescent shape commonly seen is *not* the earth's shadow. To convince your class that the moon spins about its polar axis, simulate the situation by holding your eraser at arms length in front of your face. Tell your class that the eraser represents the moon and your head represents the earth. Rotate slowly keeping one face of the eraser in your view. Call attention to the class that from your frame of reference, the eraser doesn't spin as it rotates about you — as evidenced by your observation of only one face, with the backside hidden. But your students occupy the frame of reference of the stars (each of them *is* a star). From their point of view they can see all sides of the eraser as it rotates because it spins about its own axis as often as it rotates about your head. Show them how the eraser, if not slowly spinning and rotationally frozen with one face always facing the same stars, would show all of its sides to you as it circles around you. See one face, then wait 14 days later and the backside is in your view. The moon has a spin rate that is the same as its rotational rate. (*Why* the moon is frozen with one face always toward the earth is treated in the footnote back in Chapter 7, page 120.) Misconception 2: Draw a half moon on the board. The shadow is along the diameter and is perfectly straight. If that were the shadow of the earth, then the earth would have to be flat, or be a big block shape! Discuss playing "flashlight tag" with a suspended basketball in a dark room that is illuminated by a flashlight in various locations. Ask your class if they could estimate the location of the flashlight by only looking at the illumination of the ball. Likewise with the moon illuminated by the sun!

Sketch the picture on the right on the board and ask what is wrong with it. [Answer: The moon is in a daytime position as evidenced by the upper part of the moon being illuminated. This means the sun must be above. Dispel notions that the crescent shape of the moon is a partial eclipse by considering a half moon and the shape of the earth to cast such a shadow.]

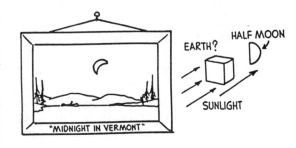

Back to Tides   Explain tides via the accelerating ball of Jell-O as in the text. Equal pulls result in an undistorted ball as it accelerates, but unequal pulls cause a stretching. This stretching is evident in the earth's oceans, where the side nearest the moon is appreciably closer to the moon than the side farthest away. Carefully draw Figure 8.13 on the board, which explains why closeness is so important for tides. The figure shows that the magnitude of ΔF rather than F itself is responsible for tidal effects. Hence the greater attraction of the distant sun produces only a small *difference* in pulls on the earth, and compared to themoon makes a small contribution to the tides on earth.

Explain why the highest high tides occur when the earth, moon, and sun are aligned — at the time of a new and a full moon.

Discuss tides in the molten earth and in the atmosphere.

Amplify Figure 8.13 with a comparison of ΔFs for both the sun and the moon as below. Clearly ΔF is smaller for the larger but farther sun.

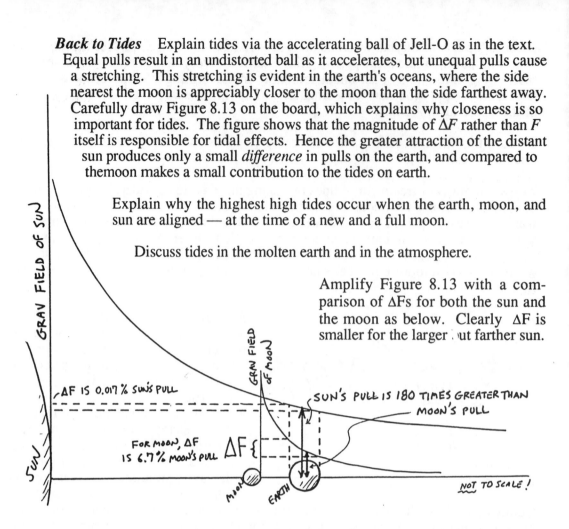

The text treats tides in terms of forces rather than fields. In terms of the latter, tidal forces are related to differences in gravitational *field* strengths across a body, and occur only for bodies in a non-uniform gravitational field. The gravitational fields of the earth, moon, and sun, for example, are inverse-square fields — stronger near them than farther away. The moon obviously experiences tidal forces because the near part to us is in a stronger part of the earth's gravitational field than the far part. But even an astronaut in an orbiting space shuttle strictly speaking experiences tidal forces because parts of her body are closer to the earth than other parts. The micro differences produce **microtides**. Farther away in deep space, the differences are less. Put another way, the earth's gravitational field is more uniform farther away. The "deepness" of a deep-space location can in fact be defined in terms of the amount of microtides experienced by a body there. Or equivalently, by the uniformity of any gravitational field there. There are no microtides in a body located in a strictly uniform gravitational field.

If there are microtides of an astronaut in orbit, would such microtides are even greater on the earth's surface? The answer is yes. This brings up Exercise 26 that concerns **biological tides**. Interestingly enough, microtides in human bodies are popularly attributed to not the earth, but the moon. This is because popular knowledge cites that the moon raises the ocean an average of 1 meter each 12 hours. Point out that the reason the tides are "stretched" by 1 meter is because part of that water is an earth diameter closer to the moon than the other part. In terms of fields, the near part of the earth is in an appreciably stronger part of the moon's gravitational field than the far part. To the extent that part of our bodies are closer to the moon than other parts, there would be lunar microtides — but enormously smaller than the microtides produced by not only the earth, but massive objects in one's vicinity.

CHECK QUESTION: Consider the tiny tidal forces that DO act on our bodies, as a result of parts of our bodies experiencing slightly different gravitational forces. What planetary body is most responsible for microtides in our bodies? [The earth, by far. When we are standing, there is a greater difference in earth gravity on our feet compared to our heads than the corresponding differences in gravity due to farther away planetary bodies.]

Simulated gravity in space habitats   The tallness of people in outer space compared to the radius of their rotating space habitats is very important. A *gravitational gradient* is appreciable in a relatively small structure. If the rim speed is such that the feet are at earth-normal one g, and the head is at the hub, then the gravitation gradient is a full 1-g. If the head is half-way to the hub, then the gradient is 1/2-g, and so forth. Simulated gravity is directly proportional to the radius. To achieve a comfortable 1/100-g gradient, the radius of the structure must be 100 times that of one's height. Hence the designs of large structures that rotate to produce earth-normal gravity.

Saturn's rings are the result of the strong gravitational gradient about Saturn. Such rings are the debris left over from bodies torn apart by Saturn's tidal forces. Such would occur for our moon if it comes closer to the earth. Too close, and the earth's tidal forces would tear the moon into a billion pieces, likely forming a ring similar to that of Saturn.

Tidal forces reach an extreme in the case of a **black hole**. The unfortunate fate of an astronaut falling into a black hole is not encountering the singularity, but the tidal forces encountered far before getting that close. Approaching feet first, for example, his closer feet would be pulled with a greater force than his midsection, which in turn would be pulled with a greater force than his head. The tidal forces would stretch him and he would be killed before these forces literally pulled him apart.

[This is a good place to break your lecture until next time.]

Gravitational Fields   Introduce the idea of force/mass for a body, and the gravitational force field. Relate the gravitational field to the more visible magnetic field as seen via iron filings. Since the field strength of the gravitational field is simply the ratio of force per mass, it behaves as force — it follows an inverse-square relationship with distance. Sketch Figure 8.19 on the board, but only the part of the graph that represents the field from the surface of the planet outward — the inverse-square part. This you have practically done before via Figure 8.6.

It's interesting to consider the field strength *inside* a planet, and to consider a tunnel bored clear through the earth. It's easy to convince your students that the gravitational force on a body located at the exact center of the tunnel would be zero — a chalkboard sketch showing a few symmetrical force vectors will do this. Hence the gravitational field at the earth's center is zero. Then consider the magnitude of force the body would experience between the center of the earth and the surface. A few more carefully drawn vectors will show that the forces don't cancel to zero. The gravitational field is between zero and the value at the surface. You'd like to easily show that it's half for an earth of uniform density, to establish the linear part of the graph of Figure 8.19. Careful judgement should be exercised at this point. For most classes I would think the geometrical explanation would constitute "information overload" and it would be best to simply say "It can be shown by geometry that half way to the center the field is half that at the surface..." and get on with your lecture. For highly motivated students it may be best to develop the geometrical explanation (given 3 pages back in this manual.)

Class time might better be spent on speculating further about the hole drilled through the earth. Show with motion of your hand how if somebody fell in such a tunnel they would undergo simple harmonic motion — and that this motion keeps perfect pace with a satellite in close circular orbit about the earth. The time for orbit, nearly 90 minutes, is the time to make a to and fro trip in the tunnel. Consider going further and explain how ideally the period of oscillation of a body traveling in such a tunnel under the influence of only gravity would be the same for any straight tunnel — whether from New York to Australia, or from New York to Hawaii or China. You can support this with the analogy of a pendulum that swings through different amplitudes with the same period. In non-vertical tunnels, of course, the object must slide rather than drop without friction. But the period is the same, and timetables for travel in this way would be quite simple; any one-way trip would take nearly 45 minutes!

Gravitational Field Inside a Hollow Planet   Consider the case of a body at the center of a completely *hollow* planet. Again, the field at the center is zero. Then show that the field everywhere inside is zero — by careful explanation of the following sketch. [Consider sample point P, twice as far from side A than side B. A solid cone defines area A and area B. Careful thought shows A has 4 times the area of B, and therefore has 4 times as much mass as B. That would mean 4 times as much gravitational pull, but being twice as far has only 1/4 as much pull. 1/4 of 4 gives the same gravitational pull as the pull toward B. So the forces cancel out (as they of course do in the center). The forces cancel everywhere inside the shell provided it is of uniform composition. If you stress this material (which will likely be on the heavy-duty side for many students) the following check question will measure the worth of your lecture effort.

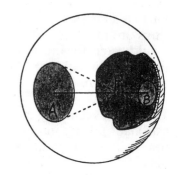

CHECK QUESTION: Sketch a graph similar to that in Figure 8.19 to represent the gravitational field inside and outside a hollow sphere. (The graphical answers should look like the following: A thin shelled planet is on the left, a thick shelled one is on the right.)

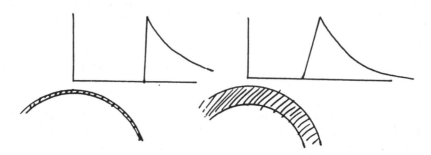

Speculate about the living conditions of a civilization inside a hollow planet. For example, as Exercise 38 asks, what happens to the g field inside, when a massive spaceship lands on the outside surface of the hollow planet? The situation is interesting!

Black holes: Begin by considering an indestructible person standing on a star, as in Figure 8.22. Write the gravitational equation next to your sketch of the person on the star, and show how only the radius changes in the equation as the star shrinks, and how the force therefore increases. Stress that the force on the person who is able to remain at distance R as the star shrinks experiences no change in force — the field there is constant as the star shrinks, even to a black hole. It is near the shrinking surface where the huge fields exist.

CHECK QUESTION: Consider a satellite companion to a star that collapses to become a black hole. How will the orbit of the companion satellite be affected by the star's transformation to a black hole? [Answer is not at all. No terms in the gravitation equation change.]

Universal Gravitation   Discuss the expanding theory of the universe, and its possible oscillating mode. You can get class interest into high gear with speculations as to the possibility of past and future cycles. After discussion, you can end your class on a high note by doing the following: State that you wish to represent a single cycle with the positions of the chalk you are holding in your hand above the lecture table. Place the chalk on the table and let that represent the time of the primordial explosion. Then as if the chalk were projected upward, raise the chalk to a point just above your head and state that this position represents the point where the universe momentarily stops before beginning its inward collapse — then move your hand slowly down, speeding up and back to its starting point — the completion of one cycle. Then hold the chalk a foot or so above the table, to a point corresponding to where we are today — a point representing about 15 to 20 billion years from the beginning of the cycle. Holding the chalk steady, and purposefully, ask where the chalk should be positioned to represent the dawning of civilization. Then move the chalk very intently to a position about a quarter of an inch below the present point. State that that's where we were, and this is where we are, as you move the chalk back to the present position. Still holding it there, ask for a speculation of where humankind will be and what the world will be like when we move to ... and then raise the chalk upward about a quarter of an inch. That point, of course, represents a time on earth that we can't begin to comprehend. It is conceivable that by then we will have evolved to beings with so powerful an intelligence as to be completely beyond present human imagining — to a point that by today's standards would be deemed God-like.

The continued evolution of humankind holds much promise.

CHECK QUESTION: Draw the figure below on the board. Ask the following:

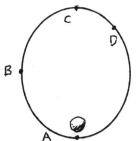

At which position is the gravitational force on the satellite the greatest? The least?
At which position is the speed greatest?
At which position is the momentum greatest?
At which position is the kinetic energy greatest?
At which position is the potential energy greatest?
At which position is the acceleration greatest?

Don't be surprised to find many of your students missing the last of these Check Questions, even though they answer the first about force correctly. If they use either equation for acceleration as their "guide," the answer is at hand; that is, from $a = F/m$, the acceleration is seen to be maximum where the force is maximum — at A. Or from a = (change in v)/t, acceleration is seen to be greatest where most of the change is happening, where the satellite whips around A. This Check Question summarizes important ideas in four chapters. Go over the answers carefully.

9

Satellite Motion

The Falling Apple
The Falling Moon
Satellite Motion
    Circular Orbits
    Elliptical Orbits
Energy Conservation and Satellite Motion
Escape Speed

Satellite Motion nearly began Mechanics back in Chapter 3 and now ends our treatment of Mechanics. This chapter is not prerequisite to others, and can be omitted for a short treatment of Mechanics.

For a more thorough treatment of the falling apple and falling moon, pages 164 and 165, see Volume I of *The Feynman Lectures On Physic*, pages 7 - 3 and 7 - 4. The fact that an object released from rest falls a vertical distance of 4.9 m, introduced in Chapter 2, is utilized here in the development of Newton's theory of gravitation.

The spin of the earth is helpful in launching satellites, which gives advantage to launching cites closest to the equator. The launch site closest to the equator is Kaurou, French Guiana, in South America, 5° 08', used by the European Space Agency. The U.S. launches from Cape Canaveral, 28° 22', and Vandenberg, 34° 38'. Russia used to launch at Kapustin Yar, 48° 31', Plesetsk, 62° 42', and Tyuratam (Baikonur) 45° 38'. Is Hawaii, less than 20° in our space launching future?

If you haven't shown the 15-minute NASA film, "Zero g", be sure to show it now. It is of footage taken aboard Skylab in 1978, narrated by astronaut Owen Garriott. Newton's laws of motion are reviewed with excellent and entertaining examples.

Practicing Physics has two pages on material in this chapter; one a vector approach to circular and elliptical orbits, and another that is a mechanics wrap-up that nicely ties concepts from preceding chapters together with satellite motion.

The **Laboratory Manual** has no material on satellites for this chapter.

SUGGESTED LECTURE PRESENTATION

Begin by discussing the falling apple story and Newton's insight about the falling moon. Reiterate the idea that if no force were acting on the moon, it would follow a straight line in space, and that Newton saw that the force of gravity extended to the moon. Discuss Figures 9.2 and 9.3.

Moving Perpendicular vs Moving Non-Perpendicular to Gravity Draw a sketch of a cannon on a mountain as shown. Simulate a cannonball fired horizontally and curving to the ground. Now suppose the

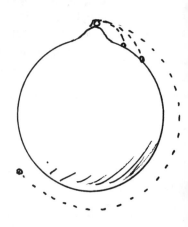

cannonball leaves the cannon at a velocity of say 1 km/s. Ask the class whether the speed when it strikes the ground will be 1 km/s, more than 1 km/s, or less than 1 km/s (neglecting air resistance). The answer is that it strikes at more than 1 km/s, because gravity speeds it up. (Toss your keys horizontally from a one-story window and catching them would pose no problem. Now toss your keys horizontally from the top of a mountain. Ask if a person below would care to catch them!) Now draw "Newton's Mountain" on the whole world as shown, and sketch a trajectory that meets the earth. Suppose the firing speed is now 4 km/s. Repeat your question: Will it be traveling faster, slower, or 4 km/s when it hits the ground? Again, faster, because it moves in the direction of the gravitational field. Caution: Do not draw a trajectory that meets the earth's surface at a point beyond the half-way mark (unfortunately, the Zero-g film makes this error). Why? Because the parabolic path is actually a segment of a Keplerian ellipse, Figure 9.9. Half way around puts it all around. Now draw the circular trajectory that occurs when the firing speed is 8 km/s. Ask if the speed increases, decreases, or remains the same after leaving the cannon. This time it remains the same. Why? Neighbor checking time!

Before answering the question, pose the case of rolling a ball along a bowling alley. Does gravity pull on the ball? [Yes.] Does gravity speed up or slow down the ball? [No.] Why? The answer to this question is the answer to the satellite question. [In both cases, the ball criss-crosses gravity — with no component of the gravitational field in the direction of motion. No change in speed, no work, no change in KE, no change in PE. Aha! The cannon ball and the bowling ball simply coast.

Circular Orbits Erase the mountain from your sketch of the world and draw a huge elevated bowling alley that completely circles the world. You're extending Figure 9.5. Show how a bowling ball on such an alley would gain no speed because of gravity. But now cut part of the alley away, so the ball rolls off the edge and crashes to the ground below. Does it gain speed after falling in the gap? [Yes, because a component of its motion is in the direction of the earth's gravitational field.] Show how if the ball moves faster it will fall farther before crashing to the ground. Ask what speed would allow it

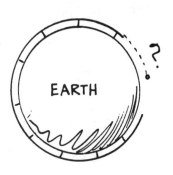

to clear the gap (like a motorcyclist who drives off a ramp and clears a gap to meet a ramp on the other side). [8 km/s, of course.] Can the gap be bigger at this speed? Sketch a gap that nearly circles the world when you ask this question. Then ask, what happens with no alley? And your class sees at 8 km/s no supporting alley is needed. The ball orbits the earth.

Elliptical Orbits Back to Newton's Mountain. Fire the cannonball at 9 km/s. It overshoots a circular path. Your sketch looks like the one here. Ask, at the position shown, is the cannonball moving at 9 km/s, more than 9 km/s, or less than 9 km/s. And why? After a neighbor check, toss a piece of chalk upward and say you toss it upward at 9 m/s. When it's half way to the top of its path, is it moving 9 m/s, more than 9 m/s, or less than 9 m/s? Equate the two situations. [In both cases the projectile slows because it is going against gravity.]

Continue your sketch and show a closed path — an ellipse. As you draw the elliptical path, show with a sweeping motion of your arm how the satellite slows in receding from the earth, moving slowest at its farthermost point, then how it speeds in falling towards the earth, whipping around the earth and repeating the cycle over and over again. Move to a fresh part of the chalkboard and redraw with the mountain at the bottom, so your sketch is more like Figure 9.8. (It is more comfortable seeing your chalk moving slowest when farthest coincides with the direction "up" in the classroom. I quip that Australians have no trouble seeing it the first way.)

Sketch in larger ellipses for still greater cannon speeds, with the limit being 11.2 km/s, beyond which the path does not close — escape speed.

Work-Energy Relationship for Satellites   You already have sketches on the board of circular and elliptical orbits. Draw sample satellites and then sketch in force vectors. Ask the class to do likewise, and then draw component vectors parallel and perpendicular to instantaneous directions of motion. Then show how the changes in speed are consistent with the work-energy relationship.

Draw a large ellipse on the board with a planet in various positions and ask your class for a comparison of the relative magnitudes of KE and PE along the orbit. You can do this with different size symbols for KE and PE. Stress that the two add up to be the same.

Escape Speed   Distinguish between ballistic speed and sustained speed, and that the value 11.2 km/s refers to ballistic speed. (One could go to the moon at 1 km/s, given a means of sustaining that speed and enough time to make the trip!) Compare the escape speeds from different bodies via Table 9-1.

Maximum Falling Speed   The idea of maximum falling speed, footnote on page 170, is sufficiently interesting for elaboration. Pretend you throw your car keys from ground level to your friend at the top of a building. Throw them too fast and they continue by your friend; throw them too slow and they never reach her. But if you throw them just right, say 11 m/s, they just barely reach her so she has only to grab them at their point of zero speed. Question: It took a speed of 11 m/s to get the keys up to her — if she simply drops them, how fast will they fall into your hands? Aha! If it takes a speed of 11.2 km/s to throw them to her if she is somewhat beyond Pluto, and she similarly drops them, how fast will they fall into your hands? Now your students understand maximum falling speed.

CHECK QUESTIONS: This reviews several chapters of mechanics; draw an elliptical orbit about a planet as shown on the board. Pose the following questions (from the *Practice Book*): At which position does the satellite have the maximum

(1) gravitational force on it?
(2) speed?
(3) momentum?
(4) kinetic energy?
(5) gravitational potential energy?
(6) total energy?
(7) acceleration?
(8) angular momentum?

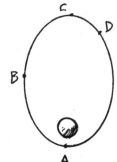

10

Atomic Nature of Matter

Atoms
Molecules
Molecular and Atomic Masses
Elements, Compounds, and Mixtures
Atomic Structure
Antimatter
The States of Matter

The treatment of atoms in this chapter is rather basic, and provides a good background for the chapters on heat. It also provides background for Chapters 21, 23, 29, 30, 31, 32, and 33. An extended treatment of atoms is given in Chapter 31.

This chapter is the most important chapter in Part II, and should not be skipped.

An excellent 10-minute film that makes an excellent tie from the solar system, galaxies, and the universe, discussed briefly in the preceding chapter, to the atom — comparing sizes as positive and negative powers of ten is *Powers of Ten*, by Charles and Ray Eames, and narrated by Philip Morrison. (Pyramid Films,1978).

This chapter is not represented in the student workbook, **Practicing Physics**.

Two excellent experiments in the **Laboratory Manual** are *Diameter of a BB* and *Oleic Acid Pancake*. The first nicely leads into the second, and both may be combined.

Although only one neighbor check question is identified in the suggested lecture here, please make your own as your lecture unfolds.

SUGGESTED LECTURE PRESENTATION

Begin by posing the situation of breaking a boulder into rocks, rocks into stones, stones into pebbles, pebbles into gravel, gravel into sand, sand into powder, and so forth until you get to the fundamental building block — the atom. Relate how from the earliest days of science people wondered how far the idea of breaking boulders into stones, pebbles, sand, powder, and so on, would go. Does it ever end? Hundreds of years ago, people had no way of finding out, and they instead carried on with philosophical speculation. Not until "modern" chemistry in the late 1700's did people begin to get indirect evidence of some basic order in the combinations of things. The first real "proof" that there were atoms was given by Einstein in 1905, the same year he published his paper on relativity. He calculated what kind of motion there ought to be in Brownian motion, based on ideas we've considered already, like energy and momentum conservation, and the idea of heat as atomic motion. Many of the "heavies" in physics at that time didn't believe in atoms until Einstein's work.

Smallness of Atoms   Give examples to convey the idea of the smallness of the atom, i.e., an atom is as many orders of magnitude smaller than a person as an average star is larger than a person — so we stand between the atoms and the stars. The size of an atom is to the size of an apple as the size of an apple is to the size of the earth. So if you want to imagine an apple full of atoms, think of the earth, solid-packed with apples.

> CHECK QUESTION: Ask what an atom would "look like" if viewed through a vertical bank of about 40 high-powered optical microscopes stacked one atop the other. [It turns out they wouldn't have an appearance, at least not in the range of frequencies we call light. The atom is smaller than the wavelength of light.]

You might allude to the later study of Chapter 31 and state that the electron beam in the electron microscope has the properties of high-frequency light. Acknowledge the wave nature of matter — the fuzziness in the distinction between particles and waves at the atomic level — that "solid" particles seem to be congealed standing waves of energy.

Recycling of Atoms   You can lead into the idea of more mole-cules in your lungs than there are breaths of air in the world with the following: State that if you put a drop of ink in a bathtub full of water, that you (the students) know that in a short time you can sample any part of the water and find ink in it. The atoms of ink spread out. We can get an idea of how small atoms are from this fact: There are more atoms in a thimbleful of ink than there are thimblefuls of water in the Atlantic Ocean. That means if you throw a thimbleful of ink into the Atlantic Ocean and give it enough years to mix uniformly, and then dip anywhere in the ocean with a thimble, you'll have some atoms of ink in your sample. You may want to discuss Problem 1 at this point and demonstrate its solution. (Note that the data for this problem concerns all the oceans of the world, not just the Atlantic.) By now your class is ready for the more interesting bit about breaths of air in the atmosphere. Relate this to Problem 2 and the statement made by my grandson Manuel on page 177.

Empty Space   Discuss ths Bohr model of the atom and the electrical role of the nucleus and surrounding electrons. Stress the emptiness of the atom and lead into the idea of solid matter being mostly empty space. State how our bodies are 99.999% empty spaces, and how a particle, if tiny enough and not affected by electrical forces, could be shot straight through us without even making a hole! Making a direct hit with an atomic nucleus or an electron is as improbable as making a direct hit with a planet or the sun if you throw a gravity-free dart from outer space at the solar system. Both the solar system and an atom are mostly empty space. Walk through a beam of neutrons and very few if any will interact with your body. Still smaller neutral particles called neutrinos (footnote page 606), the most elusive yet most numerous and fastest of all particles, pass though us every moment. But they do so without consequence, for only very rarely, perhaps once or so per year, do any make a bull's-eye collision with any of our atomic nuclei. They freely pass through the entire earth with rare inter-actions. (Interestingly enough, the neutrino flux from the 1987 supernova was so enormous that about 1 out of every 240 people on earth absorbed one of its neutrinos. This tidbit from John Learned, University of Hawaii.)

Electrical Forces   Discuss the role of electrical forces in preventing us from oozing into our chairs and so forth. Ask the class to imagine that the lecture table is a large magnet, and that you wear magnetic shoes that are repelled by the table you "stand" on. Ask them to imagine whether or not a sheet of paper could be passed between your shoes and the table. For there is a space there. Then state that on the submicroscopic scale that this is indeed what happens when you walk on any solid surface. Only the repelling force isn't magnetic, its electric! Discuss the submicroscopic notion of things touching. Acknowledge that under very special circum-stances the nucleus of one atom can physically touch the nucleus of another atom — that this is what happens in a thermonuclear reaction.

Discuss the relative distances between positive and negative charges in neighboring atoms and the role of the electric forces in molecular structure. (You're discussing the implications of Coulomb's law at short distances — combined with the ideas you previously discussed in your treatment of tides and tidal forces, namely the importance of relative distances.)

Atomic Number and Periodic Table   Schematically show the hydrogen atom, and add a proton and neutrons to build a helium atom, and then a lithium atom, and so on. Discuss atomic number, and the role that the number of protons play in the nucleus in dictating the surrounding electron configuration. Call attention to and briefly discuss the periodic table that is located inside the front cover of the text. Point out that the atomic configurations depicted in Figure 10.8 are simply models not to be taken seriously. For example, if the nuclei were drawn to scale they would be scarcely visible specks. And the electrons don't really "orbit", as the drawings suggest — such terms don't seem to have much meaning at the atomic level. It would be more precise to say they "swarm", or are "smeared", around the central nuclei. You might state that the configuration of electrons and their interactions with each other is basically what the field of chemistry is about.

Antimatter   Discuss antimatter, and the speculations that other galaxies may be composed of antimatter. There are even antiquarks. Or knowledge of quarks is relatively new, newer than the first edition of this text. Until recent times it was a fact that the fundamental building block of matter was the protons, neutrons, and electrons discussed in this chapter. Now it is a fact that the proton and neutron are not the fundamental particles, but are composed of quarks. This change of view or advancement in our knowledge, like others, is often cited as a weakness by people who do not understand what science is about. Science is not a bag of answers to all the questions of the world, but is a process for finding answers to many questions about the world. We continue to refine our models and add new layers to our understanding — sometimes building onto layers and other times replacing layers. It is unfortunate that some people see this as a weakness. This is remindful of Bertrand Russell, who publicly changed his mind about certain ideas in the course of his life — changes that were part of his growth, but were looked upon by some as a sign of weakness (as discussed in Chapter 1). Likewise with physics. Our knowledge grows. And that's nice!

States of Matter   Briefly discuss the states of matter, and how changes in molecular motion (temperature) are responsible for changes from the solid to liquid to gaseous to plasma states.

11

Solids

Crystal Structure
Density
Elasticity
Tension and Compression
Arches
Scaling

The treatment of the crystalline nature of solids and bonding are very brief in this chapter. More emphasis is on macroscopic structures in this edition — elasticity, tension and compression, and the application to arches. Students should find the section on "Scaling" of particular interest. A fascinating source of additional scaling examples is George Barnes' fascinating article, "Physics and Size in Biological Systems" — April 1989 issue of *The Physics Teacher*.

Scaling is becoming enormously important as more devices are being miniaturized. Researchers are finding that when something shinks enough, whether it is an electronic circuit, motor, film of lubricant, or an individual metal or cermaic crystal, it stops acting like a miniature version of its larger self and starts behaving in new and different wys. Paladium metal, for example, which is normally composed of grains about 1000 nanoseconds in size, is found to be five times as strong when formed from 5 nanometer grains.

A page on *scaling* is in **Practicing Physics**.

Three activities, one on *scaling*, one on *density,* and one on *elasticity,* and one experiment on *Hooke's Law* are in the **Laboratory Manual**.

This chapter may be skipped with no particular consequence to following chapters. If this chapter is skipped and Chapter 12 is assigned, density should be introduced at that time.

SUGGESTED LECTURE PRESENTATION

Crystal Structure Begin by calling attention to the micrograph on page 192, and explain how Dr. Mueller made the photograph. The micrograph is evidence not only for the crystalline nature of the platinum needle, but also evidence for the wave nature of atoms is seen in the resulting diffraction pattern. It is easy to imagine the micrograph as a ripple tank photo made by grains of sand sprinkled in an orderly mosaic pattern upon the surface of water.

Density Measure the dimensions of a large wooden cube in cm and find its mass with a pan balance. Define density = mass/volume. (Use the same cube when you discuss flotation in the next chapter.) Some of your students will unfortunately conceptualize density as massiveness or bulkiness rather than massiveness per bulkiness, even when they give a verbal definition properly. This can be helped with the following:

> CHECK QUESTIONS: Which has the greater density, a cupful of water or a lakeful of water? A kilogram of lead or a kilogram of feathers? A single uranium atom or the world?

I jokingly relate breaking a candy bar in two and giving the smaller piece to my friend who looks disturbed. "I gave you the same density of candy bar as I have."

Contrast the density of matter and the density of atomic nuclei that comprise so tiny a fraction of space within matter. From about 2 gm/cm^3 to 2 x 10^{14} gm/cm^3. And in a further crushed state, the interior of neutron stars, about 10^{16} gm/cm^3.

Elasticity

> DEMONSTRATION: Drop glass, steel, rubber, and spheres of various materials onto an anvil and compare the elasticities.

> DEMONSTRATION: Hang weights from a spring and illustrate Hooke's Law. Set a pair of identical springs up as in Problem 3, and ask the class to predict the elongation before suspending the load.

Tension, Compression, and Arches Bend a meter stick held at both ends and ask which side is being stretched and which side is being compressed. Stretching is tension, and compressing is compression. If one side is being stretched and the other compressed, there must be a "crossover" place — where neither stretching nor compression occur. This is the neutral layer.

Compare a cantilever and a simple beam.

Discuss the shape of an I beam, and Exercise 9.

Discuss the strength of arches. Before the time of concrete, stone bridges and the like were self supporting by virtue of the way they pressed toward one another — in an arch shape. Wooden scaffolding allowed their construction, and when the keystone was inserted, the structures stood when the scaffolding was removed. The same practice is used today. The set of top bricks in Figure 11.12 serve as a keystone.

Area-Volume Introduce the relationship between area and volume as Chelcis Liu does by showing the following: Have a 500-ml spherical flask filled with colored water sitting on your lecture table. Produce a tall cylindrical flask, also of 500 ml (unknown to your students), and ask for speculations as to how high the water level will be when water is poured into it from the spherical flask. You can ask for a show of hands for those who think that the water will reach more than half the height, and those who think it will fill to less than half the height, and for those who guess it will fill to exactly half the height. Your students will be amazed when they see that the seemingly smaller spherical flask has the same volume as the tall cylinder. To explain, call attention 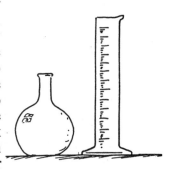 to the fact that the *area* of the spherical flask is considerably smaller than the surface area of the cylinder. We see a greater area and we unconsciously think that the volume should be greater as well. Be sure to do this. It is more impressive than it may first seem.

On the matter of shapes, if you haven't already done so back in Chapter 3, you might ask why manhole covers are round. The answer is so some bozo doesn't drop them accidentally into the manhole. If they were square, they could be tipped up on edge and dropped through the hole on the diagonal. Similarly with ovals. But a circular hole will defy the most determined efforts in this regard. Of course there is a lip around the inside of the manhole that the cover rests on, making the diameter of the hole somewhat less than the diameter of the cover.

Scaling   Now for the most interesting part of your lecture: Have at least 8 large cubes on your lecture table as you explain Figures 11.15 and 11.16. Support the figures with further examples as found in the Haldane and Thompson essays (Suggested Reading, page 206).

> CHECK QUESTIONS: Which has more surface area, an elephant or a mouse? 2000 kilograms of elephant or 2000 kilograms of mice? (Distinguish carefully between these different questions.)

> CHECK QUESTION: Cite two reasons why small cars are more affected by wind.

> CHECK QUESTION: Why do Chinese cooks chop food in such small pieces for cooking quickly in a wok?

> CHECK QUESTION: In terms of surface area to volume, why should parents take extra care that a baby is warm enough in a cold environment.

Your lecture can continue by posing exercises from the chapter end material and having your class volunteer answers. The examples posed in the exercises will perk class interest. (The answer to Exercise 15 may need more explanation. How much more surface area is there for a body with twice the volume? Consider a cube; twice the volume means each side is the cube root of two, 1.26 times the side of the smaller cube. Its area is then 1.26 x 1.26 = 1.587 times greater than the smaller cube. So the twice as heavy person at the beach would use about 1.6 times as much suntan lotion.)

Regarding Figure 11.18, note that the span from eartip to eartip is almost the height of the elephant. The dense packing of veins and arteries in the elephant's ears finds a difference in five degrees in blood entering and leaving the ears. A second type of African elephant that resides in cooler forested regions has smaller ears. Perhaps Indian elephants evolved in cooler climates.

12

Liquids

Pressure in a Liquid
Buoyancy
Archimedes' Principle
Density Effects on Submerged Objects
Flotation
Pascal's Principle
Surface Tension
Capillarity

The depths of the ocean as well as the expanse of outer space are of current interest, yet liquids are seldom studied in introductory physics classes anymore. Perhaps this is because Archimedes' Principle and the like are too far from the frontiers of present research. But because much of the physics in this chapter is more than 2000 years old is no reason that it should not be in your physics course. Liquids are a very real part of your students' everyday world.

It is well known that falling from great heights into water has much the same effect as falling to solid ground. Less well known are the new "water saws," with pressures of about 5500 lb/in^2 used for cutting through armor-plate steel.

Regarding Figure 12.2, you may point out that the average mass of a giraffe's heart is about 40 kilograms. That's quite a pump.

In student laboratory exercises, it is more common to work with mass density than with weight density, and floating or submerged materials are more often described in units of mass rather than weight. Displaced liquid is also described in units of mass rather than weight. This is why buoyant force in this chapter is treated as "the weight of so many kilograms," rather than "so many newtons." The expression of buoyancy in terms of mass units should be more in keeping with what goes on in lab.

A page on Archimedes' Principle is in **Practicing Physics**.

Three activities and 1 experiment on chapter material are in the **Laboratory Manual**.

Prerequisite to this chapter is understanding of density, covered in the previous chapter. So if you skipped Chapter 11, discuss density here. This chapter is prerequisite to the following chapter but is not prerequisite to the remaining chapters of the text.

SUGGESTED LECTURE PRESENTATION

Force versus Pressure Begin by distinguishing between force and pressure. Illustrate with examples: Somebody pushing on your back with a force of only 1 N — with a pin! As you're lying on the floor, a 400-N lady stands on your stomach —

perched atop spike heels! Indian master lying on a bed of 1000 nails — apprentice considering starting with one nail! Why the importance of jewel bearings (remember them old timer?) in watches, diamond stylus (still around!) in record players, rounded corners on tables, sharp blades on cutting knives, and the absurdity of standing tall while pointing your toes downward when caught in quicksand.

Have students compare in their hands the weights of a small steel ball and a large styrofoam ball, and after agreeing that the little ball is heavier (since density was treated in the previous chapter), weigh them and show the styrofoam ball is heavier! Another example of pressure (on the nerve endings).

Liquid Pressure Liquid pressure = density x depth: After a few words about density, you may want to derive or call attention to the derivation of this relationship (footnote on page 211).

> DEMONSTRATION: Pascal's Vases (similar to Figure 12.3) — rationalize your results in terms of the supporting forces exerted by the sloping sides of the vases. [That is, in the wide sloping vase, the water pushes against the glass, and the glass reacts by pushing against the water. So the glass supports the extra water without the pressure below increasing. For the narrow vase that slopes outward near the bottom, the water pushes up against the sloping glass. By reaction, the glass pushes down on the water, so the pressure at the bottom is as if water were present all the way to the surface.]

Discuss Figure 12.2 and why your heart gets more rest if you sleep in a prone position versus sitting up. Call attention to the fact that when swimming, the pressure one feels against the eardrums is a function of only depth — that swimming 3 meters deep in a small pool has the same effect as swimming 3 meters deep in the middle of a huge lake.

> CHECK QUESTION: Would the pressure be greater swimming 3 m deep in the middle of the ocean? (Then compare the densities of fresh and salt water.)

Ask why dams are built thicker at the bottom, and after discussing Figure 12.4 sketch the top view of a couple of dams on the board and ask which design is best (Exercise 10, previous chapter). Then relate this to the shape of stone bridges (which actually need no mortar), and the arched shape of the tops of windows in old brick buildings (Figure 11.12, previous chapter). Another illustration is the concave ends of large wine barrels (Exercise 11, previous chapter).

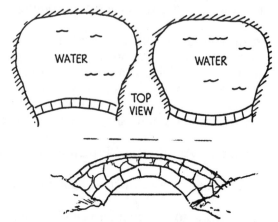

Buoyant Force Show that a consequence of pressure being depth dependent is the phenomenon of buoyancy. Sketch Figure 12.7 on the board. Follow this up with a sketch and explanation of Figure 12.12.

> DEMONSTRATION: Show how an overflow can enables the measure of an object's volume. Ask how one could measure a quarter of a cup of butter in a liquid measuring cup using this method.

DEMONSTRATION: Archimedes' Principle, as shown in Figure 12.11.

You may find that many students who have trouble with conceptualizing buoyant force are confused about the distinction between area and volume. Be sure to make this distinction clear, (as elementary as it seems!). (If you didn't pour the contents of the spherical flask into the tall cylindrical flask of the same volume as described in the suggested lecture of the previous chapter, be sure to do so here.) Also, point out that because a liquid is incompressible (practically incompressible, as the volume of water decreases by only 50 one-millionths of its original volume for each atmosphere increase in pressure, or equivalently, for each addition 10.3 m in depth) its density is not depth dependent. The density of water near the surface is practically the same as the density far beneath the surface. You may wish to acknowledge that some variation occurs due to temperature differences. Usually a student will inquire about water-logged objects which lie submerged yet off the bottom of the body of water. Such objects are slightly denser than the warmer surface water and not quite as dense as the cooler water at the bottom. Stress that this is unusual and that objects appreciably denser than water always sink to the bottom, regardless of the depth of the water. Scuba divers do not encounter "floating" rocks near the bottoms of deep bodies of water!

> CHECK QUESTION: Two solid blocks of identical size are submerged in water. One block is lead and the other is aluminum. Upon which is the buoyant force greater?

After discussion, try this one:

> CHECK QUESTION: Two solid blocks of identical size, one of lead and the other of wood, are put in the same water. Upon which is the buoyant force greater? [This time the BF is greater on the lead, because it displaces more water than the wood that floats!]

> CHECK QUESTION: What is the buoyant force on a ten-ton ship floating in fresh water? In salt water? In a lake of mercury? [Same BF, but different *volumes* displaced.]

The unit "ton" is used in several places in this text. It may be taken to mean a metric tonne, the weight of 1000 kg, or the British ton, 2000 lbs. Either interpretation is sufficient in treating the idea involved.

Flotation Discuss boats and rafts and the change of water lines when loaded.

> CHECK QUESTIONS: What is the approximate density of a fish? Of a person? What can you say of people who can't float?

> DEMONSTRATION: Cartesian diver (inverted partially filled small bottle submerged in a larger flexible plastic bottle that you squeeze to increase and decrease the weight of water in the small bottle to make it rise and fall).

Discuss the compressibility of the human body in swimming — how the density of most people a meter or two below the surface of the water is still less than the density of water, and that one need only relax and be buoyed to the surface. But that at greater depths, the greater pressure compresses one to densities greater than the density of water, and one must swim to the surface. Simply relaxing, one would sink to the bottom! Relate this to the Cartesian diver demonstration. Also state why one cannot snorkel with a tube that goes deeper than a half meter or so.

Side point: Contrary to those old Tarzan movies, you cannot sink in quicksand. Quicksand is the name given to a mass of sand particles that are supported by circulating water rather than by each other. Its density s greater than the density of human bodies, so you can float on it. If you struggle, you'll unfortunately succeed in digging yourself deeper in. So if you're ever stuck in it, keep yourself still until you stop sinking (you will), and then use slow swimming motions to get yourself into a horizontal position and then roll onto the ground.

Pascal's Principle Begin by pushing against the wall with a meter stick and state that the stick affords a means of applying pressure to the wall — then state that the same can be done with a confined fluid. Explain how any external pressure applied to a liquid that tightly fills a volume is transmitted to all parts of the liquid equally. Discuss Figures 12.18 and 12.19. If a hydraulic press is available, crush a block of wood with it. Point out that the pressure transmitted throughout a confined liquid is pressure over and above that already in the liquid. For example, the pressure in a hydraulic system at any point is equal to the applied pressure plus the density x depth.

Surface Tension An interesting example of surface tension (not in the text) involves the tallness of trees. The cohesive forces of water explains the transport of water from roots to the top of tall trees. When a single water molecule evaporates from the cell membrane inside a leaf, it is replaced by the one immediately next to it due to the cohesive forces between water molecules. A pull is created on the column of water which is continuous from leaves to roots. Water can be lifted far higher than the 10.2 m that atmospheric pressure would serve — even to 100 m in this way, the height of the largest trees.

NEXT-TIME QUESTION: Show your class an ordinary rectangular chunk of wood with square cross-section, and ask how it will float if placed in water: [Unless it is very low density, like styrofoam, it will float as in postion b. Why?]

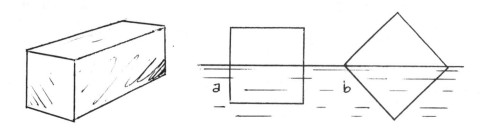

13

Gases and Plasmas

The concepts of fluid pressure, buoyancy, and flotation introduced in the previous chapter are applied to the atmosphere in this chapter. The chief difference between the common fluid water and the common fluid air has to do with the variability of density. Unlike a body of water, the density of the atmosphere is depth-dependent.

The section on Boyle's Law avoids distinguishing between absolute pressure and gauge pressure. Charles' Law is not covered, and reference is made to temperature effects only in a footnote.

Exercises 32, 33, and 34 direct the student to consider an atmosphere in a rotating space habitat. For background information on this topic, see John M. McKinley's article, "Static Atmospheres in a Rotating Space Habitat," in the Nov. 1980 issue of *The Physics Teacher*.

Although plasma seems more remote from our everyday environment than the first three states of matter, it is receiving more attention in its role in nuclear fusion.

For baseball fans, *The Physics of Baseball* by Robert K. Adair ($9.00) and *Keep Your Eye on the Ball* by Robert G. Watts and A. Terryh Bahill ($12.95), plus shipping, are available, both from Technology Review Books, MIT-W59, Cambridge, MA 02139. Adair explains the physics behind pitching, batting, the flight of the ball, curving, and how cork affects a bat. Watts and Bahill answer questions like "Could Sandy Koufax's curve really have acted like it 'fell off a table'?"

If you're into lecture demonstrations, this is the chapter material for a show. There are two good sources I have found useful: *A Demonstration Handbook for Physics*, by G.D. Frier and F.J. Anderson, published by AAPT, and *Invitations to Science Inquiry*, by Tik L. Liem, at St. Francis Xavier University, in Antigonish, Nova Scotia.

In discussing the atmosphere, if you get into the abuses that the atmosphere is undergoing, acid rain, etc., please do not end on a sour note. Also get into what can be done to better the situation. Our students have no shortage of inputs telling them about the abuses of technology, but they don't often hear how technology can be used to improve the quality of life in the world.

There are no exercises in **Practicing Physics** for this chapter.

An activity on Bernoulli's Principle is in the **Laboratory Manual**.

This chapter is not prerequisite to the following chapters.

SUGGESTED LECTURE PRESENTATION

Weight of Air   Hold out an empty drinking glass and ask what's in it. It's not really empty, for it's filled with air, and has weight. It is common to think of air as having very little mass, when the truth is air has a fairly large mass — about 1 1/4 kilogram for a cube one meter on a side (at sea level). The air that fills your bathtub has a mass of about 1/2 kilogram. We don't feel the weight of this mass only because we are immersed in an ocean of air. A plastic bag full of water, for example, has a significant weight, but if the bag is taken into a swimming pool it weighs nothing (Figure 13.4). Likewise for the surrounding air. A bag of air may have a fairly large mass, but as long as the bag is surrounded by air, its weight is not felt. We are as unconsious of the weight of air that surrounds us as a fish is unconsious of the weight of water that surrounds it.

> CHECK QUESTION: Open the door of a refrigerator and inside is a large
> lonely grapefruit. Which weighs more, the air in the frig or the grapefruit?
> [The inside volume of a common refrigerator is between 1/2 and 3/4 m^3,
> which corresponds to nearly a kilogram of cold air (about 2 pounds). So
> unless the grapefruit is more than a 2-pounder, the air weighs more.]

The Atmosphere   Draw a circle as large as possible on the chalkboard, and then announce that it represents the earth. State that if you were to draw another circle, indicating the thickness of the atmosphere surrounding the earth to scale, that you would end up drawing the same line — for over 99% of the atmosphere lies within the thickness of the chalk line! Then go on to discuss the ocean of air in which we live.

> DEMONSTRATION: While discussing the preceding, have a gallon metal
> can with a bit of water in it heating on a burner. When steam issues, cap it
> tightly and remove from the heat source. Continue your discussion and the
> collapsing can will interrupt you as it crunches. If you really want to
> impress your class, do the same with a 50-gallon drum! [The explanation
> is that pressure inside the can or drum decreases as cooling occurs and the
> steam condenses. Atmospheric pressure on the outside produces the
> crunching net force on the can or drum.]

> DEMONSTRATION: Here's a goodie! Heat some aluminum soda pop
> cans on a burner, empty except for a small amount of water that is brought
> to a boil to make steam. With a pot holder or tongs, pick up a can and
> quickly invert it into a basin of water. Crunch! The atmospheric pressure
> immediately crushes the can with a resounding WHOP! Very impressive.
> [Condensation of the steam and vapor occur and the interior pressure is re-
> duced as above. Interestingly enough, I have found this works even when
> the temperature of the water bath into which the can is inverted is nearly
> boiling temperature. What happens is a "flypaper effect;" water molecules
> in the vapor state condense when they encounter the water into which

they're placed, even hot water. When you get into Chapter 16 your students will learn that both condensation and vaporization occur at any water surface, and the net effect is generally spoken of as "evaporation" or "condensation." In this case, if the can is inverted into boiling water, the condensation of vapor is countered by as much vaporization so the pressure in the can remains the same. But when plunged into water slightly cooler, the rate of condensation exceeds the vaporization of the hot water and the pressure is reduced. But these are "second-order effects" at this stage of your lecture.]

Atmospheric Pressure   While this is going on, state that if you had a 30-km tall bamboo pole of cross section 1 square cm, the mass of the air from the atmosphere in it would amount to about 1 kg. The weight of this air is the source of atmospheric pressure. The atmosphere bears down on the earth's surface at sea level with a pressure that corresponds to the weight of 1 kg per square cm. (Remember the old days when we could talk about plain old 14.7 lb/in^2? Since the unit of force is now the newton and the unit of area is the square meter, conceptualizing atmospheric pressure is less simple than before. Nevertheless, continue with the following description.) To understand the pressure of the atmosphere in terms of newtons per square meter, ask your class to imagine a 30-km tall sewer pipe of cross section 1 square m, filled with the air of the atmosphere. How much would the enclosed air weigh? The answer is about 10^5 N. So if you draw a circle of one square meter on the lecture table, and ask what the weight is for all the air in the atmosphere above, you should elicit a chorus, silent or otherwise of "10^5 N!" If your table is above sea level, then the weight of air is correspondingly less. Then estimate the force of the air pressure that collapsed the metal can — both for a perfect vacuum and for a case where the pressure difference is about half an atmosphere.

Estimate the force of the atmosphere on a person. You can estimate the surface area by approximating different parts of the body on the board — leg by leg, arm by arm, etc. (This can be quite funny, if you want it to be!)

DEMONSTRATION: This great one from John McDonald of Boise State University consists of a square sheet of soft rubber with some sort of handle at its center. A 50-gram mass hanger poked through its center works well. Toss the rubber sheet on any perfectly flat surface — best on the top of a lab stool. Picking the rubber up by a corner is an easy task,  because the air gets under it as it is lifted. But lifting it by the middle is another story. As the middle is raised, a low-pressure region is formed because air cannot get in. The rubber sheet behaves as a suction cup, and the entire stool is lifted when the handle is raised.

DEMONSTRATION: Whap a toilet plunger or other suction cup on the wall. (Instruct your class to inquire with their neighbors to see if there is a consensus as to the reason.)

DEMONSTRATION: Place a wooden shingle on the lecture table so that it overhangs the edge a bit. Cover the shingle with a flattened sheet of newspaper, and strike the overhanging part of the shingle with a stick or your hand (be careful of splinters). Promote more "discuss with your neighbor" activity.

Barometers State that a better vacuum source than sucking would remove much more air, and if all the air were removed, a very large column of water would be needed to balance the atmosphere on the other side. This would be about 10.3 m, but depends a little on today's atmospheric pressure. Such devices made up the first barometers. They are impractically large, so mercury is instead commonly used. Since mercury is 13.6 times as dense as water, the height of water needed to balance the atmosphere is 1/13.6 of 10.3 m = 76 cm. If you have the opportunity, construct a mercury barometer before the class.

> CHECK QUESTION: How would the barometer level vary while ascending and descending in the elevator of a tall building? [You might quip about the student who was asked to find the height of a building with a sensitive barometer who simply dropped it from the top and measured the seconds of fall — or who exchanged it with the builder of the building for the correct information.]

Discuss ear popping in aircraft, and why cabin pressure is lower than atmospheric pressure at high altitudes.

> DEMONSTRATION: As the sketch shows, try sucking a drink through a straw with two straws; one in the liquid and the other outside. It can't be done because the pressure in your mouth is not reduced because of the second straw (although with some effort a bit of liquid can be drawn). Invite your students to try this, and to share this (and other ideas!) at parties.

> DEMONSTRATION: The siphon. Careful! Many instructors have found in front of their classes that they misunderstood the operation of a siphon. The explanation does not have to do with differences in atmospheric pressures at the ends of the tube, but with the difference in liquid pressures in the short and long sides of the bent tube. Unless the long end of the tube exceeds 10.3 m, atmospheric pressure acting upwards against the liquid in the tube is greater than the downward pressure of liquid. The situation is analogous to pushing upward against the bottom ends of a see-saw with unequal pushes. Liquid in the short end of the tube is pushed up with more net force than the liquid in the long end of the tube. (Or it's analogous to a chain hanging over a peg, with one end longer and heavier than the other end.)

Boyle's Law Discuss Boyle's Law. At the risk of information overload you may or may not want to get into the differences between absolute and gauge pressures. (I avoid it in the text.)

Consider discussion Home Project 1, estimating the weight of a car by the pressure in its tires and the amount of tire contact area. Now your students know why trailer trucks commonly have 18 wheels — the air pressure in the tires multiplied by the area of contact of the 18 tires is the weight of the truck and its load. Fewer tires means greater air pressure in the tires.

Discuss or show Home Project 2 (dunking a glass mouth downwards in water to show the "empty" glass contains air — and how air is compressed with deeper depths) and relate this to the compressed air breathed by scuba divers. Discuss the reason for the difficulty of snorkeling at a depth of 1 m and why such will not work for greater depths; i.e., air will not of itself move from a region of lesser pressure (the air at the surface) to a region of greater pressure (the compressed air in the submerged person's lungs).

Recall the sinking balloon problem from the previous chapter (Exercise 28 in Chapter 12) and relate this to the smaller volume to which a swimmer is subjected with increasing depth. Hence the need for pressurized air for scuba divers. Without the pressurized air, one's volume and therefore buoyancy is decreased, making it more difficult to return to the surface. Whereas at shallow depths the average swimmer can passively return to the surface, at greater depths a passive swimmer will sink to the bottom.

Buoyancy of Air Hold your hands out, one a few centimeters above the other, and ask if there really is any difference in air pressure at the two places. The fact that there is can be demonstrated by the rising of a helium-filled balloon of the same size! The balloon rises only because the atmospheric pressure at its bottom is greater than the atmospheric pressure at its top. Pressure in the atmosphere really is depth dependent!

> CHECK QUESTION: Which is greater, the buoyant force on the helium-filled balloon, or the buoyant force on you? [Assuming the balloon has less volume than you, there is more buoyant force on you.] Discuss why.

Interestingly enough, atmospheric pressure halves with every 6 km increase in elevation, so a freely expanding balloon becomes twice as big with each 6 km rise. Does this increase the buoyant force? No, because the displacement of twice as much half-as-dense air has the same weight!

> CHECK QUESTION: A large block of styrofoam and a small block of iron have identical weights on a weighing scale. Which has the greater mass? [Actually the styrofoam has the greater mass. This is because it has a greater volume, displaces more air, and experiences a greater buoyant force. So it's weight on the scale is its "true weight," minus the buoyant force of the air, which is the case for all things weighed in air. The fact that it reads the same on the scale as the iron means it must have more mass than the iron. (A lobster that walks on a bathroom scale on the ocean bottom has more mass than the reading indicates.)]

> CHECK QUESTION: What would happen to the bubbles in a beer mug if you dropped the mug of beer from the top of a high building? Would the bubbles rise to the top, go to the bottom, or remain motionless with respect to the mug? [First of all, you'd likely be apprehended for irresponsible behavior. As for the bubbles, they'd remain motionless relative to the mug, since the local effects of gravity on the beer would be absent. This is similar to the popular demo of dropping a cup of water with holes in the side. When held at rest the water spurts out, but drop it and the spurting stops.]

Bernoulli's Principle Introduce Bernoulli's principle by blowing across the top surface of a sheet of paper, Figure 13.17. Follow this up with a variety of demonstrations such as making a beach ball hover in a stream of air issuing from the reverse end of a vacuum cleaner or a Ping-Pong ball in the airstream of a hair dryer.

> DEMONSTRATION: Line a cardboard tube with sandpaper and sling a Ping-Pong ball sidearm. The sandpaper will produce the friction to make the ball roll down the tube and emerge spinning — you'll see that the ball breaks in the correct direction. Point out that paddles have a rough surface like the sand-paper for the same reason — to spin the ball when it is properly struck — that is, to apply "English" to the ball.

83

DEMONSTRATION: Place a pair of upright empty aluminum soft drink cans on a few parallel straws on your lecture table. Blow between the cans and they roll toward each other. Or do the same with the nearby cans suspended by strings. A puff of air between them makes them click against one another, rather than blowing them apart as might be expected. [Some people avoid Bernoulli's principle because in some cases, like plane flight, there are alternate models to account for the forces that occur. These clicking cans, however, are straight Bernoulli!]

DEMONSTRATION: Show the sailboat demo described earlier on page 46 of this manual; first with the flat sail, and then with the curved sail. The difference is apparent.

DEMONSTRATION: Swing a Ping-Pong ball taped to a string into a stream of water as shown in Figure 13.24. Follow this up with the shower curtain bit of page 242.

Plasma Describe the changes of state of matter as the rate of molecular motion is increased in a substance, say a piece of ice changing to water, and then to steam. State how increased motion results in the molecules shaking apart into their constituent atoms, and how still increased motion results in the freeing of orbital electrons from the atomic nuclei — and you have a plasma. Acknowledge the partial plasmas in the everyday world — advertising signs, fluorescent lamps, street lamps, and the like. Discuss the role of plasma in power production.

NEXT-TIME QUESTION: Place a small birthday-type candle in a deep drinking glass. When the glass is whirled around in a circular path, say held at arm's length while one is spinning like an ice skater, which way does the flame point? And most important, why? (Note the similarity of this with Exercise 25.)

14

Temperature, Heat, and Expansion

Temperature
Heat
Quantity of Heat
Specific Heat Capacity
Expansion
Expansion of Water

Just as the chapters on Properties of Matter placed particular emphasis on water and the atmosphere, the chapters on Heat do the same. Note that no attempt is made to familiarize the student with methods of temperature conversion from one scale to another. The effort saved can be better spent on physics.

The concept of heat flow between temperature differences provides some background to the concept of current flow between electric potential differences in Chapter 22. Here we introduce the concept of KE/molecule, *temperature*, which is analogous to the later concept of PE/charge, *voltage*. Both high temperatures and high voltages are ordinarily harmful only when large energies are transferred in a relatively short time (that is, when large power is transferred). The white-hot sparks of a 4th-of-July sparkler have very high temperatures, but their energies are very small. So they are quite harmless. Similarly, a balloon rubbed on your hair may have thousands of volts, but the energy stored is very small. Energy per molecule or energy per charge may be high, but if the molecules or charges involved are small in number, the energy content is also small. Aside from the parallels between heat and electricity, the chapter serves as a prerequisite only for the three following chapters dealing with heat transfer, change of state, and thermodynamics.

In the text, temperature is treated in terms of the kinetic energy per molecule of substances. Although strictly speaking, temperature is directly proportional to the kinetic energy per molecule only in the case of ideal gases, we take the view that temperature is related to molecular translational kinetic energy in most common substances. Rotational kinetic energy, on the other hand, is only indirectly related to temperature, as is illustrated in a microwave oven. There the H_2O molecules are set oscillating with considerable rotational kinetic energy. But this doesn't cook the food. What does is the translational kinetic energy imparted to neighboring molecules that are bounced from the oscillating H_2Os like marbles that are set flying in all directions when they encounter the spinning blades of fans. If neighboring atoms did not interact with the oscillating H_2O molecules, the temperature of the food would be no different before and after the microwave oven was activated. Temperature has to do with the translational kinetic energy of molecules. Degrees of freedom, rotational and vibrational states, and the complications of temperature in liquids and solids are not treated. Next course!

Quantity of heat is spoken of in terms of calories, a departure from the SI unit, joules.

Note that the term *thermal energy* is not used in this edition. Because it means different things to different people, I avoid any confusion, I hope, by simply leaving it out. In most all cases, *internal energy* is the proper term anyway.

In this edition we speak of *specific heat capacity*, rather than *specific heat* as in previous editions. Why? Because it carries more meaning for nonscientists.

The definition of the calorie, page 256, implies that the same amount of heat will be required to change the temperature of water 1°C — whatever the temperature of the water. Although this relation holds true to a fair degree, it is not exactly correct: a calorie is precisely defined as the amount of heat required to raise a gram of water from 14° to 15° Celsius.

The exaggeration of the volume vs temperature scale in Figure 14.14 should be pointed out, for it is easy for a student to erroneously conclude that a great change in the volume of water occurs over a relatively small temperature change. Despite the warning in the following page, some students will interpret the volume at 0°C to be that of ice rather than ice water.

Linear expansion is treated on a page in **Practicing Physics**.

There are two activites and one experiment in the **Laboratory Manual** that go with this chapter.

Check questions are few in the following suggested lecture. By now it is hoped that this technique is a major part of your lecture method. Take pity on students who sit through lectures where the instructor poses questions that he or she immediately answers without involving the students, who are passive observers rather than participants in the learning process. Pose check questions before you move onto new material.

SUGGESTED LECTURE PRESENTATION

Begin by asking what the difference is between a hot cup of coffee and a cold cup of coffee. Think small for the answer: The molecules in the hot cup of coffee are moving faster — they are more energetic. Heat and temperature have to do with the kinetic energies of the molecules in substances. Heat and temperature are different: To begin with, **heat** is energy that is measured in joules, or calories. **Temperature** is measured in degrees. More on this soon.

Temperature Calibration Describe how the increased jostling of molecules in a substance result in expansion and show how this property underlies the common thermometer. Draw a sketch of an uncalibrated thermometer on the board, with its mercury vessel at the bottom, and describe how the energy of jostling molecules is transferred from the outer environment to the mercury within. If placed in boiling water, energy of the jostling water molecules would be transferred to the mercury, which would expand and squeeze up the tube. State that one could make a scratch on the glass at this level and label it 100. And then describe how, if placed in a container of ice water, the molecules of mercury would give energy to the cold water and slow down, contract, and fall to a lower level in the tube. One could again make a scratch and call this point zero. Then, if 100 equally-spaced scratches are made between the two reference points, one would have a centigrade thermometer.

In a vein of humor draw a second uncalibrated thermometer on the board and repeat your discussion (in abbreviated fashion) of placing it in boiling water. State that the upper level needn't be called 100, that any number would do so long as all thermometers were calibrated the same. Ask the class for any random number. Someone will say 212. Casually acknowledge the 212 response and write that on your diagram. Repeat the bit about placing the instrument in ice water and state that the position on the scale needn't be called zero, that any number would do. Ask for a random number. You'll have several students volunteer 32, which you graciously accept. The class should be in a good mood at this point, and you briefly discuss the two scales and lead into the idea of absolute zero and the Kelvin scale. (Name after "Lord Scale?")

Did Fahrenheit have a fever on the day he calibrated his temperature scale? Was a 1.4° above normal responsible for his placement of the 100° mark where he wished to be the standard for 100°? Your class may wish to speculate how he placed his zero.

> CHECK QUESTION: Which has the largest degrees, a Celcius thermometer or a Fahrenheit thermometer? [Celcius.]

> CHECK QUESTION: True or false: Cold is the absence of fast-moving molecules. [False; cold refers to very slow-moving molecules, not their absence. If you have no molecules at all, the concept of temperature is meaningless. That's why its technically incorrect to speak of the "cold of outer space". Space has no temperature, although because it acts as a heat sink (Chapter 17), an object in it will soon become very cold.]

Absolute Zero   The treatment of the Kelvin scale is very brief in this chapter, and it is not really treated until Chapter 17. So you can gloss over it and explain that it is "nature's scale" and begins at the coldest possible value for its zero point. In case your treatment of heat is brief and you will not be including the Thermodynamics Chapter 17, you may want to develop the idea of absolute zero here, in which case you should consider the following lecture skit [which is repeated in the suggested lecture of Chapter 17].

Begin by supposing you order at your friendly restaurant a piece of hot apply pie. The waitress brings you cold pie, straight from the frig and at $0°$C. You tell her you'd like hotter pie, in fact, twice as hot. Question: What will be the temperature of the pie? Encourage neighbor discussion. Many will say zero degrees. Then ask what the new temperature would be if the pie were initially $10°$C, and acknowledge that the answer is *not* $20°$C! Now you're ready for the "Celsius, the Village Tailor" story.

> **Celsius, the Village Tailor**   To answer the pie temperature questions and develop the idea of absolute zero, hold a measuring stick against the wall of the lecture room (so that the bottom of the vertically-oriented stick is about 1 meter above the floor) and state that that you are Celsius, the village tailor, and that you measure the heights of your customers against the stick, which is firmly fastened to the wall. You state that there is no need for the stick to extend to the floor, nor to the ceiling, for your shortest and tallest customers fall within the extremities of the stick. Mention that all tailors using the same method could communicate meaningfully with each other about the relative heights of their customers providing the measuring sticks in each shop were fastened the same distance above the "absolute zero"of height. It just so happens that the distance to the floor, the "absolute zero," is 273 notches — the same size notches on the stick itself. Then one day, a very short lady enters your shop and stands against the wall, the top of her head coinciding with the zero mark on the measuring stick. As you take her zero reading, she comments that she has a brother who is twice her height. Ask the class for the height of her brother. Then ask for the temperature of the twice-as-hot apple pie. When this is understood, ask why the pie will not *really* be $273°$C. Or that for the initially $10°$C pie, the temperature will not really be $293°$C. [Considerable heat has gone into changing the state of the water in the pie, which ac-

counts for it being "dried out." If you wish to avoid the change of state factor, begin your discussion with the temperature of something such as a piece of metal that will not change state for the temperature range in question.]

Heat   Distinguish between *heat* and *temperature*. Heat has to do with energy flow while temperature is a ratio of energy per molecule. They are very different. A Fourth-of-July-type sparkler emits sparks with temperatures exceeding 2000°C, but the heat one receives when one of these sparks lands on ones face is very small. High temperature means a high ratio of heat per molecule. The *ratio* and the *amount* of heat energy transferred are different things. Relatively few molecules comprise the tiny bit of white-hot matter that makes up the sparks of the sparkler. (Later you'll invoke a similar argument when you discuss the small energy associated with the high voltage of a charged van de Graaff generator or party balloon rubbed on your hair.)

> CHECK QUESTION: How are the sparks from a sparkler that strike your skin akin to tiny droplets of boiling water striking your skin? [Both have high temperatures, but safe levels of internal energy to transfer to your skin.]

Distinguish between *heat* and *internal energy*. (Internal energy is treated in more detail in Chapter 17.) Internal energy is loosely referred to as heat energy, although by definition, heat is the energy that flows from one place to another by virtue of a temperature difference. Heat is energy in transit.

Quantity of Heat   Define the calorie, and distinguish it from the Calorie, the concern of people who watch their diet.

Specific Heat Capacity   Lead into a distinction between the difference between calories and degrees, and the concept of specific heat capacity by asking your class to consider the difference in touching an empty iron frying pan that has been placed on a hot stove for one minute (ouch!) and doing the same with a frying pan of water. With the water, you could place your hand in it safely even if it were on the stove for several minutes. Ask which has the higher temperature, the empty pan or the one filled with water. Clearly, it is the empty pan. Ask which absorbed the greater amount of energy. The answer is the water-filled pan, if it was on the stove for a longer time. The water has absorbed more energy for a lesser rise in temperature! Physics types have a name for this idea — specific heat capacity, or for short, specific heat. Cite the different specific heat capacities of cooked foods, of a hot TV dinner and the aluminum foil that can be removed with bare hands while the food is still to hot to touch.

Water's High Specific Heat   Cite examples of water's high specific heat — hot water bottles on cold winter nights, cooling systems in cars, and the climate in places where there is much water. With the aid of a large world map, globe, or chalkboard sketch, show the sameness of latitudes for England and the Hudson Bay, and the French and Italian Riverias with Canada. State how the fact that water requires so long a time to heat and cool, enables the Gulf Stream to hold heat energy long enough to reach the North Atlantic. There it cools off. But if the water cools, then according to the conservation of energy, something else has to warm. What is that something? The air. The cooling water warms the air, and the winds at that latitude are westerly. So warmed air moves over the continent of Europe. If this weren't the case, Europe would have the same climate as regions of northern Canada. A similar situation occurs in the United States. The Atlantic Ocean off the coast of the eastern states is considerably warmer than the Pacific Ocean off the coast of Washington, Oregon and California, yet in winter months the east coast is considerably colder. This has to do with the high specific heat of water and the westerly winds. Air that is warmed by cooling water on the west coast moves landward and gives mild winters to Washington, Oregon, and California. But on the east coast, this warmed air moves seaward, leaving the east coast frigid in winter months. In summer months, when the air is warmer than the water, the air cools and the water warms. So summer months on the west coast states are relatively cool, while the east coast is relatively hot. The high specific heat of water serves to moderate climates. The climates on islands, for example, are fairly free of temperature variations. Even San Francisco, a peninsula that is close to being an island, has the most stable climate of any city in continental America.

4°C Water   To lead into the idea of water's low density at 4°C you can ask if anyone in class happens to know what the temperature at the bottom of Lake Michigan was on a particular date, New Year's eve in 1905, for example. Then for the bottom of Lake Tahoe in California for any other date. And for another, until many are responding "4°C".

> CHECK QUESTION: Ask the same for the bottom of a rain puddle outside the building, and be prepared for some to say 4°C.

Then ask why 4°C was the right answer for the deep lakes but the wrong answer for puddle. Then go into the explanation as given in the book — how the microscopic slush forms as the freezing temperature is approached, yielding a net expansion below 4°C. (I haven't done this, but I have thought of showing a Galileo-type thermometer in class — a small flask with a narrow glass tube filled with colored water, so changes in temperature would be clearly evident by different levels of water in the narrow tube. Then surround the flask with perhaps dry ice to rapidly chill the water. The water level drops as the temperature of the water decreases, but its rate slows as it nears 4°C, and then the direction reverses as cooling continues. This expansion of the water is due to the formation of "microscopic slush." The level of water observed, as a function of time, yields the graph of Figure 14.14.)

Ice Formation on Lakes   Discuss the formation of ice, and why it forms at the surface and why it floats. And why deep bodies of water don't freeze over in winter because all the water in the lake has to be cooled to 4°C before colder water will remain at the surface to be cooled to the freezing temperature, 0°C. State that before one can cool a teaspoon full of water to 3°C, let alone 0°C, all the water beneath must be cooled to 4°C and that winters are neither cold or long enough for this to happen in the United States.

Expansion   (Note the order differs from the text — in lecture I keep running with water) State that steel lengths expand about 1 part in 100 000 for each 1°C increase in temperature. Show a steel rod and ask if anybody would be afraid to stand with their stomach between the end of the rigidly held steel rod and a wall while the temperature of the rod is increased a few degrees. This is a safe activity, for the slight expansion of the rod would hardly be noticeable. Now ask for volunteers for a steel rod several kilometers in length. This is much different, for although the rate of change in length is the same, the total change in length could well impale you! Then discuss the expansion joints of large structures (Figures 14-9 and 14-10).

> DEMONSTRATION: Place the middle of a bimetallic strip in a flame to show the unequal expansions of different metals, and the subsequent bending.

Point out that different substances expand or contract (length, area, and volume) at their own characteristic rates [coefficients of expansion]. Cite examples such as the need for the same expansion rate in teeth and teeth fillings; iron reinforcing rods and concrete; and the metal wires that are encased in glass light bulbs and the glass itself. Provision must be made when materials with different expansion rates interact; like the piston rings when aluminum pistons are enclosed in steel cylinders in a car, and the rockers on bridges (Figure 14.9), and the overflow pipe for gasoline in a steel tank.

CHECK QUESTION: How would a thermometer differ if glass expanded with increasing temperature more than mercury? [Answer: The scale would be upside down, because the reservoir would enlarge (like the hole enlarged in the heated metal ring) and mercury in the column would tend to fill it up with increasing temperature.]

NEXT-TIME QUESTION: Ask your students to place an ice cube in a glass of ice water at home, and compare the water level at the side of the glass before and after the ice melts. Ask them to account for the volume of ice that extends above the water line after it melts. The answer to the original question is, of course, that the level remains unchanged. This can be explained from the principles learned in Chapter 12. The floating ice cube displaces its own weight of water, so if the cube weighs say a newton, then when placed in the glass, one newton of water is displaced and the water level rises. If it is first melted and then poured in the glass, again the water line would be higher, but by one newton, the same amount. More interesting is to account for the volume of floating ice that extends above the water line (Exercise 26). The ice expanded upon freezing because of the hexagonal open structures of the crystals. Ask the class if they have any idea of how much volume all those billions an billions of open spaces constitute. Their combined volume is essentially that of the part of ice extending above the water line! When the ice melts, the part above the water line fills in the open structures as they collapse. Discuss this idea in terms of icebergs, and whether or not the coastline would change if all the floating icebergs in the world melted. The oceans would rise a bit, but only because icebergs are composed of fresh water. (They form above sea level and break off and then fall into sea.) The slight rise is more easily understood by exaggerating the circumstance — think of ice cubes floating in mercury. When they melt, the depth of fluid (water on mercury) is higher than before.

NEXT-TIME QUESTION: Exercise 19 (The size of the hole in the iron ring when heated): Many students will correctly reason that the thickness of the ring will increase, but they will then conclude that the hole becomes smaller. When you treat the answer, consider cutting the ring into 4 quadrants, and put the pieces into a hot oven. They all expand. Now bring them back together to form a ring. This should make it clear that the hole expands when the ring is heated. More simply, the circumference as well as the thickness and every other dimension increases. Support this by demonstration and by the examples of opening a stuck metal jar lid by placing it under hot water, and the fitting of iron wheel rims on wooden wagon wheels by first placing the slightly smaller iron rims into the blacksmith's fire.

NEXT-TIME QUESTION: Problem 4, the ring around the earth.

15

Heat Transfer

This chapter begins with conduction, convection, and radiation of heat with emphasis again on bodies of water and the atmosphere. The section on radiation serves as some background to later chapters on light.

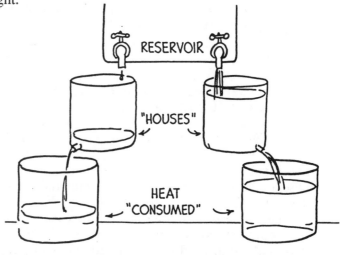

To turn your thermostat down or off in order to save energy, Exercise 36, makes an excellent NEXT-TIME QUESTION. To illustrate its answer [turn it off!], make up the apparatus shown, which consists of a main reservoir that feeds "heat" into two identical "houses," that leak heat to the environment. The amount of leakage is caught by the bottom jars and can be compared at a glance. Arrange the input flow rates so that equilibrium is established when the "houses" are nearly full: then input = outflow. Turn one input off altogether. After some time, turn it back on until it fills to the level of the other "house." Now compare the differences in leaked water! Make comparisons of turning it down partway instead of off. This roughly approximates Newton's law of cooling. Leak rate is highest when ΔT, or in this case, ΔP, is greatest.

Adiabatic expansion is suggested in this chapter, and a molecular model is described to account for the cooling that expanding air undergoes. This idea is picked up again in more detail in Chapter 17.

Calorimetry is treated on a page in **Practicing Physics**.

An activity on heat transfer is in the **Laboratory Manual**.

The material on the earth's seasons from the suggested lecture in Chapter 14 can be worked into your lecture for this chapter if you didn't cover it last time. It is not covered in the text, but is related to comments on the climate of either Chapter 14 or this chapter.

SUGGESTED LECTURE PRESENTATION

Conduction Begin by asking why pots and pans have wooden or plastic handles, why little Joshua on page 251 can safely touch wood at a high temperature — then discuss conduction from an atomic point of view, citing the role of the electrons in both heat and electrical conductors. You might demonstrate the oldie of melting wax on different metal rods equidistant from a hot flame, and illustrate relative conductivities. Other materials can be compared in their ability to conduct heat, like newspaper when having to sleep out-of-doors. Discuss the poor conductivity of water, which ties to the previous lecture where you discussed the $4°C$ temperature of the bottom of deep lakes all year round.

> DEMONSTRATION: Do Home Project 1 with ice wedged at the bottom of a test tube. Some steel wool will hold the ice at the bottom of the tube. It is impressive to see that the water at the top is brought to a boil by the flame of a burner while the ice below barely melts!

> DEMONSTRATION: Do Home Project 2 and wrap a piece of paper around a thick metal bar and attempt to burn it in the flame. The paper does not reach its ignigion temperature because heat is conducted into the metal.

> DEMONSTRATION: Extend the previous demo and place a paper cup filled with water in the flame. Again, the paper will not reach its ignition temperature and burn because heat from the flame is conducted into the conductor — this time water. Water is not *that* poor a conductor — its high specific heat comes into play here also (this is Exercise 13.)

Discuss the poor conductivity of air, and its role in insulating materials — like snow. Discuss thermal underwear, and how the fish-net open spaces actually trap air between the skin and the undergarment. Discuss double-window thermopane. If your lecture was preceded by Chapter 13, cite the case of the manufacturer in the midwest who sent a shipment of thermopane windows by truck over the Rocky Mountains only to find that all the windows broke at the higher altitude. The atmospheric pressure between the panes was not matched by the same pressure outside. Ask if the windows "imploded" or "exploded".

Convection and rising Warm Air Illustrate convection by considering the case of rising warm air. Discuss Figure 15.5. An analogy is a drunk who is moving haphazardly in the middle of a large dance floor where there is a "gradient" of people, crowded near the bandstand, and sparce toward the opposite end of the room. If the drunk rambled around for a few minutes, wouldn't you be most prone to find him on the side of the room farthest from the crowded bandstand? You can sketch this situation on the board, your sketch being essentially that of Figure 15.5.

> CHECK QUESTION: Why does smoke from a cigarette rise and then settle off?

CHECK QUESTION: Why does helium rise to the very top of the atmosphere? Why doesn't it settle like the smoke? [The answer to this is detailed in the long footnote on page 269.]

After explaining that for the same temperature, the relatively small mass of helium is compensated for by a greater speed at whatever temperature and altitude, state that helium is not found in the air but must be mined from beneath the ground like natural gas. (The helium nucleus is the alpha particle that emanates from radioactive ores.) This idea of faster-moving helium underscores the relationship of kinetic energy to temperature. Stress it.

Expanding Air Cools (The rising of warm air and its subsequent cooling is treated thermodynamically in Chapter 17 — the treatment here and the later treatment complement each other nicely.) Now you're into the cooling effect of expanding air. Depart from the order of topics in the text and first treat the warming of compressed air. The familiar bicycle pump offers a good example. Why does the air become warm when the handle is depressed. It's easy to see that the air molecules speed up when the piston slams against them. A Ping-Pong ball similarly speeds up when a paddle hits it. Now, consider what happens to the speed of a Ping-Pong ball when it encounters a receeding paddle! Can your students see that its rebound speed will be less than its incident speed? Now you're ready to discuss the cooling of expanding air, Figure 15.6, and compare this to the case of the slowing Ping-Pong balls with molecules that are on the average receding from one another.

Here's a great one: Have everyone in class blow against their hands with open mouths. Their breaths feel warm. Then repeat with mouth openings very small. Their breaths are remarkably cooler (Figure 17.6 in Chapter 17). They **experience** first hand that expanding air *really does* cool!

> DEMONSTRATION: Heat water in a pressure cooker, remove the cap and place your hand in the expanding steam that is ejected to show the cooling of expanding air, as Millie does in Figure 15.7. Mixing of water vapor with the outside air also contributes to this cooling. Cite that the students don't see steam as such, for the steam is actually not visible. The cloud they see is not steam but condensed water vapor — and considerably cooled at that!

Discuss the role of convection in climates. Begin by calling attention to the shift in winds as shown in Figure 15.8. This leads you into radiation, the heat from the sun.

Warm at the Equator; Cold at the Poles You may want to discuss why the earth is warmer at the equator than at the poles, and get into the idea of solar energy per unit area. A neat way to do this is to first draw a large circle on the board that represents the earth (like the one below, only without the sun's rays at this point). Ask for a neighbor check and speculate why it is warm near the equator and cold at the poles. To dispel the idea that the farther distance to the poles is the reason, do the following:

SKIT: Ask the class to pretend there is a vertical rainfall, into which you reach out your window with two sheets of paper — one held horizontally and the other held at an angle as shown. You bring the papers inside as a friend strolls by and inquires what you're doing. You remark that you have been holding the sheets of paper out in the rain. Your friend sees that the horizontally held paper is much wetter and asks why. You repeat with both papers held outward as before, and your friend says, "Oh, I see why. You're holding the tilted sheet further away from the clouds!" Ask your class if you are holding it farther away from the overhead clouds. The answer is yes. Ask if this is the reason the paper is not as wet. The answer is no!

Seasons Depending on time, you might consider departing from the text and continue with the solar energy per unit of area idea to the seasons. The plane of the earth's equator is not parallel to the plane of the earth's orbit. Instead, the polar axis is inclined at 23 1/2 degrees (the ecliptic). Draw the sketch below on the board, first with only the two positions of the earth at the far left and far right. Ask which of these two positions represents winter months and which represents summer months. Encourage neighbor discussion.

Once it is clear that winter is at the left, show the position of the earth in autumn and in spring. Shift the position of the sun closer to the earth in winter, for this is actually the case. From your drawing, your class can see why northern hemisphere types enjoy an extra week of spring and summer! Southern hemisphere types are compensated by a somewhat milder climate year round due to the greater amount of ocean in the southern hemisphere (80% as compared to about 60% for the northern hemisphere).

Radiation Discuss the radiation one feels from red hot coals in a fireplace. And how the radiation decreases with distance. Consider the radiation one feels when stepping from the shade to the sunshine. Amazing! The heat is not so much because of the sun's temperature, because like temperatures are to be found in the torches of some welders. One feels hot not because the sun is hot, but because it is *big*. Comfortably big!

Acknowledge that everything emits radiation — everything that has any temperature. But everything does not become progressively cooler because everything absorbs radiation. We live in a sea of radiation, everything emitting and everything absorbing. When emission rate equals absorption rate, temperature remains constant. Some materials, because of their molecular design, emit better than others. They also absorb better than others. They're easy to spot, because they absorb visible radiation as well and appear black.

DEMONSTRATION: Make up and show the black hole in the white box, as shown by Helen Yan in Figure 15.11. (Helen, now a physicist, was a 21-year-old student at CCSF when this was taken in 1983.)

94

DEMONSTRATION: Pour hot water into a pair of vessels, one black and the other shiny silver. Ask for a neighbor check as to which will cool faster. Have thermometers in each that you ask a student to read aloud at the beginning and a few minutes later. (You can repeat this demo with initially cold water in each vessel.)

Explain the frost in the above-freezing mornings bit, page 275.

Newton's Law of Cooling   If you're into graphical analysis, construct a large plot of the exponential decrease of the temperature of either of the vessels in the previous demonstration. Its easy to see the curve is steep at first (when the water is hotter) and less steep as it cools. The slope of your curve is of changing temperature per time interval — the slope decreases as time increases. But one can as well say the slope decreases as the temperature approaches the ambient temperature. This is Newton's law of cooling.

The rate will be different for the black and silver vessels, so we see the difference between a proportionality sign and an equals sign for the formula here. The actual rate of cooling or warming is not only proportional to the difference in temperatures, but in the "emissivities" of the surfaces.

Relate Newton's law of cooling to Exercises 30 (cream in the coffee), 36 (thermostat on a cold day), and 37 (air conditioner on a hot day). These exercises make excellent Next-Time Questions.

Greenhouse Effect   Compare the window glass of the florist's greenhouses to the carbon-dioxide window glass of the earth's atmosphere. CO_2 builds up year by year by increased usage of fossil fuels that spew carbon into the atmosphere. Interestingly enough, the carbon that is spewed by burning is the same carbon that is absorbed by tree growth. So a realistic step in the solution to the greenhouse-effect problem is to simply grow more trees (while decreasing the rate at which they are cut down)! Johnny-Appleseed types — to the task! This would not be an end-all to the problem, however, because the carbon returns to the biosphere when the trees ultimately decay. More general than the name greenhouse effect is *global warming*.

State that terrestrial radiation rather than solar radiation is directly responsible for the warmth of the air around us. Air is primarily warmed by the earth, which is an important reason we don't freeze at night when we're not in the sun's light. Three cheers for terrestrial radiation!

Interesting point: The earth is always "in equilibrium" whether it is overheating or not. At a higher temperature, as global warming produces, the earth simply radiates more terrestrial radiation. Income and outgo match in any case; the important consideration is the temperature at which this income and outgo match.

Solar Power   Solar power has been with humans from the beginning. We see its application whenever we see clothes hung on a line (do you see that much anymore?) and we see it as an energy source on rooftops that provide hot water (Figure 15.19). If you have up-to-date information on this growing technology, share it with your class here.

Excess Terrestrial Heat Discuss the overheating of the earth problem, and tie it to Exercise 38.

As an interesting side point that has to do with heat, it has long been known that a frog cannot discern small changes in temperature, and if sitting comfortably in a pan of water that is slowly heated on a stove, it will make no effort to jump out as the water as temperature increases. It will just sit there and be cooked. But this is not limited to

95

frogs. According to accounts given by cannibals who cook their victims in large pots of water, the same is true of humans. More recent evidence took place several years ago in Mill Valley, CA, where water in a hot tub gradually overheated (due to a faulty heater) and resulted in the death of the unsuspecting and drowsy occupants. You can compare this to other cases where if adverse conditions are increased gradually, humans will tolerate what otherwise would be completely unacceptable to them: smog, noise, pollution, crime, and so on.

NEXT-TIME QUESTION: Those who missed the expansion of the ball and ring question can mend their ways with this one: Consider the gap in a piece of metal in the shape of a C. When the metal is heated, will the gap get wider or narrower? [Wider, as is seen better if it is first cut into several sections, then rearranged when all parts have expanded.]

16

Change of State

Again the emphasis is on bodies of water and the atmosphere. Material from this chapter is not prerequisite to the chapters that follow.

We speak of change of *state*; many other texts speak of change of *phase*, perhaps to avoid confusion with "energy state." Should I change to phase in the next edition?

Note that the units calories are used in this chapter, particularly with heats of fusion and vaporization of water. I find the SI units 334.88 kJ/kg and 2.26 MJ/kg too conceptually difficult compared to the 80 and 540 calories that many students are familiar with in chemistry courses. If you're a 100% SI type, the footnotes on page 297 give the SI units, and you can lecture with SI units and point out the very few places where the units calories occur.

Thanks to Jearl Walker for the classroom photo of his famous firewalk. With the recent interest in firewalking, and its exploitation by various mystics and a few charlatans, Jearl's physics explanation scores another point for rationality.

Regarding Home Project 6: The considerable amount of energy that goes into vaporization explains why under some conditions hot water will freeze faster than warm water. This occurs for water hotter than $80°C$, and is evident when the surface area that cools by rapid evaporation is large compared to the amount of water involved — like washing a car with hot water on a cold winter day, or flooding a skating rink to melt and smooth out the rough spots and freeze quickly. That 540 calories per gram of water that evaporates is substantial. To simplify, consider the cooling of boiling water with a 25% evaporation rate. Then for every gram of water that evaporates, three grams are left behind. If the 540 calories is supplied by the 3 grams of remaining water, each gram gives up 180 calories. From the 180 calories, 100 calories will bring boiling water to $0°C$. This leaves 80 calories. What happens when 80 calories is taken away from a gram of $0°C$ water? It turns to ice. Hence the rapid evaporation of 1 gram of boiling water converts the other 3 grams of boiling water to ice. In practice, of course, evaporation rates are considerably lower than this, and not all the energy for this change of state is supplied by the remaining water. Will boiling water freeze before cold water? No. But boiling water will freeze before water warmer than $60°C$. A plot showing freezing times (again, thanx to Jearl Walker) is shown at the right. Surprisingly, water at 80°C takes longer to freeze than water at 99°C. But for water temperatures less than 80°C, common sense prevails. (Another factor that I haven't checked is that freezing may be enhanced in hot water because dissolved oxygen has been taken out of it during heating.)

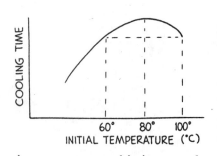

If you wish to introduce the idea of distribution curves in your course, this is a good place to do it. Treat the cooling produced by evaporation with plots of relative numbers of molecules in a liquid vs their speeds, and show how the distribution shifts as the faster-moving molecules evaporate. You may wish to point to the bell-shapes distribution curves that represent the distributions of so many things, from molecular speeds to examination scores to people's IQ scores. Regretably, many people tend to regard such distributions not as bell-shaped, but as spikes. This makes a difference in attitudes. For example, suppose you compare the grade distributions for two sections of your course, Group 1 and Group 2, and that the average score for Group 1 is somewhat greater than that for Group 2. For whatever reason, Group 1 outperforms Group 2. With this information can we make any judgement about individuals from either group? One who looks at these distributions as spiked shaped behaves as if he can - he'll say (or not say but think) that individuals from Group 1 are "better" than particular individuals from Group 2. On the other hand, one who thinks in terms of the broad shape of the bell shaped distribution will not make any assumptions about such individuals. He is well aware of the region of overlap in the two distribution curves. His attitude toward individuals from either group is unbiased by unwarranted prejudice. Hence the difference between narrow-mindedness and broad-mindedness!

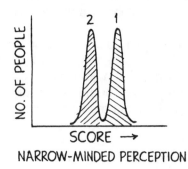

NARROW-MINDED PERCEPTION

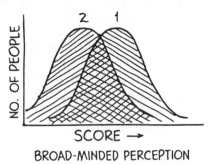

BROAD-MINDED PERCEPTION

There is a page in **Practicing Physics** for this chapter — *Energy Changes of State.*

There are four activities on *change of state* in the **Laboratory Manual.**

I feel compelled to interject here (as I mean to stress all through this manual) the importance of the "check with your neighbor" technique of teaching. Please do not spend your lecture talking to yourself in front of your class! The procedure of the "check with your neighbor" routine keeps you and your class together. I can't stress enough its importance to effective teaching!

SUGGESTED LECTURE PRESENTATION

Evaporation Begin by citing the familiar case of leaving the water when bathing and feeling chilly in the air, especially when it is windy. Explain the cooling of a liquid from an atomic point of view, and reinforce the idea of temperature being a measure of the average molecular kinetic energy, and acknowledge molecules that move faster and slower than the average.

CHECK QUESTION: Why does cooling occur in the water of a leaky canvas water bag? [Water seeps through the canvas. More faster-moving molecules leak and vaporize, leaving less energy per molecule behind.]

CHECK QUESTION: Cite at least two ways to cool a hot cup of coffee. [You can increase evaporation by blowing on it or pouring it into the saucer to increase the evaporating area. You can cool it by conduction by putting silverware in it, which absorbs heat and provides a radiating antenna.]

Sketch a bell-shaped distribution curve on the board to represent the wide array of molecular speeds in a container of water. The peak of the curve represents the speeds that correspond to the temperature of the water. (It is not important to distinguish here between the mean speed, the rms speed, and the most probable speeds.) Stress the many lower and higher speeds to the left and right of the peak of your curve at any moment in the water. Which molecules evaporate? The fast ones, which you clip from the right hand tail of your curve. What is the result? A shift toward the left of the peak of the curve — a lowering of temperature. [Actually, this approach is highly exaggerated, for the molecules that do penetrate the surface and escape into the air have energies that correspond to 3400K! See my article on page 492 of *The Physics Teacher*, October, 1981.]

The relatively strong bond between water molecules (hydrogen bonding) prevents more evaporation than presently occurs. It also enhances condensation.

Condensation   If evaporation is a cooling process, what kind of process would the opposite of evaporation be? This is condensation, which is a warming process.

CHECK QUESTION: Why is it that many people after taking a shower will begin drying in the shower stall before getting outside. [While still in the shower region, appreciable condensation offsets the cooling by evaporation.]

Make the point that a change of state from liquid to gas or vice versa is not merely one or the other. Condensation occurs while evaporation occurs and vice versa. The net effect is usually what is spoken about. If you haven't shown the collapsing can demo in your atmospheric pressure lecture, now is a good time:

DEMONSTRATION: Heat some aluminum soda pop cans on a burner, empty except for a small amount of water that is brought to a boil to make steam. With a pot holder or tongs, pick up a can and quickly invert it into a basin of water. Crunch! The atmospheric pressure immediately crushes the can with a resounding WHOP! Very impressive. Do this first by inverting cans into a cold basin of water. It is evident that condensation of the steam and vapor on the inside takes place, pressure is correspondingly reduced, and the atmospheric pressure on the outside crunches the can. Then repeat but this time invert cans into a basin of very hot water, just short of the boiling temperature. Crunch again, but less forceful than before. Steam molecules stick to the water surface, hot or cool, like flies sticking to fly paper. Then repeat, but this time invert cans into *boiling* water. No crunch. Lead your class into the explanation wherein the *net* effect is no change, as condensation of steam is met with just as much vaporization from the boiling water.

And make clear just what is cooling when evaporation occurs. To say that one thing cools is to say that another warms. When a hot cup of coffee cools by evaporation, the surrounding air is warmed. Conservation of energy reigns!

Condensation in the Atmosphere An interesting way to present the condensation of water vapor to droplets is the following: Ask why a glass containing an iced drink becomes wet on the outside, and why a ring of moisture is left on the table. I inject a bit of humor here and state that the reason is... and then write a big 16.7 on the board. Then ask why the walls of the classroom would become wet if the temperature of the room were suddenly reduced. State that the answer is...then underline your 16.7. Ask why dew forms on the morning grass, and state the answer is...another underline for 16.7. Ask why fog forms, and how the clouds form, and back to your 16.7. By now your class is wondering about the significance of 16.7. Announce you're discussing *Figure* 16.7, and with class attention and interest go on to discuss the formation of fog and clouds (and even rain, hail, and snow). [Snow crystalizes from vapor; hail is rain that freezes when tossed upward, often repeatedly, by strong updrafts.]

For years I have been unclear about the mechanics of energy release to the surrounding air by water vapor when it condenses. Now I think I know. H_2O molecules simply give most of their KE to the air during their last collision before condensation. The details are shown in the three sketches below.

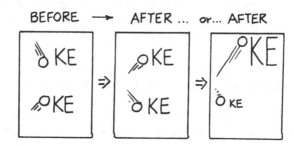

Consider two pairs of molecules, say with equal KEs before collision (Sketch 1). After collision, individual KEs may be quite unequal, for molecules that transfer much of their KE to others are left with corresponding less KE of their own (Sketch 2). So far, there is no change in the air's total KE score. But if the slower molecules happen to be H_2O, they are candidates for condensation if their next collisions are with other H_2Os that have similarly just given most of their KE to neighboring molecules (Sketch 3). Upon condensation of the slow-moving H_2Os, molecules left in the air have an increase in average KE. Viola! *H_2O molecules transfer KE to the surrounding air during their last collision while in the gaseous state* — the collision that immediately precedes condensation. The energy gained by the air is the well-known heat of vaporization — about 540 calories per gram of condensed H_2O for an ambient temperature of 100°C. It's greater for lower temperatures (molecules bopped to high speeds in a low-speed environment gain more energy than molecules bopped to the same high speeds in higher-speed environments). So all things being equal, a rainy day really is warmer than a cloudy day.

Condensation is enhanced by the presence of ions, dust, or tiny particles that act as the nuclei of dropplets. London became much foggier when coal burning provided more particles in the air to initiate condensation.

Boiling Discuss boiling and the roles of adding heat and pressure in the boiling process. A tactic I use throughout my teaching is to ask the class members to pretend they are having a one to one conversation with a friend about the ideas of physics. Suppose a friend is skeptical about the idea of boiling being a cooling process. I tell my class just what to say to convince the friend of what is going on. I tell them to first point out the distinction between heating and boiling. If the friend knows that the temperature of boiling water remains at 100°C regardless of the amount of heat applied, point out that this is so because the water is cooling by boiling as fast as it is being warmed by heating. Then if this still is not convincing, ask the friend to hold her hands above a pot of boiling water — in the steam. She knows she'll be burned.

But burned by what? By the steam. And where did the steam get its energy? From the boiling water; so energy is leaving the water — that's what we mean by cooling! Bring in the role of pressure on boiling, and illustrate this with the pressure cooker.

> CHECK QUESTIONS: In bringing water to a boil in the high mountains, is the time required to bring the water to a boil longer or shorter than at sea level? Is the time required for cooking longer or shorter? (Preface this second question with the statement that you are posing a different question, for any confusion about this is most likely due to failing to distinguish between the two questions.)

> DEMONSTRATION: Evacuate air from a flask of water that is at room temperature, enough so that the water in the flask will boil from the heat of the students' hands as it is passed around the classroom. [Take care that the flask is strong enough so that it doesn't implode!]

Geyser Explain how a geyser is like a pressure cooker. Discuss the operation of a coffee percolator.

Boiling and Freezing at the Same Time This must be seen to be appreciated!

> DEMONSTRATION: The triple-point demonstration, Figure 16.13. [A film loop should be made of this impressive demo for those who don't have the equipment!]

Melting and Freezing

> DEMONSTRATION: Regelation of an ice cube with a copper wire, Figure 16.15. (The wire must be a good heat conductor for this to work, as discussed in the footnote on page 294.)

Energy and Changes of State Ask if it is possible to heat a substance without raising its temperature, and why a steam burn is more damaging than a burn from boiling water at the same temperature. In answering these, discuss the change of state graph of Figure 16.17, and relate this to Figure 16.16. After citing examples of changes of state where energy is absorbed, cite examples where energy is released — like raining and snowing. People sometimes say that it is too cold to snow. Explain that this statement arises from the fact that when it is snowing, the temperature of the air is higher than would otherwise be the case — that it is really never too cold to snow, but that whenever it is snowing the air is relatively warm. Ask about cooling a room by leaving the refrigerator door open, and compare it to putting an air conditioner in the middle of a room instead of mounting it in a window. Ask what the result would be of mounting an air conditioner backwards in a window.

Air Conditioning In view of the ozone-destroying chemicals used as refrigerants, cite present efforts you are acquainted with in developing alternative systems. One approach introduced in mid 1992 by ICC Technologies in Philadelphia uses ordinary water in place of chlorofluorocarbons, with reports of providing cooling for a small fraction of the energy of conventional systems. The device utilizes the evaporation condensation cycle with a new type of desiccant, or drying agent, that chills air without increasing its humidity. Alternative air conditioning systems will likely be in the forefront of news on new technologies. Its needed.

Chicanery If any of your students want to acquire large sums of money by preying on the ignorance of the public, there may still be enough people left that don't know their physics who may be willing to shell out $300 each to learn how to walk barefoot on red-hot coals. Just be sure to use wood coals with a low heat conductivity. Different woods will give different results. After the surfaces of coals with a low heat conductivity give up their heat, it will take a sufficient time before appreciable internal energy from the inside reheats the surface. Lead your walkers to believe they are apart from nature, do not tell them about physics, and above all, do not have them walk on red-hot rocks or stones (unless you get that $300 first). Don't fret taking the $300, for that's a small violation of ethics compared to your robbing them of a rational view of the world — not that they had one to begin with, but you *are* leading them further astray. To gain community respect, consider incorporating and calling yourself a church.

NEXT-TIME QUESTION: Exercise 29 or 31.

17

Thermodynamics

Absolute Zero
Internal Energy
First Law of Thermodynamics
    Adiabatic Processes
    Meteorology and the First Law
Second Law of Thermodynamics
Entropy

In keeping with the preceding chapters on heat, this chapter focuses on the environment. Particular emphasis is given to the atmosphere. What do most people talk about in casual conversations? The weather, of course. This chapter provides some physics insights that underlie the weather.

There is no **Practicing Physics** page for this chapter.

An activity on the *mechanical equivalent of heat* is in the **Laboratory Manual.**

The topics absolute zero and internal energy were introduced in Chapter 14 and are treated in somewhat more detail in this chapter. This chapter concludes Part 3 and is not prerequisite to chapters that follow. It may be skipped if a brief treatment of heat is required.

SUGGESTED LECTURE PRESENTATION

Absolute Zero Review the temperature scales and lead into the thermodynamic temperature scale. If you did not discuss "Celsius, the Village Tailor", related in the suggested lecture for Chapter 14, (page 87), this would be the time to do so. Begin by considering the ordering of a piece of hot apple pie and then being served cold pie — ice cold pie, at $0°C$. Suppose you ask the waiter to put the pie in the oven and heat it up. How hot? Say twice as hot. Question: what will be the temperature of the pie? Move your class to the "check-your-neighbor" routine. Change your mind about the $0°C$ initial temperature of the piece of pie, and ask if the problem is easier if you begin with, say, a $10°C$ piece of pie. Tell your class to beware of neighbors who say the problem is simplified, and the answer is $20°C$. This should spark interest. Now you're ready for "Celsius, the Village Tailor" story.

> **Celsius, the Village Tailor** Hold a measuring stick against the wall of the lecture room (so that the bottom of the vertically-oriented stick is about 1 meter above the floor) and state that that you are Celsius, the village tailor, and that you measure the heights of your customers against the stick, which is firmly fastened to the wall. You state that there is no need for the stick to extend to the floor, nor to the ceiling, for your shortest and tallest customers fall within the extremities of the stick. Mention that all tailors using the same method could communicate meaningfully with each

other about the relative heights of their customers providing the measuring sticks in each shop were fastened the same distance above the "absolute zero"of height. It just so happens that the distance to the floor, the "absolute zero," is 273 notches — the same size notches on the stick itself. Then one day, a very short lady enters your shop and stands against the wall, the top of her head coinciding with the zero mark on the measuring stick. As you take her zero reading, she comments that she has a brother who is twice her height. Ask the class for the height of her brother. Then ask for the temperature of the twice-as-hot apple pie. When this is understood, ask why the pie will not *really* be 273°C. Or that for the initially 10°C pie, the temperature will not really be 293°C. [Considerable heat has gone into changing the state of the water in the pie, which accounts for it being "dried out." If you wish to avoid the change of state factor, begin your discussion with the temperature of something such as a piece of metal that will not change state for the temperature range in question.]

Internal Energy Distinguish internal energy from temperature. A neat example is the 4th of July type sparklers, even if you've mentioned it earlier. The sparks that fly from the firework and strike your face have temperatures in excess of 2000°C, but they don't burn. Why? Because the energy of the sparks is extremely low. They have a low internal energy. It is the amount of energy you receive that burns, not the ratio of energy/molecule. Even with a high ratio (high temperature), if a relatively few molecules are involved, the energy transfer is low. (Again, this is similar to the high voltage of a balloon rubbed against your hair. It may have thousands of volts, which is to say thousands of joules per charge. But if there are a relatively small number of charges, the total energy they carry is small.)

First Law of Thermodynamics Introduce the first law of thermodynamics by citing the findings of Count Rumford: that when cannon barrels were being drilled and became very hot, that it was the friction of the drills that produced the heating. Recall the definition of work, *force x distance*, and cite how the metal is heated by the frictional force x distance that the various parts of the drill bit move. Have your students rub their hands together and feel them warm up. Or warm part of the chair they sit on by rubbing.

Follow this up with the account of Joule with his paddle wheel apparatus and his measuring the mechanical equivalent of heat. Of interest is Joule's attempt to extend this experiment to a larger scale while on his honeymoon in Switzerland. Joule and his bride honeymooned near the Chamonix waterfall. According to Joule's conception of heat, the gravitational potential energy of the water at the top should go into increasing the internal energy of the water when at the bottom. Joule made a rough estimate of the increased difference in water temperature at the bottom of the waterfall. His measurements did not substantiate his predictions, however, because considerable cooling occurred due to evaporation as the water fell through the air. Without this added complication, however, his predictions would have been supported. What happens to the temperature of a penny, after all, when you slam it with a hammer? Likewise with water. Emphasize that the first law is simply the law of energy conservation for thermal systems.

Adiabatic Processes Cite the opposite processes of compression and expansion of air and how each affects the temperature of the air. It's easy to see that compressing air into a tire warms the air; and also that when the same air expands through the nozzle in escaping, it cools. Discuss cloud formation as moist air rises, expands, and cools.

CLASS DEMONSTRATION: Blow on your hands first with wide-open mouth, and then with puckered lips so the air expands. This is a first-hand demo of adiabatic cooling!

If you have a model of an internal combustion engine, such as is shown in Figure 17.5, strongly consider showing and explaining it in class. Many of your students likely have little idea of the process. (It still amazes me that automobile engines are as quiet as they are!)

Meteorology and the First Law   Discuss the adiabatic expansion of rising air in our atmosphere. Ask if it would be a good idea on a hot day when going for a balloon ride to only wear a T-shirt. Or would it be a good idea to bring warm clothing? A glance at Figure 17.7 will be instructive.

Discuss the check question in the text, page 311, about yanking down a giant dry-cleaner's garment bag from a high altitude and the changes in temperature it undergoes. Interesting stuff. Then follow this with the second footnote on page 309, which is of considerable interest: but don't assume that because it's in the text that you can't introduce it to your class as if it were brand new information. (I'm past that stage, thinking that everything really interesting in the text is absorbed by my students in their reading — or are my students really less scholarly than yours?)

There is more to Chinook winds than is cited in the text. As Figure 17.8 suggests, warm moist air that rises over a mountain cools as it expands, and then undergoes precipitation where it is gains latent heat energy as vapor changes state to liquid (rain) or solid (snow). Then when the energetic dry air is compressed as it descends on the other side of the mountain, it is appreciably warmer than if precipitation hadn't occurred. Without the heat given to the air by precipitation, it would cool a certain amount in adiabatically expanding and warm the same amount in adiabatically compressing, with have no net increase in temperature.

Discuss temperature inversion and the role it plays in air pollution; or at least in confining air pollution. On the matter of pollution, we find now that even rain is polluted. Acid rain has wrecked havoc with the environment in many parts of the world. Interestingly enough, it isn't the destruction of vast forests or poisoning of wildlife that has evoked the loudest public outcry — acid rain dulls the high-tech finishes on automobiles, and *that* is going too far!

Second Law   Introduce the second law by discussing Exercise 8 on page 320, about immersing a hot tea cup in a large container of cold water. Stress that if the cup were to become even warmer at the expense of the cold water becoming cooler, the first law would not be violated. You're on your way with the second law.

According to my friend Dave Wall who worked for a couple of years in the patent office in Washington D.C., the greatest shortcoming of would-be inventors was their lack of understanding the first and second laws of thermodynamics. The patent office has long been besieged with schemes that promise to circumvent these laws. This point is worth discussion, which you can direct to Carnot's efficiency equation and its consequences, like why better fuel economy is achieved when driving on cold days. [Remember in pre-SI days we talked of "mileage" — now it's fuel economy, because "kilometerage" just doesn't have the right ring yet.]

CHECK QUESTION: Temperatures must be expressed in kelvins when using the formula for ideal efficiency, but may be expressed in either Celsius of kelvins for Newton's law of cooling. Why? [In Carnot's equation, ratios are used; in Newton's law of cooling, only differences.]

CHECK QUESTION: Now there are new "electronic bulbs" that use a quarter of the energy that standard bulbs use to emit the same amount of light (these bulbs generate a radio signal that mixes with the same gas used in conventional fluorescent lampls). Can it be said that these bulbs generate less heat? [Yes, of course.]

CHECK QUESTION: Common incandescent lamps are typically rated only 5% efficient, and common fluorescent lamps are only 20% efficient. Now we say that incandescent lamps are 100% heat efficient. Isn't this contradictory? [5% and 20% efficient as *light* sources, but 100% efficient as *heat* sources. All the energy input, even that which becomes light, very quickly becomes heat.]

Entropy Conclude your treatment of this chapter with your best ideas on entropy — the measure of messiness.

18

Vibrations and Waves

Vibration of a Pendulum
Wave Description
Wave Motion
Wave Speed
Transverse Waves
Longitudinal Waves
Interference
    Standing Waves
Doppler Effect
Wave Barriers
Bow Waves
Shock Waves

Some teachers begin the study of physics with waves, vibrations, and sound, topics that have greater appeal to many students than mechanics. Your course could begin with Part 4 and then move to Part 6, Light. If this chapter is used as a launch point, only the concept of speed needs to be introduced.

There is a page on shockwaves from the workbook **Practicing Physics** for this chapter.

There are six activities that go with this or the following chapter in the **Laboratory Manual** that go with this material.

This chapter serves as a necessary background for the following two chapters, as well as a useful background to the chapters in Part 5.

SUGGESTED LECTURE PRESENTATION

Vibration of a Pendulum   Demonstrate the periods of pendula of different lengths, and compare the strides of short and tall people, and animals with short and long legs. (Tie this to rotational inertia, as studied in mechanics.)

Wave Description   Move a piece of chalk up and down, tracing and retracing a vertical straight line on the board. Call attention to how "frequently" you oscillate the chalk, and tie this to the definition of frequency. Also discuss the idea of amplitude. With appropriate motions, show different frequencies and different amplitudes. Then do the same while walking across the front of the board tracing out a sine wave. Show waves of different wavelengths.

> DEMONSTRATION: Show waves on a Bell Telephone torsion type wave machine (if you're fortunate enough to have one).

DEMONSTRATION: In jest, do as Tom Gordon at Bronx High School does and suspend a harmonica from a spring, bob it up and down, and ask, "What do we have here?" Answer: Simple "harmonica" motion!

Swing a pendulum to and fro and discuss the reciprocal relationship between frequency and period: $f = 1/T$, and $T = 1/f$. Or $fT = Tf = 1$.

Distinguish between wiggles in time — vibrations, and wiggles in space and time — waves. Stress the sameness of the frequency of a wave and the frequency of its vibrating source.

Wave Speed Explain or derive the wave speed = frequency x wavelength formula. Support this with examples, first the freight car question on page 327, and then the water waves as in Problem 1, and then lead into electromagnetic waves as suggested in Problem 3. Calculate the wavelength of one of your local popular radio stations. If you discuss electromagnetic waves, be sure to contrast them with longitudinal sound waves and distinguish between them. You may refer ahead to the family of electromagnetic waves in Figure 25.3 on page 452.

Transverse and Longitudinal Waves

DEMONSTRATION: You and a student hold the ends of a stretched spring or a slinky and send transverse pulses along it, stressing the idea that only the disturbance rather than the medium moves along the spring. Shake it and produce a sine wave. Then send a stretch or compression down the spring, showing a longitudinal pulse, and wave. After some discussion, produce standing waves.

Interference Explain interference, beginning with water waves, and then apply your explanation to standing waves. Overhead transparencies showing various interference patterns may simplify your presentation. The Ealing film loops are helpful also.

CHECK QUESTION: Can waves overlap in such a way as to produce a zero amplitude? [Yes, this is the destructive interference that is characteristic of all waves.]

(Impressive interference demos of sound are treated in the lecture for the next chapter.)

Doppler Effect Introduce the Doppler Effect by throwing a ball, perhaps sponge rubber or styrofoam, around the room. In the ball you first place an electronic whistle that emits a sound of about 3000 Hz. Relate this to the sound of a siren on a fire engine (Figure 18.16) and radar of the highway patrol. [Note that sound requires a medium; radar is an E&M wave and doesn't.]

Wave Barriers, Bow Waves, and Shock Waves Describe the Doppler effect via the bug in water sequence as treated in the text. From this lead into bow and shock waves. After sketching Figures 18.14, 18.15, and 18.17, ask the class to consider the waves made by two stones thrown in the water. Sketch the overlapping waves as shown to the right. Ask where the water is highest above the water level, then indicate the two places where the waves overlap with X's. Then show that this is what happens with a bow wave, that a series of such overlaps make up the envelope of many circular waves forming a V-shape. Then discuss the shock waves produces by supersonic aircraft.

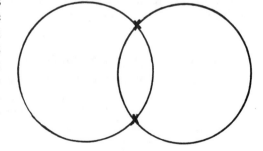

The analogy between bow waves in water and shock waves in air is very useful. Questions raised by students about shock waves and the sonic boom can be effectively answered by translating the question from one of an aircraft in the air to one of a speedboat knifing through the water, a much easier-to-visualize situation.

If you wish to go further with shock waves than is treated in the text, consider explaining how the speed of an aircraft can be estimated by the angle of its shock wave (shock waves are visible (Chapter opener on page 322 and Figure 18.20), for light is refracted in passing through the denser air).

Shock Wave Construction   Construct a shock wave on the board by the following sequence: first place your chalk on the board anywhere to signify time zero. Draw a meter-long horizontal line, say to the right, to represent how far an aircraft has traveled in a certain time. Suppose it travels twice the speed of sound (Mach 2). Then during the time it travels your one meter, the sound it made initially has traveled half this distance, which you mark on the midpoint of your line. State that the initial sound has expanded spherically, which you represent two-dimensionally by drawing a circle as shown. Explain that this circle represents only one of the nearly infinite circles that

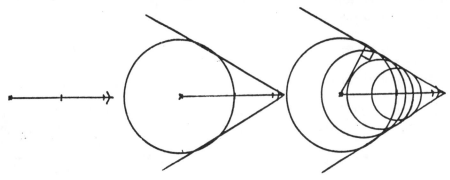

make up the shock wave, which you draw. The shock wave should be a 60 degree wedge (30 degrees above your horizontal line, and 30 degrees below). The next line you draw is important: draw the radius of the circle, from its center to a point tangent to the shock wave. Explain how the speed of the craft is simply the ratio of the horizontal line to this radial distance. (If your students are science students, at this point and not before, introduce the sine function). Now your test of all this: Construct a shock wave of different angle on the board and ask your class to estimate the speed of the craft that generated it. In making constructions, working backwards now, the most common student error is constructing the right angle from the horizontal line rather than from the shock wave line that is tangent to the circle.

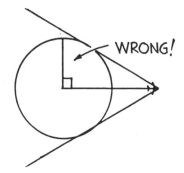

Such geometrical constructions are the subject of this chapter's activity in the **Practice Book**.

19

Sound

Origin of Sound
Nature of Sound in Air
Media that Transmit Sound
Speed of Sound
Reflection of Sound
Refraction of Sound
Energy in Sound Waves
Forced Vibrations
Natural Frequency
Resonance
Interference
    Beats
Radio Broadcasts

This chapter lends itself to interesting lecture demonstrations: a ringing doorbell inside a vacuum jar being evacuated — the easily seen vibrations of a tuning fork illuminated with a strobe lamp — resonance and beats with a pair of tuning forks mounted on sound boxes — and the 8-mm film loop of the "Tacoma Narrows Bridge Collapse".

Forced vibrations, resonance, and interference provide a very useful background for the same concepts applied to light in Chapters 25, and 26.

For more about dolphins and ultrasound, see *Mind In The Waters*, by J. McIntyre, pp 141, 142. Sierra Club Books, San Francisco, 1974.

There is no worksheet for this chapter in **Practicing Physics.**

In addition to activities, there are two experiments in the **Laboratory Manual** that go with the material in this chapter. One is the speed of sound demonstration with tuning forks held over the long vertical tube paratially filled with water. Do as Paul Hickman does and drop a couple of Alka Selzer tablets into the water. The air column above soon is filled with CO_2 and the tone of the reverberating sound undergoes a marked change.

SUGGESTED LECTURE PRESENTATION

Origin of Sound   Begin by stating that the source of sound or all wave motion, is a vibrating object. Ask your class to imagine a room filled with Ping Pong balls and that you hold a giant Ping Pong paddle. When you shake the paddle to and fro you set up vibrations of the balls. Ask how the frequency of the vibrating balls will compare with the frequency of the vibrating paddle. Sound is understood if we "think small."

> DEMONSTRATION: Tap a large tuning fork and show that it is vibrating by dipping the vibrating prongs in a cup of water. The splashing water is clear evidence that the prongs are moving! (Small forks do not work as well.)

DEMONSTRATION: Hold an aluminum rod (a meter long or so) horizontally at the midpoint and strike one end with a hammer. You will create vibrations that travel and reflect back and forth along the length of the rod. The sustanined sound heard is due to energy "leaking" from the ends, about 1% with each reflection. So at any time the sound inside is about 100 times as intense as that heard at the ends. (This is similar to the behavior of light waves in a laser.) Shake the rod to and fro as Paul Doherty does and illustrate the Doppler effect.

DEMONSTRATION: Rub some pine pitch or rosin on your finges and stroke the aluminum rod. If you do it properly, it will "sing" very loudly. Do this while holding the rod at its midpoint and then at different places to demonstrate harmonics. (Of course you practiced this first!)

Nature of Sound in Air

DEMONSTRATION: Ring the doorbell suspended in a bell jar that is being evacuated of air. While the loudness of sound diminishes, discuss the movement of sound through different media — gases, liquids, and solids. Ask why sound travels faster in warm air — then faster through moist air.

Media That Transmit Sound Discuss the speed of sound through different media — four times as fast in water than in air — about eleven times as fast in steel. The elasticity of these materials rather than their densities accounts for the different speeds. Cite how the American Indians used to place their ears to the ground to hear distant hoofbeats. And how one can put the ear to a track to listen for distant trains.

Speed of Sound Discuss the speed of sound and how one can estimate the distance from a lightning storm.

Compute or state that a radio signal takes about 1/8 second to go completely around the world, while in the same time sound travels about 42.5 m. Pose the following: Suppose a person attends a concert that is being broadcast over the radio, and that he sits about 45 m from the stage and listens to the radio broadcast with a transistor radio over one ear and the non-broadcast sound signal with the other ear. Which signal will reach his ear first? The answer is that the radio signal would reach his ear first, even if the radio signal traveled completely around the world before reaching his radio!

Reflection of Sound Bats and echoes, charting of the ocean bottom, reverberations in the shower, and acoustics in music halls — go to it.

Refraction of Sound Explain refraction with a chalkboard drawing similar to Figure 19.7. As an example different than the sound of the bugle waking the dog, consider the temperature inversion over a lake at night, and how one can hear whispers of people on the opposite side of the lake. You may want to follow this up with the similar case of refraction by wind, where wind speed is greater higher up than near the ground.

A useful medical application of sound refraction is ultrasound technology (Figure 19.8), especially in examining the unborn children in pregnant women. Fortunately, the method appears to be relatively free of dangerous side effects.

The most fascinating example of reflection and refraction of sound is the dolphin. Dolphins have been doing all along what humans have just learned to do. Add to the material about dolphins on page 345, that unlike humans, dolphins breathe voluntarily. They cannot be put to sleep for medical operations because they will cease breathing and die. They are subject to drowning, as any mammal is. When in

111

trouble other dolphins hold the troubled dolphin at the surface so breathing can take place. When sick, they will beach themselves so they won't drown. Many shipwrecked sailors owe their lives to dolphins who have beached them. Fascinating creatures!

Forced Vibrations, Natural Frequency Tap various objects around you and explain what is happening at the atomic level — that crystalline or molecular structures are made to vibrate, and that due to the elasticity and bonding of the material constituents, natural modes of vibration are produced. Objects have their own characteristic frequencies. The organs of humans have a natural frequency of about 7 hertz.

Resonance

> DEMONSTRATION: Show resonance with a pair of tuning forks, explaining how each set of compressions from the first fork push the prongs of the second fork in rhythm with its natural motion. Compare this to pushing somebody on a playground swing. Illuminate the forks with a strobe light for best effect!

When you are adjusting the frequency of one of your tuning fork boxes, by moving the weights up or down the prongs, call attention to the similarity of this with tuning a radio receiver. When one turns the knob to select a different station, one is adjusting the frequency of the radio set to resonate with incoming stations.

Cite other examples of resonance — the chattering vibration of a glass shelf when a radio placed on it plays a certain note — the loose front end of a car that vibrates at only certain speeds — crystal wine glass shattering by a singer's voice, — troops breaking step in bridge crossing.

Conclude your treatment of resonance with the exciting film loop "The Tacoma Narrows Bridge Collapse". This short film is by far the most impressive of the physics films.

Interference Introduce interference by sketching a sine wave on the board — a water wave. Then superpose another identical wave on it and ask what happens. Nothing spectacular, simply a wave of twice the amplitude. Now repeat and superpose the second wave a half-wavelength out of step. State that physicers don't say "out of step," but "out of phase." Same thing.

> DEMONSTRATION: Play a stereo radio, tape or CD player, on a mono setting and demonstate the different quality of sound when the speakers, set apart from each other, are out of phase. I have mine connected to a DPDT switch to flip the phase. The difference in sound is obvious, especially for students on the center line. You might point out in Figure 19.15 that in position *b* cancellation will occur for a few particular wavelengths, whereas in position *a* cancellation can occur for all wavelengths — when both speakers emit the same signal. Of course, wall reflections fill in any pure cancellations. In an acoustic chamber, however, cancellation would occur.

> DEMONSTATION: Do as Meidor does in Figure 19.16 and face the stereo speakers toward each other, at arm's length apart. Flip one speaker out of phase and gradually bring them closer. The volume of sound fades dramatically as they are brought face to face. Interference. This may likely be one of the more memorable of your demos.

The question may arise as what happens to the sound energy when sound cancels. Interestingly enough, each radio loudspeaker is also a microphone. When the speakers face each other they "drive" each other, inducing back voltages in each other that cut the currents down in each. Thus energy is diminished, but not cancelled.

> DEMONSTRATION: Show the reason for speakers mounted in boxed enclosures by producing a bare speaker connected to a music source. The sound is "tinny". State why; that as compressions are produced by one side of the speaker cone, rarefactions are produced by the other. Superposition of these waves results in destructive interference. Then produce a square piece of board (plywood or cardboard) close to a meter on a side with a hole the size of the speaker in its center. Place the speaker at the hole and let your class hear the difference in the fullness of the sound that results. You have diminished the superposition of waves that previously cancelled. The effect is dramatic.

I kid around about my keen ability to completely cancel sound by striking one tuning fork and then the other at precisely the time to produce cancellation. When I do this I quickly grab and release the prongs of the sounding fork while not really making contact with the second. It is especially effective for students who weren't watching carefully. I exclaim that when I'm lucky enough to achieve complete cancellation on the first try, I never repeat it. Is this real physics? No, but its a mood elevator so that my students are receptive to the real physics I discuss the rest of the time.

> DEMONSTRATION: Do as Paul Hickman does and sound a tuning fork mounted on a sounding board and position the open end at various places from a reflecting wall. Areas of cancellation and reinforcement are readily located.

Beats Acknowledge you were kidding around before about producing interference with the pair of tuning forks, but now you're for real with them. Strike the slightly different frequency forks and hear the beats. This is even nicer when your students see an oscilloscope trace what they hear.

Demonstrate beats as Paul Robinson does by bouncing laser light off a pair of vibrating tuning forks. Quite lively!

20

Musical Sounds

Pitch
Loudness
Quality
Musical Instruments
Musical Scales
Fourier Analysis
Laser Discs

As in the preceding chapter, this chapter should be supported with lively lecture demonstrations. This material is not prerequisite to following material, and the entire chapter can be disregarded if a short treatment of sound is desired. In any event, the material in this chapter should be treated lightly. The information of musical scales, for example, is a useful thumbnail sketch to those versed in music, but information overload to those not. Imagine the dread of one not into music confronted with all the information on musical scales to be mastered for your exam! A waste of good time. Please make it clear that you don't expect this detailed material, like the periodic table, is to be learned. The musical scales material is in the book because it does relate to physics, and the detail is meaningful primarily to those who have a musical background.

Recommended reading: *The Physics of Musical Instruments*, reviewed in *Physics Today*, December 1991, p 75, and an article, *The Acoustics of Drums*, in *Physics Today*, March 1992, pp 40-47, reviewed in *Science*, June 21, 1991, pp 1728-9, both by Neville H. Fletcher and Thomas D. Rossing. It is well known that Richard Feynman loved drums.

There is no worksheet in **Practicing Physics** for this chapter, but there is both an acitivity and an experiment in the **Laboratory Manual**.

SUGGESTED LECTURE PRESENTATION

Bring out the oscilloscopes, the audio oscillator, microphones, loudspeakers, and musical instruments.

Pitch, Loudness, and Quality   Waveforms can be displayed on the screen of an oscilloscope. An audio oscillator connected to a loudspeaker and an oscilloscope will demonstrate the relationships between pitch, frequency, and wavelength, and between amplitude and loudness. You can speak into the loudspeaker and display a wave pattern on the oscilloscope screen, showing that the loudspeaker serves as a microphone. (It may or may not be appropriate to briefly discuss the electromagnetic induction that takes place in the electromagnet of the loudspeaker at this point.) The waveforms of various musical instruments can be displayed and compared on the oscilloscope screen. Show the different harmonics for the same notes played on different instruments. Discuss quality.

If you display a decibel meter, show that for mid-range frequencies a decibel is the just-noticeable sound level difference that humans can detect.

Demonstrate Chladni figures with a fastened metal plate, violin bow, and fine sand (or show the Ealing Film Loop of the same). Discuss nodes and antinodes.

Musical Instruments Although *standing longitudinal waves* are not treated in the text, you may wish to introduce this topic and relate it to musical instruments. If so, begin by demonstrating the resonance of standing air columns with a resonance water tube (a long glass tube partially filled with water, the level of which can be adjusted by raising or lowering an external reservoir). Hold a vibrating tuning fork over the open tube and adjust the water level until the air in the tube resonates loudly to the sound being sent into it by the fork. Show and explain that several heights will result in resonance. Measure the wavelengths of a high and a low frequency sound. Consider doing as Paul Hickman does and drop a couple of Alka Selzer tablets into the water. The air column above soon is filled with CO_2 and the tone of the reverberating sound undergoes a marked change. Relate the relative sizes of the respective sound cavities to the relative sizes of musical instruments; the bigness of a bass fiddle, and the smallness of a piccolo. These ideas underlie the tones one produces when blowing over the top of a soda pop bottle.

Fourier Analysis You may want to discuss Fourier Analysis and the superposition of waves and show on the chalkboard how the composite wave in Figure 20.10 is a sum of the fundamental and the second and third harmonics.

Ask your class how many grooves there are on a typical record. (The answer is one!) If your class is somewhat familiar with vectors you may want explain how stereo signals are captured into the wavy groove of a record and how the vibrations of the stylus are sorted into perpendicular components for each channel.

CDs Discuss the operation of a the compact disc.

21

Electrostatics

Electrical Forces
Electric Charges
Conservation of Charge
Coulomb's Law
Conductors and Insulators
    Semiconductors
Charging
    Charging by Contact
    Charging by Induction
Charge Polarization
Electric Field
    Electrical Shielding
Electric Potential
Electric Energy Storage
    Van de Graaff Generator

The study of electricity begins with electrostatics. The material in this chapter should be supported with lecture demonstrations, such as the electrophorus (a metal plate charged by induction that rests on a sheet of plexiglass which has been charged with cat's fur, or equivalently, a pizza pan that rests on a charged phonograph record), the Whimshurst machine (electrostatic generator), and the Van de Graaff generator.

Electric shielding and the zero E field inside metals is briefly treated in the chapter, but not explained. Instead, reference is made to the similar case of the zero G field inside a hollow spherical shell in Chapter 8. You may want to expand this idea in lecture.

New to this edition is a brief treatment of capacitors.

You may note also, as Paul Doherty pointed out to me, that different colored balloons acquire different amounts of charge, likely due to the different effects of dyes in the rubber.

Approximately 44,000 thunderstorms and 8 million lightning flashes take place daily around the world. In the U.S. alone, lightning causes about 150 deaths each year. For an update on lightning see *The Electrification of Thunderstorms* by Earle R. Williams in the Nov 88 issue of *Scientific American*.

There is a worksheet on *Electric Potential* in **Practicing Physics**.

There are two activities on *charging* in the **Laboratory Manual**.

This chapter is prerequisite to the following chapters in Part 5.

The order of topics in the lecture sequence below departs somewhat from the order of topics in the chapter. The ideas of each demo flow nicely to the next. Have your lecture table set up with rods, pith ball, and charging demos at one end of the table, then an electrophorus, then a Whimshurst or whatever electrostatic machine, and finally the Van de Graaff generator. Then your lecture begins at one end of the table and proceeds in order to the opposite end.

SUGGESTED LECTURE PRESENTATION

Electrical forces Begin by comparing the strength of the electric force to gravitational force — billions of billions of times stronger. Acknowledge the fundamental rule of electricity: That *like charges repel and unlike charges attract*. Why? Nobody knows. Hence we say it is fundamental.

Electric Charges Electrical effects have to do with electric charges, minus for the electron and plus for the proton. Discuss the near balance that exists in common materials, and the slight imbalance when electrons transfer from one material to another. Different materials have different affinities for electrons, which explains why charge transfers from fur to rubber when rubbed. It also explains why its painful for people with silver fillings in their teeth to chew aluminum spitballs. Silver has more affinity for aquiring electrons than aluminum. The mildly acidic saliva in your mouth facilitates a flow of electrons, which when transmitted to the nerves of your teeth produce that familiar unpleasant sensation. Discuss **charging**.

> DEMONSTRATION: Bring out the cat's fur, rubber and glass rods, and suspended pith balls. An alternative to the pith ball is a copper-painted ping-pong ball. Explain the transfer of electrons when you rub fur against rubber rod (and silk against glass). Explain what it means to say an object is electrically charged, and discuss the **conservation of charge**.

Rubbing a rubber rod on cat's fur or a glass rod on silk illustrates charging by friction, but charge separation can occur without friction, by the simple contact between dissimilar insulating materials. In this case charge simply peels from one material to another, like dust is peeled from a surface when a piece of sticky tape is peeled from it.

> DEMONSTRATION: Show the effects of electrical force and **charge by induction** by holding a charged rod near the ends of a more-than-a-meter-long wooden 2 x 4, that balances and easily rotates sideways at its midpoint on a protrusion such as the bottom of a metal spoon. You can easily set the massive piece of wood in motion. This is quite impressive!

> DEMONSTRATION: Rub a balloon on your hair and show how it sticks to the wall. Draw a sketch on the board (Figure 21.13) and show in induction how the attracting charges are slightly closer than the repelling charges. Closeness wins and it sticks!

> DEMONSTRATION: Charge the electrophorus, place the insulated metal disk on top of it, and show that the disk is not charged when removed and brought near a charged pith ball. Why should it be, for the insulating surface of the electrophorus has more grab on the electrons than the metal plate. But rest the plate on the electrophorus again and touch the top of the plate. You're grounding it (producing a conducting path to ground for the repelling electrons). Bring the plate near the pith ball and show that it is charged. Then show this by the flash of light produced when the charged metal plate is touched to the end of a gas discharge tube — or a fluorescent

lamp. Engage neighbor discussion of the process demonstrated. Only after this is generally understood, proceed to the next demo.

DEMONSTRATION: Move up the lecture table to the Whimshurst machine, explaining its similarity to the electrophorus (actually a rotating electrophorus!). Show sparks jumping between the spheres of the machine and so forth, and discuss the sizes (radii of curvature) of the spheres in terms of their capacity for storing charge. [The amount of charge that can be stored before discharge into the air is directly proportional to the radius of the sphere.] Fasten a metal point, which has a tiny radius of curvature and hence a tiny charge storing capacity, to one of the Whimshurst spheres and demonstrate the leakage of charge.

If you wish to expand upon charge leakage from a point, you might simplify it this way: On the surface of an electrically charged flat metal plate, every charge is mutually repelled by every other charge. If the surface is curved, charges on one part of the plate will not interact with charges on some distant part of the plate because of the **shielding** effect of the metal — they are "out of the line of sight" of each other. Hence for the same amount of work or potential, a greater number of charges may be placed on a curved surface than on a flat surface. The more pronounced the curvature, the more shielding and the more charge may be stored there. To carry this idea further, consider a charged needle. Under mutual repulsion, charges gather to the region of greatest curvature, the point. Although all parts of the needle are charged to the same electric potential, the charge density is greatest at the point. The **electric field** intensity about the needle, on the other hand, is greatest about the point, usually great enough to ionize the surrounding air and provide a conducting path from the charge concentration. Hence charge readily gathers at points and readily leaks from points. DEMONSTRATE this leakage and the reaction force (ion propulsion) with a set of metal points arranged to rotate when charged. This is the "ion propulsion" that science fiction buffs talk about in space travel. Interestingly enough, this leaking of charge from points causes static with radio antennas; hence the small metal ball atop automobile antennas.

Discuss **lightning rods** and show how the bottoms of negatively charged clouds and the resulting induced positive charge on the surface of the earth below are similar to the electrophorus held upside down; where the charged plexiglass plate is analogous to the clouds and the metal plate is analogous to the earth. After sketching the charged clouds and earth on the chalkboard, be sure to hold the inverted electrophorus pieces against your drawing on the board in their respective places. Discuss the lightning rod as a preventer of lightning while showing the similar function of the metal point attached to the Whimshurst machine. [Notice that one idea is related to the next in this sequence — very important, as the ideas of electricity are usually difficult to grasp the first time through. So be sure to take care in moving through this sequence of demonstrations and their explanations.]

Benjamin Franklin's kite, by the way, was not struck by lightning. It it had, he would likely have not been around to report his experience. Franklin showed that the kite collected charges from the air during a thunderstorm. Hairs on the kitestring stood apart, implying that lightning was a huge electric spark.

After establishing the idea that charge capacity depends on the size and curvature of the conductor being charged, advance to what your students have been waiting for: **The Van de Graaff generator** (invented by the way, by Robert Generator).

DEMONSTRATION: When showing the long sparks that jump from the dome of the generator to the smaller grounded sphere, do as Bruce Bernard suggests and hold a lightning rod (any sharp pointed conductor) in the vicinity of the dome and the sparking will stop. Bring the lightning rod farther away and the frequency of sparking will resume.

DEMONSTRATION: Set a cup of puffed rice or puffed wheat on top of the Van de Graaff generator. Your students will like the fountain that follows when you charge it. Or do as Marshall Ellenstein does and place a stack of aluminum pie plates on the dome and watch them one by one levitate and fly away. Then snuff out a match by holding it near the charged dome. Introduce (or reintroduce) the idea of the **electric field** at this time, the aura of energy that surrounds all charged things. Compare electric and gravitational fields.

Fields are called "force fields" because forces are exerted on bodies in their vicinity, but a better term would be "energy field," because energy is stored in a field. In the case of an electric field, any charges in the vicinity are energized. We speak about the potential energy that electrically charged bodies have in a field — or more often, the potential energy compared to the amount of charge — **electric potential**. Explain that the field energy, and correspondingly the electric potential, is greatest nearest the charged dome and weaker with increased distance (**inverse-square law**).

DEMONSTRATION: Hold a fluorescent lamp tube in the field to show that it lights up when one end of the tube is closer to the dome than the other end. Relate this to potential difference, and show that when both ends of the fluorescent tube are equidistant from the charged dome, light emission ceases. (This can be effected when your hand is a bit closer to the dome than the far end of the tube, so current does not flow through the tube when the dome discharges through you to the ground. There is no potential difference across the tube and therefore no illuminating current, which sets the groundwork for your next lecture on electric current.)

The Van de Graaff generator nicely illustrates the difference between **electric potential energy** and **electric potential**: Although it is normally charged to thousands of volts, the amount of charge is relatively small so the electric potential energy is relatively small. That's why you're normally not harmed when it discharges through your body. Very little energy flows through you. In contrast, you wouldn't intentionally become the shortcircuit for household 110 volts because although the voltage is much lower, the transfer of energy is appreciable. Less energy per charge, but many many more charges!

Storage of charge is accomplished with a **capacitor**.

DEMONSTRATION: Show one of the most impressive capacitors, the Leyden Jar, and a sparking demonstraton.

NEXT-TIME QUESTION: Why does current flow when one end of the fluorescent tube is held closer to the charged Van de Graaff generator, but not when both ends are equidistant? [The simplified answer you're looking for at this point is that the close end is in a stronger part of the field than the far end. More energy per charge means more voltage at the near end. With a voltage difference across the tube, you get a current. When both ends are equidistant, there is no voltage difference across the tube, and no current. This leads into the next chapter. Strictly speaking, the current path is more than simply between the ends of the tube; it goes through you also and to ground where it returns to the generator.]

22

Electric Current

This chapter seeks to build a good "everyone's understanding" of current electricity, and to dispel some of the popular misconceptions about electricity. The treatment of series and parallel circuits avoids the calculation of equivalent circuit resistances, multiple emfs, and the like. This chapter may be skipped, as a knowledge of elementary circuits is not needed elsewhere in the text.

If you're into puns in your lectures on rainy days, Marshall Ellenstein has a few pictorial puns on the symbol for resistance that he and coworkers Connie Bownell and Nancy McClure came up with ("Ohmwork" or $\Omega F \times D$, *Physics Teacher* magazine, Sept 91, page 347). A few are:

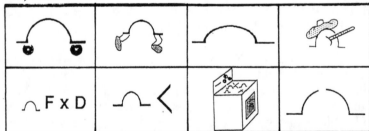

Answers in order are: Mobile Ohm; Ohm Run; Ohm Stretch; Ohm Sick; Ohmwork; Ohmless; Ohm on the Range; Broken Ohm.

There are two worksheets for this chapter, one on series circuits, the other on parallel circuits, in **Practicing Physics**.

Choose from 3 activites and 2 experiments on circuits in the **Laboratory Manual**.

SUGGESTED LECTURE PRESENTATION

Flow of Charge; Electric Current   Define electric current and relate it to the lighting of the lamp via the Van de Graaff Generator at the end of your last lecture. Explain this in terms of current being directly proportional to a difference in voltage. That is, one end of the lamp was in a stronger part of the energy field than the other — more energy per charge on one end than the other — more voltage at one end than the other. Write on the board *Current ~ voltage difference*. (You're on your way to Ohm's law. Strictly speaking, the voltage term in Ohm's law implies the difference in potential, so voltage difference is redundant. Nevertheless, it underscores a point that may be missed, so go for it.)

Voltage Sources   Relate voltage to the idea of electrical pressure. Emphasize that a *difference* in electric potential must exist — or as above, a voltage difference. Cite how a battery provides this difference in a sustained way compared to suddenly discharging a Van de Graaff generator. Generators at power plants also provide a voltage difference across wires that carry this difference to consumers (more detail on this in Chapter 24). Cite examples of voltage differences in cases of birds sitting on bare high-voltage wires, walking unharmed on the third rail of electric-powered train tracks, and the inadvisability of using electric appliances in the bathtub.

Discuss the function of the **third prong on electric plugs** (that it provides a ground wire between the appliance and the ground). The ground prong is longer than the pair of flat prongs. Why? (So it will be first to be connected when plugging it into a socket, establishing a ground connection slightly before the appliance is electrically connected. This path to ground prevents harm to the user if there is a short circuit in the appliance that would otherwise include the user as a path to ground.)

Discuss **electric shock** and why electricians put one hand behind their back when probing questionable circuits [to prevent a difference in potential across the heart of the body]. Discuss how being electrified produces muscle contractions that account for such instances as "not being able to let go" of hot wires, and "being thrown" by electric shock.

Electrical Resistance   Introduce the idea of electrical resistance, and complete Ohm's law. Compare the resistances of various materials, and the resistances of various thickness of wires of the same metal. Call attention to the glass supports on the wires that make up high-voltage power lines; the rubber insulation that separates the pair of wires in a common lamp cord.

Ohm's Law   Complete your chalkboard equation by introducing resistance and you have Ohm's law.

> DEMONSTRATION: Connect two or three lamps to a battery and relate the current, as viewed by the emitted light, to the voltage of the battery and the resistance of the lamps. (Be sure the lamps are not bright enough to make viewing uncomfortable). Interchange lamps of low and high resistance, relating this to the brightness of the lamps.

DC and AC   Discuss the differences between DC and AC. Compare the DC current that flows in a circuit powered with a battery to the AC current that flows in a household circuit (powered by a generator). A hydrodynamic analogy for AC is useful: Imagine powering a washing-machine agitator with water power. Verbally describe with gestures a pair of clear plastic pipes connected to a paddle wheel at the bottom of the agitator, fashioned so water that sloshes to and fro in the pipes causes the agitator to rotate to and fro. Suppose the free ends of the plastic pipe are connected to a special socket in the wall. The socket is powered by the power utility. It supplies no water, but consists of a couple of pistons that exert a pumping action, one out and the other in, then vice versa, in rapid alternation. When the ends of the pipe containing water are connected to the pistons, the water in the pipes is made to slosh back and forth: power is delivered to the washing machine. There is an important point to note here: The **source** of flowing substance, water or electrons, is supplied by you. The power company supplies no water, just as the power utilities supply no electrons! The greater the load on the agitator, the more energy the power company must deliver to the action of the alternating pistons, affording a visual model for household current — especially with the transparent plastic pipes where your students can "see" the sloshing water!

The water analogy also serves to show the function of a **capacitor** in smoothing the conversion of AC to DC, Figure 22.11.

Speed of Electrons in a Circuit   To impart the idea of how DC current travels in a circuit, use the following analogy. Ask the class to suppose that there is a long column of marchers at the front of the room, all standing at rest close together. Walk to the end of this imaginary column and give a shove to the "last person." Ask the class to imagine the resulting impulse traveling along the line until the first marcher is jostled against the wall. (Or use the analogy of loosely coupled railroad cars.) Then ask if this is a good analogy for how electricity travels in a wire. The answer is no. Such is a good analogy for how sound travels, but not electricity. Cite how slowly the disturbance traveled, and how slowly sound travels compared to light or electricity. Again call attention to the column of marchers and walk to the far end and call out, "Forward march!" As soon as the command reaches each individual, each steps forward. The marcher at the beginning of the column, except for the slight time required for the sound to get to her, steps immediately. State that this is an analogy for electricity. Except for the brief time it takes for the electric *field* set up at the power source to travel through the wire, nearly the speed of light, electrons at the far end of the circuit respond immediately. State that the speed at which the command "forward march" traveled is altogether different from how fast each marcher moved upon receiving that command — and that the velocity of the electric signal (nearly the speed of light) is quite a bit different than the drift velocity of electrons (typically 0.01 cm/s) in a circuit.

> CHECK QUESTION: When you turn on your key to start your car, electrons migrate from the negative battery terminal through the electric network to the starter motor and back to the positive battery terminal. About how long is required for electrons to leave the negative terminal and go through the circuit and back again? Less than a millisecond? Less than a second? About a second or two? Or about a day? (Class interest should be high when you announce the latter answer!)

Ask for an estimate of the number of electrons pumped by the local power plant into the homes and industries locally in the past year. Then stress the idea that power plants do not sell electrons — that they sell energy. Discuss the origin of electrons in electric current flow.

Electric Power   Distinguish between energy and power. Electric power is usually expressed in kilowatts, and electric energy in kilowatt-hours. It is effective if you use an actual electric bill to make your point. Note that a kilowatt-hour is 1000 joules per second times 3600 seconds, or 3600 kJ.

Electrical Circuits   You simply must use an automobile storage battery with extended terminals as shown below. The extended terminals are simply a pair of rigid rods, welding rods or simply pieces of thick wire. They are easily inserted and removed if female connectors are permanently fastened into the battery terminals. Also fasten alligator clips to the ends of short lengths of wire fastened to about three or so lamps of equal resistance.

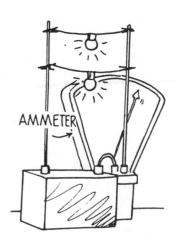

DEMONSTRATION: Connect the ends of one of the lamps directly to the battery terminals. It glows, evidence of current flow. Then insert the rods and repeat. It glows as before. Slide the lamp farther up the rods and its glow is the same. It is easily accepted that the 12-volt potential difference between the terminals is also established along and across the full length of the rods. State how the rods could extend across campus and someone far away could similarly light up a lamp. State how the resistance of the rods is very small compared to the resistance of the lamp filament. Compare the rods to a long lamp cord. Then to power lines from power plants to consumers. Take your time with these ideas, for they are central!

Series Circuits

DEMONSTRATION CONTINUED: Attach two lamps in series via alligator clips. Before connecting the double lamp circuit to the rods, ask for a neighbor check about the relative brightness of light. [Since the resistance is doubled, the current is halved and the brightness diminished — brightness is "less than half" because most of the energy is going to heat and not light. The effects of heat can be discerned for low currents when no light is seen.] Point out that the voltage across each lamp is 6 volts when connected in series. Repeat the process for three lamps in series, where three lamps share the 12 volts, and describe the reduced current in terms of Ohm's law. This is even more effective if you connect a lecture-size ammeter to your circuit.

Parallel Circuits

DEMONSTRATION CONTINUED: Now connect a pair of lamps in series. Before making the second connection, ask for a neighbor check about the relative brightnesses. It's easy to see that the voltage across each lamp is not reduced as with the series connection, but each is impressed with a full 12 volts. [Nearly a full 12 volts; line voltage diminishes with increased current through the battery — perhaps information overload at this stage of learning.] Repeat with three lamps after a neighbor check. Ask about the "equivalent resistance" of the circuit as more lamps are attached in parallel (or the equivalent resistance to people flow if more doors are introduced to the classroom). The lesser resistance is consistent with Ohm's law. An ammeter between one of the rods and the terminal shows line current, which is seen to increase as lamps are added. This is the simplest and most visually comprehensible demo of parallel circuits I have discovered. Neat?

CHECK QUESTION: Consider two resistors to be connected in a circuit. Which will have more resistance, if they are connected in series or in parallel? [A series connection will have more resistance, regardless of the values of resistance; the equivalent resistance of a parallel connection will always be less than that of the smaller resistor.]

Home Circuits and Fuses Discuss home lighting circuits. Draw a simple parallel circuit of lamps and appliances on the board. Estimate the current flowing through each device, and point out that it makes no difference how many of the other devices are turned on. Show on your diagram the currents in the branches and in the lead wires. Show where the fuse goes and describe its function. Then short your circuit and blow the fuse.

Overloading Discuss the consequences of too many appliances operating on the same line, and why different sets of lines are directed to various parts of the home. Most home wiring is rated at 30 amperes maximum. A common air conditioner uses about 2400 watts, so if operating on 120 volts the current would be 20 amps. To start, the current is more. (Why the starting current is larger would be premature to explain here — if it comes up you can explain that every motor is also a generator, and the input electricity is met with a generated output that reduces the net current flow.) If other devices are drawing current on the same line, the fuse will blow when the air conditioner is turned on, so a 220-volt line is usually used for such heavy appliances. Point out that most of the world operates normally at 220 - 240 volts.

CHECK QUESTION: How does the amount of line current in the school building differ from the amount of current that lights the lamps overhead in this room? [Unless your room is the only room in the school to be using electricity at the moment, the current that feeds the lights to the room is only part of the line current that services the whole school.]

124

23

Magnetism

This chapter, like others, links the subject matter to the environment. It concludes with a bit of paleomagnetism, and the magnetic sensors in living organisms.

The quip on James Van Allen's name on page 427 is done with his permission.

Show the Ealing film loop (#A80-2033/1, Ferromagnetic Domain Wall Motion).

Make iron-filing permanent displays by spraying water on iron filings on a paper atop a magnet. The rust strains will leave a permanent impression of the magnetic field. (This idea from Matt Keller.)

For more on magnetic pole reversals read *Ancient Magnetic Reversals: Clues to the Geodynamo*, by Kenneth A. Hoffman in <u>Scientific American</u>, May 1988.

There is no workbook page for this chapter in **Practicing Physics**, but one activity in the **Laboratory Manual.**

The material in this chapter is prerequisite to the next chapter.

SUGGESTED LECTURE PRESENTATION

Magnetic Force Begin by holding a magnet above some nails or paper clips on your lecture table. State that the nails or clips are flat on the table because every particle of matter in the whole world is gravitationally pulling them against the table. Then show that your magnet outpulls the whole world and lifts the nails or clips off the table.

Show that iron is not the only ferromagnetic substance. Certain Canadian nickels and quarters (1968 to 1981 which are pure nickel) are easily attracted to a magnet. The U.S. 5 cent piece is no longer pure nickel, is 75% copper, and won't respond to a magnet.

Magnetic Poles Show how a bar magnet affects a large lecture compass and discuss magnetic poles. Similar to the fundamental rule of electricity, *like poles repel and opposite poles attract*.

Magnetic Fields Show field configurations about bar magnets with the use of an overhead projector and iron filings. Simply lay a magnet on the glass surface of the projector and cover it with a sheet of plastic, and sprinkle iron filings over the plastic. Acknowledge the alignment of **magnetic domains** in the magnet material.

Magnetic Induction Explain magnetic induction, and show how bringing a non-magnetized nail near a magnet induces it to become a magnet and be attracted. Then contrast this with an aluminum rod — discuss unpaired electron spins and magnetic domains. Compare magnetic induction (Figure 23.5) to the electric induction shown in Figures 21.11 and 21.12 back on page 382. Stress the similarities of electrically inducing charge polarization and magnetically inducing the alignment of magnetic domains.

Electric Currents and Magnetic Fields Discuss the source of magnetism — the motion of charges. All magnetism starts with a moving electric charge: in the spin of the electron about its own axis (like a top), in the revolution about the nuclear axis, and as it drifts as part of an electric current.

> DEMONSTRATION Place a lecture compass near a wire and show the deflection when current is passed through the wire.

It should be enough to simply acknowledge that the magnetic field is a relativistic "side effect" or "distortion" in the electric field of a moving charge. (Unless you've already treated special relativity, the relativistic explanation may be too involved to be effective.)

Side point: When the magnetic field about a current-carrying wire is undesirable, double wires are used, with the return wire adjacent to the wire. Then the net current for the double wire is zero, and no magnetic field surrounds it. Wires are often braided to combat slight fields where the cancellation is not perfect.

Electromagnets Call attention to the circular shape of the magnetic field about a current-carrying wire (Figure 23.9 and the photos of field lines of Figure 23.10). It's easy to see how the magnetic field is bunched up in a loop of current-carrying wire, and then in a coil of many loops. Then place a piece of iron in the coil and the added effect of aligned domains in the iron produces an electromagnet.

> DEMONSTRATION: Make a simple electromagnet in front of your class. Simply wind wire around a spike and pick up paper clips when you put a current through the wire. Mimick the operation of a junk yard magnet, where the clips are dropped when the current is turned off.

> DEMONSTRATION: Show your department's electromagnets, and your superconducting electromagnets!

If you have an electromagnetic levitator, discuss the train application when you are fascinating your students with its demonstration. The idea of a **magnetically-**

levitated train was described in 1909 by Robert Goddard, an American better known for inventing the liquid-fueled rocket. Although Europe and Japan now have the lead in this field, the first modern design for a maglev train comes from Americans, nuclear-engineer James R. Powell, and particle-acceleration physicist Gordon T. Danby. They were awarded a patent in 1968 for their design.

Whatever the present variations in design, once the train is levitated there is no mechanical friction to contend with, so only modest force is needed to accelerate it. Fixed electromagnets along the guideway alternately pull and push by switching polarity whenever one of the train's propulsion magnets passes it. The phased switching is timed by computers under the control of the driver to accelerate or decelerate the train, or simply keep it moving. Various designs have the overall result of propelling the train like a surfboard riding a wave. Speculation by co-inventor Danby is that future travel in partially evacuated tubes will permit cross-country passage in about an hour. Maglev trains may play a large role in transportation in the coming century.

Magnetic Force on Moving Charges

> DEMONSTRATION: Show how a magnet distorts the electron beam of an oscilloscope or TV picture. Stress the role of motion.

Discuss the motion of a charged particle injected into a magnetic field perpendicularly, and explain how it will follow a circle. The perpendicular push is a centripetal force that acts along the radius of its path. Briefly discuss cyclotrons and bevatrons, with radii ranging from less than a meter to more than a kilometer.

Magnetic Force on Current-Carrying Wires   Simple logic tells you that if forces act on electrons that move through a magnetic field, then forces act on electrons traveling through a wire.

> DEMONSTRATION: Show how a wire jumps out of (or into) a magnet when current is passed through the wire (Figure 23.14). Reverse current (or turn wire around) to show both cases.

If you have a large lecture galvanometer, show your class the coil of wire that is suspended in the magnetic field of the permanent magnet (Figure 23.16). The same is found in ammeters and voltmeters. Now you are ready to extend this idea to the electric motor.

> DEMONSTRATION: Show the operation of a DC demonstration motor.

Earth's Magnetic Field   Discuss the field configuration about the earth and how cosmic rays are deflected by the magnetic field lines. In discussing pole reversals, add that the magnetic field of the sun undergoes reversals about every eleven years.

Biomagnetism   Acquaint yourself with the latest findings regarding magnetic field sensing by living things. Bacteria, bees, and pigeons are mentioned briefly in the text.

Magnetic Resonance Imaging (MRI)   As a side topic not treated in the text you might discuss what used to be called NMR — nuclear magnetic resonance — the now widely used application in medicine; particularly as a method of cancer detection. An external alternating magnetic field is applied to the part of the body of a patient to be examined. Slight differences in the natural frequencies of magnetic quadrapole moments of atomic nuclei, commonly protons, due to the environment of neighboring atoms are detected by a "magnetic echo." The resonant signals from the nuclei of atoms in living cells differs slightly for cancerous tissue and is picked up by a sensitive magnetometer. Why the name change from NMR to MRI? The word *nuclear*, honey! Its simply out with the public, who are phobic about anything with the dreaded word nuclear. Another reason for conceptual physics for the common student!

NEXT-TIME QUESTION: Given two bars, one a magnet and the other not, determine which is the magnet. You must find out by only the interaction between the two bars. (Solution: Make a T shape with the bars and the nonmagnet will not fasten itself to the middle of the magnet.)

24

Electromagnetic Induction

Electromagnetic Induction
Faraday's Law
Generators and Alternating Current
Power Production
    Turbogenerator Power
    MHD Power
Transformer
Self-Induction
Power Transmission
Field Induction
In Perspective

This chapter focuses on the important features of electromagnetic induction, and avoids such complications as reactances, back emf, Lenz's law, and the left and right hand rules that normally serve to overwhelm your students. An important function of the chapter is to implant the idea of transferring energy from one place to another without means of physical contact. The chapter should be supported with various lecture demonstrations of electromagnetic induction, such as those in the figures of the chapter.

This chapter serves as a background for the study of light.

There is a worksheet on transformers in the student book, **Practicing Physics**.

In the **Laboratory Manual** there are two activies and three experiments to choose from.

The suggested lecture will probably span two or three class periods.

SUGGESTED LECTURE PRESENTATION

This lecture is a series of demonstrations.

Electromagnetic Induction   Up to this point you have discussed how one can begin with electricity and produce magnetism. The question was raised in the first half of the 1800s; can it be the other way around — can one begin with magnetism and produce electricity? Indeed it can, enough to light entire cities with electric lighting! Now you produce your galvanometer, magnet, and wire loop — conspicuously well away from your previous electric power source.

> DEMONSTRATION: Plunge a magnet in and out of a single coil, as in Figure 24.2, and show with a galvanometer the current produced. This is nice with a large lecture demonstration galvanometer.

This need not be mysterious, for it follows from the deviations of electrons in a magnetic field, last chapter. Invoke the argument shown in Figure 24.6. [Electrons are moved across the magnetic field lines when you push the wire downward, and they experience a sideways force. This time there *is* a path for them and they move along the wire. Same physics as Figure 24.6a.] Then repeat with the wire bent into two coils — twice the effect. Many coils (Figure 24.3), many times more current.

> DEMONSTRATION: Drop a small bar magnet through a vertically held copper or aluminum pipe. It will take appreciably longer to drop through than an unmagnetized piece of iron (which you show first). The explanation is that the falling magnet constitutes a changing magnetic field in the metal pipe. It induces a voltage and hence a current flow in the conductucting pipe. The magnetic field set up by the current loops repel the falling magnet and account for its slow fall. Electromagnetic induction! [The magnetic field so induced opposes the change in the original field — Lenz's law. If the induced field enhanced the change in the original field, the falling magnet would be attracted rather than repelled and increase in its acceleration and gain more KE than its decrease in PE. A conservation of energy no no!] (This demo is a kit available from Pasco.)

Faraday's Law   We have seen that charges moving in a magnetic field experience forces. In the last chapter, the force deviated the direction of electrons, both in a free beam and traveling along a wire, in which case the wire was deviated. Now we see that if we push electrons that are in a wire into a magnetic field, the deviating force will be along the direction of the wire and current is induced. Another way to look at this is to say that *voltage* is being induced in the wire. The current then, is an outcome of that voltage. Faraday states that the voltage induced in a closed loop equals the time rate of change of the magnetic field in that loop. Another way of looking at induction. So rather than saying current is induced, Faraday says voltage is induced, which produces current.and other times saying voltage is induced).

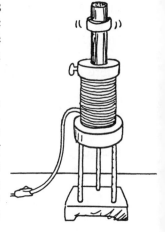

> DEMONSTRATION: Show the assorted demonstrations with the classical Elihu Thompson Electromagnetic Demonstration Apparatus — With the power on, levitate an aluminum ring over the extended pole of the Elihu Thompson device.
>
> CHECK QUESTION: Do you know enough physics to state how much electromagnetic force supports this 1-newton aluminum ring (assuming the ring weighs 1 N)? [Answer: 1 N, not particularly from a knowledge of electromagnetic forces, but from knowledges about forces in general that go back to Newton's laws. Since the ring is at rest and not accelerating, the upward electromagnetic force (in newtons!) must be equal to the downward force of gravity.]

> DEMONSTRATION: With the power off, place the ring at the base of the extended pole. When you switch on the power the current induced in the ring via electromagnetic induction converts the ring into an ac electromagnet. (By Lenz's law, not developed in the text, the polarity of the induced magnet is always such to oppose the magnetic field imposed.)

> CHECK QUESTION: Do you know enough physics to state whether or not the electromagnetic force that popped the ring was more, equal to, or less than the magnetic force that produced levitation earlier? [Answer:

More, because it accelerated upward, evidence the upward force was more than the weight. This is also understandable because the ring was lower and intercepting more changing magnetic field lines.]

As interesting examples of electromagnetic induction, consider Exercises 5, 6, and 7 (smart traffic lights, airport metal detectors, and earthquake detectors).

Emphasize the importance of this discovery by Faraday and Henry, and how its application transformed the world. Isn't it difficult to imagine having no electric lights — to live in a time when illumination after the sun goes down is by candles and whale-oil lamps? Not so long ago, really. In our older cities many buildings still have pre-electric light fixtures: gas and oil lamps.

State that underlying all the things discussed and observed is something more basic than voltages and currents — the induction of *fields*, both electric and magnetic. And because this is true we can send signals without wires — radio and TV — and furthermore, energy reaches us from the sun, sunlight.

Generators and Alternating Current   Point out that strictly speaking generators do not generate electricity — nor do batteries. What they do is pump a fluid composed of electrons. As stressed in the previous chapter, they don't make the electrons they pump. The electron fluid is in the conducting wires.

> DEMONSTRATION: Return to the motor from the previous lecture and show that when you reverse the roles of input and output, and apply mechanical energy, it becomes a generator. Light a bulb with the hand-cranked generator and show how the turning is easier when the bulb is loosened and the load removed. Allow students to try this themselves during or at the end of class.

Compare motor and generator — in principle the same. When electric energy is put in it converts it to mechanical — motor. When mechanical energy is put in it converts it to electrical energy — generator. In fact, a motor acts also as a generator creates a "back voltage" [back emf] and an opposing current. The net current in a motor is the input current minus the generated back current. The net current in a power saw will not cause its overheating and damage to its motor windings — so long as it is running and generating a back current that keeps the net current low. But if you should jam the saw so that it can't spin, without the back current generated by the spinning armature, the net current is dangerously high and can burn out the motor.

It is interesting that electric motors are used in diesel-powered railroad engines. The combustion engine cannot bring a heavy load from rest, but an electric motor can. Why? Because when the armature is not turning, the current in the windings is huge, with a corresponding huge force. As both the train and the motor gain speed, the back current generated by the motor brings the net current in the motor down to non-overheating levels.

Stress the fact that we don't get something for nothing with electromagnetic induction, and acknowledge Figure 24.4. This can be readily felt when lamps powered with a hand-cranked or a bicycle generator are switched on. Each student should experience this. The conservation of energy reigns!

Power Production   Continue with a historical theme: With the advent of the generator the task was to design methods of moving coils of wire past magnetic fields, or moving magnetic fields past coils of wire. Putting turbines beneath waterfalls, and boiling water to make steam to squirt against turbine blades and keep them turning — enter the industrial revolution.

Transformers   Explain the operation of a transformer. (I remember as a student being very confused about the seeming contradiction with Ohm's law — the idea that when voltage in the secondary was increased, current in the secondary was decreased.) Make clear that when the voltage in the coil of the secondary and the circuit it connects is increased, the current in *that* circuit also increases. The decrease is with respect to the current that powers the *primary*. So P = iV does not contradict Ohm's law!

> DEMONSTRATION: With a step-down transfer, weld a pair of nails together. This is a spectacular demonstration when you first casually place your fingers between the nail ends before they make contact, and after removing your fingers bring the points together allowing the sparks to fly while the nails quickly become red and white hot.

Cite the role of the transformer in stepping down voltages in toy electric trains, power calculators, and portable radios, and the role of stepping up voltages in TV sets and various electrical devices, and both stepping up and stepping down voltages in power transmission.

Field Induction   Point to the similarity of the field induction laws of Faraday and Maxwell — how a change in either field induces the other. This concept led Einstein to the development of his special theory of relativity. Einstein showed that a magnetic field appears when a purely electric field is seen by a moving observer, and an electric field appears when a purely magnetic field is seen from a moving vantage point.

Because of the electric and magnetic induction of fields in free space we can "telegraph" signals without wires — hence radio and TV — and furthermore, we shall see that because of field induction, there is light.

25

Properties of Light

Some instructors begin the study of physics with light, a topic that has greater appeal to many students than mechanics. Your course could begin with this chapter and continue through the following chapters of Part 6, or you could integrate chapters on vibrations, waves, and sound from Part 4 in your sequence. The way the chapters are nearly self contained allows you flexibility. If you're doing Parts 4 and 6 together, the reason for jumping in at this chapter is to avoid the more technical nature of Chapter 18. This sequence, Chapter 25, 26, 18-20, 27-29, is a gradual entrance to the study of physics. If this chapter is used as a launch point, only the definitions of speed and frequency need to be introduced. In addition, give a demonstration of resonance with a pair of tuning forks. Your students will then experience resonance, which will be a jumping off place to understand explanations of the interaction of light and matter.

Note that the "depth of the plow" in the treatment of light is respectably deep. The aim is not to separate and name categories such as transmission, reflection, and absorption, but to get into the physics. Your students will get into some good physics in this chapter — and understand it. Understanding more than you may expect, and discovering more than you thought there was, is a real joy of learning. So this should be an enjoyable chapter — why some teachers opt to begin here.

In reference to the visual illusions of Figure 25.20 on page 465: The slanted line is not broken, as can be seen looking at the book at a grazing angle. The dashes are all the same length, as a ruler will show. For a bit of humor, the vertical lines are *not* parallel. And a look at the page at a grazing angle will confirm that the tiles are not crooked. The width of the hat is the same as its height, the "fork" and "rectangular" piece could not be made in the shop, and there are two THEs in the PARIS IN THE THE SPRING.

A neat exercise on the pinhole image of the sun is featured in **Practicing Physics**. One of my very favorites! This is repeated in the **Laboratory Manual** along with two other activities. Interestingly enough, the circles or ellipses of sunlight that are cast beneath trees due to the openings between leaves, escapes the notice of most people. Many artists who paint splotches of light in the shade of trees paint irregular shapes, because they expect the shapes should be as irregular as the openings in the leaves above. Renoir, as Chapter 1 indicated, saw what was there and painted it accordingly. This exercise puts you in a beautiful role: Being the person to point out the niceties in the world that ordinarily might be missed. That's one of the niceties of being a physics instructor!

SUGGESTED LECTURE PRESENTATION

If this chapter follows E&M, and your students have just finished Chapter 24, then begin your lecture with **Begin 1** that follows. If you're jumping into light without having covered E&M, then jump ahead to **Begin 2**.

Begin 1: Electromagnetic Waves Usually I begin my lecture by asking the class to recall my recent demonstration of charging a rubber rod with cat's fur and how when I brought it near a charged pith ball, I produced action at a distance. When I moved the charged rod, the charged ball moved also. If I gently oscillate the rod, the ball in turn oscillates. State that one can think of this behavior as either action-at-a-distance or the interaction of the ball with the space immediately around it — the electric field of the charged rod. For low frequencies, the ball will swing in rhythm with the shaking rod. But the inertia of the ball and its pendulum configuration makes response poor for any vigorous shaking of the rod (that's why it's best not to actually show this, but to only describe it and go through the motions as if the equipment were present — you avoid the "that's the way it would behave" situation). You can easily establish in your students' minds the reasonableness of the ball shaking back and forth in response to the shaking electric field about the shaking rod. Carry this further by considering the ball to be simply a point charge with negligible mass. Now it will respond in synchronous rhythm with the shaking rod. Increase the frequency of the shaking rod and state that not only is there a shaking electric field about the rod, but because of its changing, there is a different kind of field.

> CHECK QUESTIONS: What kind of field is induced by the shaking rod? What kind of field in turn, does this induced field induce? And further in turn, what kind of field does this further induced field induce? And so on.

Develop the idea of the optimum speed of the field emanation, that is consistent with energy conservation, page 451.

Begin 2: Electromagnetic waves Begin by stating that everybody knows that if you placed the end of a stick in a pond and shook the stick back and forth, you'd generate waves across the water surface. But what everybody doesn't know is that if you shook a charged rod back and forth in free space, you'd generate waves also. Not waves of water, or even waves of the medium in which the stick exists, but waves of electric and magnetic fields. You'd generate *electromagnetic waves*. Shaking the rod at low frequencies generates radio waves. Shaking at a million billion times per second generates waves one could see in the dark. For those waves would be seen as light.

Electromagnetic Wave Velocity If you've just covered E&M and Chapter 24, go into some detail on the mutual induction of electric and magnetic fields, and how the critical speed of light is determined by the conservation of energy (page 451). But if you're jumping in to light without having done E&M, tell your students that this section should be treated lightly, and to move onward. A small price for jumping into the middle of a book!

> CHECK QUESTION: So the speed of light is finite; does this mean your image in the mirror is always a bit younger or a bit older than you? [Older, but of course not by very much!]

Electromagnetic Spectrum Continue by stating that, strictly speaking, light is the only thing we see. And to understand what light is, we will first try to understand how it behaves. Call attention to the rainbow of colors that are dispersed by a prism or by raindrops in the sunlight. We know white light can be spread into a spectrum of colors. Ask your students to consider the world view of little creatures who could only see a tiny portion of the spectrum, creatures who would be color blind to all the other parts. Their world view would be very limited. Then state that we are like those little creatures, in that the spectrum of colors we can see are a tiny portion of the *electromagnetic spectrum* (Figure 25.3)— less than a tenth of one percent! We are color blind to the other parts. The instruments of science have extended our view of the other parts. These instruments are not microscopes and telescopes, for they enable closer viewing of the part of the spectrum we are familiar with. It is the infrared detecting devices, microwave and radio receivers, that allow us to explore the lower-frequency end of the spectrum, and ultraviolet, X-ray, and gamma-ray detectors that let us "see" the higher-frequency end. What we see without unaided eyes is a tiny part of what's out there in the world around us.

Buckminster Fuller put it well when he stated that ninety-nine percent of all that is going to affect our tomorrows is being developed by humans using instruments that work in ranges of reality that are nonhumanly sensible.

> CHECK QUESTION: Where does sound fit in the electromagnetic spectrum? [It doesn't of course!]
>
> CHECK QUESTION: A photographer wishes to photograph a lightning bolt, and comes up with the idea of having the camera triggered by the sound of thunder. A good idea or a poor idea? [Very poor, for light travels about a million times faster than sound. By the time the sound of thunder arives, the lightning bolt is long gone!]

Transparent Materials Recall your earlier demonstration of sound resonance (or if you haven't done this, demonstrate now the resonance of a pair of tuning forks mounted on sounding boxes (Figure 25.4). The tuning fork demo provides important experience for your students in understanding the interaction of light and matter. In some cases light strikes a material and rebounds — reflection (Chapter 27). In cases where light continues through the material, we say the material is*transparent..*

> DEMONSTRATION: Show the swinging balls apparatus that is usually used to illustrate momentum and energy conservation. Here you are showing that the energy that cascades through the system of balls is analagous to light energy cascading through transparent matter. Just as the incident ball is not the same ball that emerges, the incident "photon" of light upon glass is not the same photon that emerges through the other side. Although too difficult to see, slight interaction times between balls produces a slight time delay between incidence and emergence of balls. Likewise for light.

Note that the text does not mention photons in the light-through-glass explanation. Photons aren't introduced until Chapter 29.

Point out the value of **scientific models**, in understanding physical phenomena. Hence the discussion of cascading balls, tuning forks, and imaginary springs that hold electrons to the nuclei of atoms. A model is not correct or incorrect, but useful or nonuseful. Models must be refined or abandoned as they fail to account for various aspects of a phenomenon.

> CHECK QUESTION: Compared to the speed of light in a vacuum, why is the speed of light less in transparent materials such as water or glass? [Answer: According to the model treated in the text, there is a time delay

between the absorption of light and its re-emis-sion. This time delay serves to decrease the average speed of light in a transparent material.]

Another analogy for light travelling through glass is the average speed of a basketball moving down a court. It may fly through the air from player to player at one constant speed, but its average speed down the court depends on the holding time of the players. Carrying the analogy further, different materials have different players, and although the instantaneous speed of light is always the same, the average speed depends on the number of players encountered, and the holding time of each player.

On the subject of glass, its interesting to note that we see through it for the same reasons we see through water. Despite the appearance of glass, it is really a highly viscous liquid rather than a solid. Its internal stucture is not the regular crystalline latticework of most solids, but is essentially random like that of liquids. Whereas conventional liquids have a freezing point at which they become solid, liquid glass gets stiffer as it cools. At room temperature its rate of flow is so slow that it takes centuries for it to appreciably ooze out of shape. Because of the downward flow due to gravity, window panes only several decades old show a lens effect at their bottoms due to the increased thickness there.

Opaque Materials State that light generally has three possible fates when incident upon a material: (1) reflects, (2) is transmitted through the material, or (3) is absorbed by the material. Usually a combination of all three fates occurs. When absorption occurs, the vibrations given to electrons by incident light are often great enough to last for a relatively long time, during which the vibratory energy is shared by collisions with neighboring atoms. The absorbed energy warms the material.

> CHECK QUESTION: Why in the sunlight is a black tar road hotter to the touch than a pane of window glass? [Sunlight is absorbed and turned into internal energy in the road surface, but transmitted through the glass to somewhere else.]

For the record, we say that ultraviolet light cannot penetrate glass. Hence you cannot get a sunburn through glass. But *some* ultraviolet light does pass through glass — long wavelength ultraviolet light, which has insufficient energy to cause a sunburn. Most sunlamps *aren't* made of ordinary glass — they're made of quartz or special UV-transparent glass.

Shadows Illustrate the different shadows cast by small and large sources of light. Ask why there appears no definite shadow of students hands when held above their desks, and relate this to the multiple sources and diffused light in the room.

On the chalkboard explain solar and lunar eclipses.

> CHECK QUESTION: Does the earth cast a shadow in space whenever a lunar or solar eclipse occurs? [Yes, but not only when these events occur — the earth, like all objects illuminated by light from a small source, casts a shadow. Evidence of this perpetual shadow is seen at these special times.]

> CHECK QUESTION: Why do you not cast a shadow on the ground on an overcast day? [A relatively small light source such as the sun casts a relatively sharp shadow. On an overcast day the primary sun is blocked and the whole sky, the secondary light source, illuminates you. The source is now so big that no shadow is seen.]

Point out that light from a point source follows the inverse-square law (first treated in Chapter 8, and again for Coloumb's law in Chapter 21). A camera flash is a point source, obeys the inverse-square law, something that is not understood by people who attempt to take pictures of far-away nighttime scenes with flash cameras — like snapping long-distance shots at a nightime concert, or a night view of a distant city. I cite the airline passenger I saw some years ago taking flash shots of a distant dark city below through the aircraft window! Cite how light from the flash spreads out on both the outgoing and return trip to the camera, consequently delivering very little light to the camera. And if through a window, how the light reflected from the window overwhelms what little light would survive the round trip anyway.

On the subject of flash photography, cite the futility of using a flash to take pictures of slides or a movie projected on a screen in a dark room. Of course, the flash overwhelms the image projected and the picture ends up showing a blank white screen. (This seems to not have been known by the many teachers who were flashing away at slides shown by cartoonist Gary Larson at a recent NSTA conference!)

Seeing Light: The Eye   An interesting tidbit not in the chapter is the explanation for the seemingly luminous eyes of nocturnal animals such as cats and owls at night. It turns out there are reflective membranes located in back of the rods in the animals' eyes, which provide a "second chance" for the animal to perceive light that initially misses the rods. This arrangement, common in night predators, gives excellent night vision. Hence also the reflection from their eyes when light is shone on them.

Discuss the function of the rods and three types of cones in the retina of the eye, and how color cannot be perceived in dim light, and how the colored stars appear white to us whereas they show up clearly colored with camera time exposures. (I show a colored slide that I took of the stars, and discuss the curved lines encircling the north star, and   get into a discussion of how long the camera shutter was held open.)

In discussing color vision, point out that in a bullfight, the bull is angry not at the redness of the cape that is flaunted before him, but because of the darts that have been stuck into him! Whereas a frog is "wired" to see only motion, so it is also on the periphery of our vision. Discuss the fact that we see only motion and no color at the periphery of our vision.

> DEMONSTRATION: Figure 25.16; stand at a corner of the room and shake brightly colored cards, first turned backward so the color is hidden and students can adjust the position of their heads (looking toward the other corner of the room). When they can just barely see the moving cards, turn them over and display the color. Try with different colors. This goes over well, and is surprising to most students.

Pupilometrics (Figure 25.17) is prone to misunderstanding. If you lecture on this topic, it is important to dispel misconceptions your students may associate with pupil size. It would not be well for people who normally have small pupils to feel self-conscious about this and mistakenly believe that small pupils display a negativity of some sort. Also, pupil size decreases with age. It would not be well for young people to mistakenly feel that their older peers were "emotionally down" in general. It is the change in pupil size, not the pupil size itself, that pupilometrics is about. For more on this, see the article on Pupilometrics in *Scientific American*, back in April 1965.

Figure 25.18 on lateral inhibition is just one more reminder to your students that they should be careful about believing firmly in what appears to be true. By obstructing the edge between the rectangles, a whole different picture is presented. Our eyes do indeed deceive us from time to time. We should always be open to new ways to look at what we consider is real.

26

Color

In this chapter we introduce a model of the atom in which electrons behave as tiny oscillators that resonate or are forced into vibration by external influences. If you haven't preceded light with a study of sound, and if you haven't demonstrated resonance with a pair of tuning forks, do it now, for the tuning fork model is used in the text to account for selective reflection and transmission of light

We continue to refer to color primarily by frequency rather than wavelength, in effort to reduce the number of terms students must learn to understand concepts. There is a trend toward using wavelength in nanometers (Angstroms are "out") for the color spectrum, probably because there seems to be evidence that the color sensitive elements of the retina-optic-nerve-brain system are more reasonably a function of wavelength than frequency due to velocity variation. There is a trend to terahertz (THz) in place of exponential notation for visible light frequencies.

If you haven't shown your class the black hole that appears in a box with white interior, back in the heat chapters (Figure 15.11, p 273) do it now. It nicely illustrates the "color" black.

You may wish to point out that the method of predicting colors from various mixtures, Figures 26.12, 26.13, and 26.14, are approximate. For example, the mixture of blue and yellow by the block diagram technique predicts that no color is reflected. So the blocks are not hard and fast, and for the mixture of blue and yellow one must allow a gap between the yellow and blue blocks to allow for the green that is in fact seen.

Be sure to mount three floodlights on your lecture table, red, green, and blue, of shades such that all three overlapping produce white on a white screen. Then stand in front of the lamps, illuminated one at a time and show the interesting colors of the shadows, as is shown by the shadows of the golf ball in Figure 26.9. Impressive!

The three overlapping primary colors is featured in **Practicing Physics**.

There are no activities or experiments for this chaplter in the **Laboratory Manual**.

This interesting chapter is not a prerequisite to chapters that follow.

SUGGESTED LECTURE PRESENTATION

Selected Reflection   Discuss the oscillator model of the atom, and the ideas of forced vibration and resonance as they relate to color, as you display different colored objects. A red object, for example, reflects red. It absorbs the other colors. Resonance is *not* occurring for red, by the way, for the resonant frequencies are being *absorbed*. (I was mixed up about this point for years!) Recall the absorption of resonant frequencies in the treatment of transparency in Chapter 25.

Selective Transmission   Similarly for colored glass — the resonant frequencies are absorbed and becomes the internal energy of the transparent material. The frequencies to pass through the glass are those away from the resonant frequencies. Frequencies close to resonance undergo more interactions with the molecules and take longer to travel than frequencies far from resonance. Hence different colors have different speeds in transparent materials. (If not, no rainbows, as we shall see!)

Mixing Colored Light   How many colors are there in the spectrum? Although we commonly group the colors into seven categories, red, orange, yellow, etc., there are an infinite number of colors. The "in-between" colors are not mixtures of their neighboring colors. The red-orange between red and orange, for example, is not a mixture of red and orange but is a distinct frequency present in sunlight.

DEMONSTRATION: Show the overlapping of the primary colors with the Singerman Color Apparatus (or its equivalent). Show complementary colors.

CHECK QUESTIONS: Ask several questions such as those in the Check Question on page 479.

DEMONSTRATION: Show the overlapping of light from three lamps on your lecture table aimed at a white screen behind you. The variety of colors in the shadows of you are very impressive. And their explanation by showing only the black shadow from one lamp, then two lamps where the black shadow is now the color of the second lamp, and then three lamps with explanation, is quite satisfying.

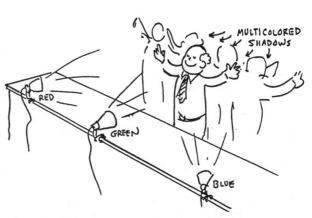

Mixing Colored Pigments   Now we address color mixing as it relates to early finger painting experience (blue + yellow = green; red + yellow = orange; red + blue = purple). This was likely the only color mixing information encountered by your students prior to this chapter. (I have never lectured about this material in detail, and have left it to the students reading.)

CHECK QUESTION: If you've gone over Figures 26.10 through 26.14, have your students do the exercise at the top of page 479 in class.

Pass a magnifying glass around and look at the cyan, magenta, and yellow dots that make up the colors on the inside back cover.

Rules for Color Mixing   Establish the concepts of complimentary colors if you haven't already.

Why the Sky is Blue   Compare the molecules in the atmosphere to tiny bells, that when struck, ring with high frequencies. They ring mostly at violet, and next at blue. We're better at hearing blue, so we hear a blue sky. On the other hand, bumble bees and other creatures that are good at seeing violet see a violet sky.

LECTURE SKIT — PART 1; Blue sky: Put a variety of six tuning forks at one end of your lecture table — a "red" one, "orange" one, "yellow" one, etc., to a "violet" one. Ask what "color" sound they would hear if you struck all the tuning forks in unison. Your class should answer, "White." Then suppose you have a mirror device around the forks so that when you "strike" them again, a beam of sound travels down the length of your lecture table. Ask what color they will hear. Several might say "White" again, but state that if there is no medium to scatter the beam that they will hear nothing (unless, of course, the beam is directed toward them). Now place a tray of tuning forks at the opposite end of your lecture table (the tray I use is simply a 2 x 4 piece of wood, about a third meter long, with about a dozen holes drilled in it to hold a dozen tuning forks of various sizes). Ask your class to pretend that the ends of your lecture table are 150 million km apart, the distance between the earth and the sun. State that your tray of assorted tuning forks represents the earth's atmosphere — point to the tuning forks, calling out their colors; a blue one, a violet one, a blue one, a blue one, a red one, a blue one, a violet one, a blue one, a green one, a blue one, a violet one, and so forth emphasizing the preponderance of blue and violet forks. Your tray of forks is perpendicular to the imaginary beam from the sun (to simulate a noonish thin atmosphere). Walk to the sun end of the table and again pretend to strike the forks and show how the beam travels down the table and intercepts and scatters from the atmospheric tuning forks in all directions. Ask what color the class hears. And you have a blue sky, especially if they're a bit deficient in hearing violet.

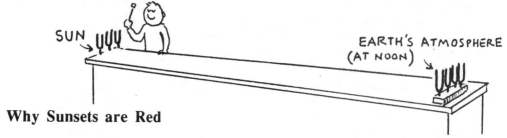

Why Sunsets are Red

PART 2; Red sunset: Sketch a rendition of Figure 26.18 on the board and show that at sunset the sunlight must travel through many kilometers of air to reach an observer — that blue light is scattered all along these kilometers. What frequencies survive, you ponder. Then back to your sun and earth forks on the lecture table. It is important to rotate the tray of forks 90° to represent the earth's thicker atmosphere at sunset. Select a student (a cooperative one, of course) from the class to sit beside the tray of earth forks. State to the class that your volunteer represents an earth observer at sunset. Go back to the sun forks which you pretend to strike. Down the table comes the beam, which you follow. Whap, into the earth's atmosphere where most of it scatters throughout the classroom. Again, ask the class what color they "hear." "Blue" is the answer. Correct. Now you ask your volunteer what color he or she heard. "Orange," is the answer! Your demonstration has been a success. For humor, by "experiment" you have proved your point. Your

140

student volunteer has simply heard a composite of the lower-frequency left-over colors after the class received most all the higher-frequency blues. So those nice colors at sunset are what? Left-over colors.

Put another way, you can say the orange of the sunset is the complementary color of the blue-violet sky.

> DEMONSTRATION: Shine a beam of white light through a colloidal suspension of a very small quantity of instant nonfat dry milk in water, to show the scattering of blue and transmission of orange.

Discuss the blueness of distant dark mountains and the yellowness of distant snow-covered mountains (Check Questions, page 482).

Why Clouds Are White Small particles scatter high frequencies. Larger molecules and particles also scatter lower frequencies (like larger bells ring at lower frequencies). Very large ones ring in the reds. In a cloud there are a wide assortment of particles — all sizes. They ring with all colors. Ask your class if they have any idea why clouds are white! (Cumulus clouds, composed of droplets, are white because of the multitude of particle sizes, but higher-altitude cirrus clouds are composed of ice crystals, which like snow, reflect all frequencies.)

Why Water is Greenish Blue Water absorbs infrared. It also absorbs visible light up into the red end of the color spectrum. Take away red from white light and you are left with the complimentary color — cyan. A piece of white paper deep in the water looks cyan. There is no red left in the sunlight to make it white. A red crab and a black crab have the same appearance on the ocean floor.

Color Vision and Color Deficiency The term color blindness is better stated as color deficiency, for one with defective cones is not blind in the true sense of the word. And its true: very few women are color blind in comparison to men. Genetics, dear one!

27

Reflection and Refraction

Reflection and refraction are introduced via Fermat's Principle of Least Time, a la Feynman. The treatment of reflection is brief, with only scant application to convex and concave mirrors. The treatment of refraction is supported by many examples. You may wish to further support the cases of atmospheric refraction by discussing the analogous case of sound refraction in a region where the temperature of air at the ground is appreciably higher or lower than the air temperature above as was treated in Chapter 19.

For a very brief treatment on light, this chapter may be covered in place of the regular sequence of Part 6. In this case, the behavior rather than the nature of light would be emphasized (which most introductory texts stress anyway).

Paul Doherty makes rainbows that his students can study first hand at the Exploratorium. You can too. Your giant water drop is a glass sphere filled with water. Cut a hole that's slightly larger than your sphere in a piece of white cardboard. Shine a bright beam of light from a slide projector or the sun through the hole so that the beam illuminates the entire water drop. The drop will project a colored circle of light onto the cardboard screen around the hole you have cut. If at first you don't see a circle of light, move the screen closer to the drop, as Paul shows to the right! (See his article on rainbows in the Exploratorium quarterly, *Exploring* (Summer 92). Thanx Paul!

Courtesy Exploratorium

I owe the conical treatment of the rainbow to one of Cecil Adams' syndicated newspaper columns, *The Straight Dope*.

An explanation of why a rainbow is bow-shaped is aided with this simple apparatus that is easily constructed: Stick three colored dowels into a sphere of clay, strofoam, wood, or whatever that represents a raindrop. One dowel is white, one violet, and the other red, to represent incident white light and refracted red and violet. The angles between dowels is shown in the sketch. A student volunteer crouching in front of your chalkboard shows the class how the only drops that cast light to him or her originate in drops along a bow-shaped region. (More on this in the lecture below.)

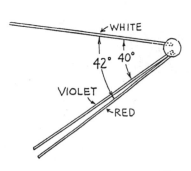

The half-size mirror problem, Exercises 4 through 7, nicely illustrate one of the valuable things about your course — that the richness in life is not only seeing the world with wide open eyes, but in knowing what to look for. Concepts in this chapter provide a lot of guidance in this respect.

There are two pages on refraction and lenses in **Practicing Physics**.
Two activities and three experiments are choices in the **Laboratory Manual**.
The following suggested lecture will probably take at least two class periods.

SUGGESTION LECTURE PRESENTATION

Principle of Least Time You can lead into Fermat's principle of least time for reflection by posing to your class the following: Consider a rectangular box, like a shoe box, with an ant inside at one of its corners, say an upper corner. Question: what would be the path of least distance along the inside surface of the box to the diagonally opposite corner? (Most will likely answer "straight down to the lower corner, then diagonally across the floor.") Then after a "talk to your neighbor" routine, provide this hint: flatten the box out and consider the shortest distance.

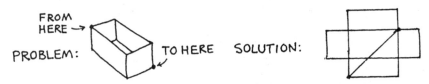

Law of Reflection Now you're ready to discuss Figures 27.2 through 27.5, and cap it off with Figure 27.6, the law of reflection.

Plane Mirrors Sketch Figure 27.7 on the board and carefully show how image and object distance are the same. Call attention to the curved mirrors of Figure 27.8 and stress that the law reigns in whatever small region a light ray strikes. Likewise with **diffuse reflection**. Discuss Exercise 12, about the diffuse dry road becoming a "plane mirror" when wet, and hence the difficulty of seeing the road in a car on a rainy night.

Refraction Discuss Fermat's principle for refraction, via the lifeguard analogy presented in the text. Contrast the path the lifeguard would take compared to the path a seal would take. Point out that the bend you draw on the board when illustrating these "refractions" depends on the relative speeds on the sand and in the water. Continue with the examples in the text, that light takes a longer path but shorter distance timewise when incident obliquely on glass; likewise through a prism, and through a lens, above the atmosphere during sunsets, and close to the ground when a mirage is produced. Consider relating the refraction of light during a mirage to the refraction of sound as treated in Chapter 19. Then to the mechanics of how light follows these incredible paths.

Cause of Refraction   Refraction hinges on the slowing of light in a transparent medium. This was established in Chapter 25. The analogy of the wheels rolling onto the grass lawn (Figure 27.22) shows that bending of path is the result of this change of speed. This is reinforced in *Practicing Physics*. So we see that the bending is the result of light changing speed, rather than the result of light "wanting" to reach a place in the least time. It is important to underscore this distinction. Here a straightforward physics explanation is much simpler than the mystical explanation. How many other mystical explanations fall in this category?

When the speed of light in a transparent object is the same as the speed of light in a fluid in which it is immersed, then it won't be seen (or in physics lingo, when the index of refraction is the same for each). This can be shown as follows:

> DEMONSTRATION: Prepare a "Magic Elixir" that consists of 590 ml carbon tetrachloride and 410 ml benzene (approximately 10:7 by volume), which has the same index of refraction as pyrex. Prior to the students entering the classroom, the solution is poured into a beaker (1 or 2 liter) and three small pyrex test tubes are placed in the solution. The test tubes are "invisible" from a distance. You might do as Herb Ringel does and tell the class the liquid has a memory. That is, if a test tube is broken and the pieces placed in the liquid, the atoms will separate and within seconds rearrange themselves and reform the test tube! Napkins and hammers are available. Invariably, someone asks for a repetition, therefore the extra test tubes! [Caution: Carbon tet and benzine are both hazardous.]

Dispersion   Now that you've established refraction as a result of changes in light speed, it follows that different speeds of different frequencies of light in transparent materials refract at different angles. This is dispersion, nicely illustrated with a prism.

Rainbows   Amplify the section on rainbows, and liken them to viewing a cone held with its apex to the eye. The deeper the misty region, the more intense the rainbow appears. The cone bit explains why the rainbow is round. Another is via the ball-and-sticks demo.

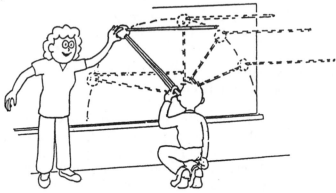

> DEMONSTRATION: Show the rainbow-sticks apparatus described earlier and compare it to the rainbow schematic drawing of Figures 27.29 and 27.30. The white stick represents incoming white light, and the red and violet sticks the refracted rays. Have a student volunteer crouch in front of the board as shown in the sketch. Place the ball near the chalkboard so the white dowel is perpendicular to the board (from the sun at the horizon for simplicity). Position the free end of the violet dowel so that it nearly meets the volunteer's eye. State that a drop at this location refracts violet light to the eye. The question follows: are there other locations that will also refract violet light to the eye? Move the "drop" to other locations along the board while keeping the white dowel perpendicular to the board. It is easy to see

144

that refracted violet from drops farther away miss the eye altogether. The only locations that send violet light to the eye are along a bow — which you trace with violet or blue chalk. This is easy to do if the students holds the end of the violet dowel near the eye while you scribe the arc in compass fashion.

CHECK QUESTION: With the ball and dowels positioned at the top of the bow, ask where the volunteer must look to see red — above the violet, or below? [Above (2° to be exact).] Show this by moving the "drop" up, whereupon the red dowel lines up with the eye. Complete your demo by sweeping this wider bow with red chalk.

Enlist a second volunteer to crouch in front of the board at a different position. Show how this volunteer must look to different drops in the sky to see a rainbow. Ask the class if the two volunteers see the same rainbow. [No, each sees his or her own personal rainbow!] Do as Marshall Ellenstein does and quip that when one person says to another, "Look at the beautiful rainbow," an appropriate response is, "Move over and let me see!"

Rainbows cannot be seen when the sun is more than 42 degrees in the sky because the bow is below the horizon where no water drops are to be seen. Hence rainbows are normally seen early and late in the day. So we don't see rainbows in midday in summer in most parts of the world (except from an airplane, where they are seen in full circles).

Point out a significant yet commonly unnoticed feature about the rainbow — that the disk segment bounded by the bow is appreciably brighter than the rest of the sky. This is clearly shown in Figure 27.33. The rainbow is similar to the chromatic aberration around a bright spot of projected white light.

Show Paul Doherty's rainbow from a sphere of water (described on page 142)

Extend rainbows to the similar phenomenon of the halo around the moon. Explain how the halo is produced by refraction of moonlight through ice crystals in the atmosphere. Note the important difference: whereas both refraction and internal reflection produce rainbows, only refraction produces halos. And whereas the observer is between the sun and the drops for seeing a rainbow, the ice crystals that produce halos are between the observer and the moon. Moonlight is refracted through ice crystals high in the atmosphere — evidence of the coldness up there even on a hot summer night.

Total Internal Reflection

DEMONSTRATION: Show examples of reflection, refraction and total internal reflection with the usual apparatus — light source (laser), prisms, and a tank of water with a bit of fluorescene dye added.

(You may notice that at the critical angle, some light skims the surface of the water. This is because your beam is slightly divergent, so where the central axis of the beam may be at the critical angle and reflect back into the medium, part of the beam is slightly beyond the critical angle and refracts.)

Ask your class to imagine how the sky would look from a lake bottom. For humor, whereas above water we must turn our heads through 180 degrees to see from horizon to horizon, a fish need only scan twice the 48 degree critical angle to see from horizon to horizon — which is why fish have no necks!

Fibre Optics Show some examples of light pipes. Discuss some of the many applications of these fibers, or "light pipes," particularly in telephone communications. The principle underlying fiber optics is similar to a boy scout signaling Morse code in flashlight to a distant friend. In fiber optics, computers fire lasers that turn on and off rapidly in digital code. Current lasers send about 1.7 billion pulses per second to optical detectors that receive and interpret the information. AT&T researches in mid 1992 sent some 6.8 billion pulses per second over a 520-mile fiber optic cable.

Today glass fibers as thin as a human hair carry 1300 simultaneous telephone conversations, compared to the only 24 that can be carried per conventional copper cable. Signals in copper cables must be boosted every 4 to 6 kilometers, whereas re-amplification in light-wave systems occurs every 10 to 50 kilometers. For infrared optical fibers, the distance between regenerators may be hundreds or perhaps thousands of kilometers. Fibers are indeed very transparent! Perhaps the legend of Figure 27.41 would better ask, "What's white and black and warm all *under*? To which the answer is a polar bear under the artic sun.

Lenses The explanation of lenses follows from your demo of light deviating through a prism. Whereas a study of lenses is properly a laboratory activity, all the ray diagrams in the world are of little value unless paired with a hands-on experience with lenses. So if a laboratory experience is not part of your course, I would recommend lenses be treated very briefly if at all in lecture.

DEMONSTRATION: Show examples of converging and diverging lenses. A white light source will do, but a neat source of light is a laser beam that is widened by lenses and then directed through a mask of parallel slits. Then parallel rays of light are incident upon your lenses.

DEMONSTRATION: Simulate the human eye with a spherical flask filled with a bit of fluorescene dye. Paint an "iris" on the flask and position appropriate lenses in back of the iris for normal, farsighted and nearsighted vision. Then show how corrective lenses placed in front of the eye put the light in focus on the retina.

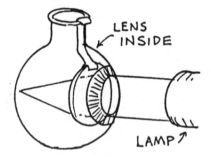

Exercise 26 about the sheet of lenses that supposedly direct more solar energy into a swimming pool makes a good lecture topic.

NEXT-TIME QUESTIONS: Be sure to ask for the minimum size mirror bit, Exercises 4 and 5. [I regret to report, that seldom do I find half of my class answering these two questions correctly — particularly when I first emphasize that the results will be surprising, and that if they are careful they will learn something about their image in a mirror that has likely escaped them all their lives (that the size of the mirror is independent of their distance from it). Most correctly get the first part, the half-size answer, but miss the second. That's where I ask them to mark the mirror where they see the top of their head and bottom of their chin, and then to step back and look carefully for the effect of distance. Perhaps like the visual illusion of Home Project 2 back on page 161, their belief in their uninvestigated answer is so strong, that they will not see what is there unless it is explicitly pointed out to them. Are your students more perceptive than mine?] In any event, when you discuss the answer, bring into class a full-length mirror or pass a few small mirrors among your students. It's worth the extra effort.

28

Light Waves

Huygens' Principle
Diffraction
Interference
    Single Color Thin Film Interference
    Interference Colors by Reflection From Thin Films
Polarization
Three-Dimensional Viewing
Colors by Transmission Through Polarizing Materials
Holography

In your treatment of light waves, empasize that light does not travel in little sine-wave lines as some diagrams of light suggest. The wavy lines represent a graph of the changes in the intensity of the E&M fields of which light is composed.

If you put some care into the two demonstrations of interference with music suggested here, you'll impress your students with the beauty of physics that should be among the high points of your course.

A page of *interference patterns* ala Figure 28.19 in detail are in **Practicing Physics**.

The **Laboratory Manual** has no activities or experiments on the material of this chapter.

SUGGESTED LECTURE PRESENTATION

Huygens' Principle   A model for understanding the propagation of light is presented in Huygens' Principle. Careful investigation of Figure 28.5, for example, illustrates *why* the angle of reflection equals the angle of incidence. The figure also shows another view of refraction. Carried further, one can see why light travels in straight lines when passing through a transparent medium. Recall the "photon" cascading in a straight line path back in Figure 25.6 on page 455. Why the cascade is along a straight line path is not clear, especially if considered from a *ray* point of view. But for many photons, wavefronts cancel one another in random directions and reinforce along the path that makes up the straight line of the ray. The overlapping wavelets of Huygens is a useful model.

Diffraction   Show examples of diffraction via some of the several Ealing film loops.

> DEMONSTRATION: After discussing diffraction, pass some index cards with razor slits in them throughout the class. Show a vertical show-case lamp or fluorescent lamp separated into three segments by colored plastic; red, clear, and blue. Have your students view the diffraction of these

three segments through the slit, or through a slit provided by their own fingers. Note the different fringe spacings of different colors.

Interference Sketch the overlapping of water waves on the board, like that shown in Figure 28.13 on the board. Point out that interference is a property of light waves, sound waves, and ALL kinds of waves.

Prepare your class for your laser demonstration by holding a piece of glass with an irregular surface (shower door glass, sugar bowl cover, crystal glassware) against a laser and show the interference pattern on a screen. Be sure to hold the glass steady so the pattern is fixed. Then make a sketch similar to Figure 28.18 on the board to explain the fringes (a dark area is the result of waves meeting out of phase; a bright area where waves meet in phase).

> DEMONSTRATION: This is a great one! With the lights out, shine laser light through the same irregular piece of glass and display beautiful interference patterns on the wall, but this time while you make slight movements of the glass. I do this in rhythm with music (Bach's Suite Three in D.) Your students will not forget this demonstration!

> DEMONSTRATION: Set up the sodium lamp and show interference fringes due to reflection from a pair of glass plates (Figure 28-22).

The worksheet that treats Figure 28-19 should be helpful at this point. Pass around diffraction gratings if available.

Interference Colors by Reflection from Thin Films

Bubble time! Your class will be delighted if you show a display of giant bubbles (made with a wide hoop in a wide tray of bubble solution — a mixture of equal amounts of Joy or Dawn dishwashing liquid, glycerine, and water). Point out that the film of the soap bubble is the thinnest thing seen by the unaided eye — 5000 times thinner than a human hair or cigarette paper. The smallness of light waves is sensed here also. Emphasize the need for two surfaces for interference colors, and why the film should be thin (Exercise 16).

Go through the text explanation of interference colors seen from splotches of gasoline on a wet street. Treat a single wave of blue light, first from only a single surface where one would see a blue reflection. This would be the case with no gasoline film on a water surface. Then draw a second surface, that of the thin film of gasoline and show that the proper thickness (1/4 wave) will produce cancellation of the blue light. Ask how many students have ever seen gasoline films illuminated with blue light. None. But sunlight, yes. And when sunlight is incident the blue part is cancelled. The complementary color of blue, yellow, is what is seen.

> CHECK QUESTION: Why are interference colors not seen from gasoline spilled on a dry surface?

The example of the bluish tint of coated lenses makes a good lecture illustration for interference. (This was Figure 29.19 in the 4th Edition of CP, if you have one of those around.)

The lightning bolt that makes up the cover of this book, of course, was taken through a diffraction grating. It was taken by physics professor William Bickel of the University of Arizona.

Polarization Distinguish between polarized and nonpolarized light.

DEMONSTRATION: Tie a rubber tube to a distant firm support and pass it through a grating (as from a refrigerator or oven shelf). Have a student hold the grating while you shake the free end and produce transverse waves. Show that when the grating "axis" and the plane of "polarization" are aligned, the wave passes. And when they are at right angles, the wave is blocked.

Crossed polaroids with another sandwiched between, as shown by the little girl in Figure 28.32 is a dandy. Second only to the sailboat sailing into the wind, it my favorite illustration of vectors. The explanation for the passage of light through the system of three polaroids is not given in the chapter, but is indicated in Figure III-12, Appendix III (repeated here more quantitatively).

$$ \text{100\%} \Rightarrow \quad \Rightarrow \quad \Rightarrow \quad \text{50\%} \quad \Rightarrow \quad (0.707)\,50\% \quad (0.707)(0.707)\,50\% $$

[For an ideal polarizer, 50% of nonpolarized incident light is transmitted. That is why a Polaroid passes so little light compared to a sheet of window pane. The transmitted light is polarized. So in the above diagram, only the electric vector aligned with the polarization axis is transmitted; this is 50% of the incident light transmitted by the first sheet. The magnitude of this vector through the second sheet is 50% cos ø, where ø is the angle between the polarization axes of both sheets, and (50% cos ø) cos Θ of the original vector gets through the third sheet, where Θ is the angle between the polarization axes of the second and third sheet. The intensity of light is proportional to the square of the emerging vector (not treated in the textbook). In any event, the polarizers are less than ideal, so less than this actually gets through the three-sheet system.]

After explaining how the light that reflects from nonmetallic surfaces is polarized in a plane parallel to the surface (by drawing an analogy of skipping flat rocks off a water surface only when the plane of the rock is parallel to the water surface), draw a couple of pair of sunglasses on the board with the polarization axes as shown on page 535 and ask which are the best for reducing road glare. If you want to discuss the viewing of three-dimensional slides and movies, you'll have a transition to such by the third choice of sunglasses with polaroids at right angles to each other.

3-Dimensional Viewing   Not everybody can flex their eyes to see the depth of Figures 28.35, 28.36, and 28.37, although with practice most students can do it. Stereograms are easy to construct. Figure 28.36 is easily done on a typewriter with simple line displacement, or can be drawn by hand. The snowflake stereogram of Figure 28.37 was made by John Dennis, editor of the magazine, Stereo World. Make your own by placing cutouts of snowflakes on a photocopier for one view, then horizontally displace them a bit for a second view. By good old trial and error, students can easily construct their own stereograms.

Colors by Transmission Through Polarizing Materials

DEMONSTRATION: The vivid colors that emerge from cellophane between crossed Polaroids makes a spectacular demonstration. Have students make up some 2 x 2 inch slides of cut and crinkled cellophane mounted on Polaroid material (which can be obtained inexpensively from Edmund Scientific Co.). Place in a slide projector and rotate a sheet of Polaroid in front of the projecting lens so that a changing montage of colors is displayed on the screen. Also include a showing of color slides of the interference colors seen in the everyday environment, as well as of microscopic crystals. This is more effective with two projectors with hand dissolving from image to image on the screen. Do this in rhythm to some music and you'll have an unforgettable lecture demonstration! [My students report that this is the best part of my course — to which I have mixed feelings. I would prefer that some of my *explanations* were the highlight of my course.]

Holograms An effective sequence for explaining holograms is the following: With the aid of Figure 28.19, develop the idea further for multiple slits, the diffraction grating. With a large diffraction grating (I use one that is the size of a full sheet of typing paper, Edmund Scientific Co.) show the spectral lines of a gas discharge tube — emphasize that there are really no physical lines where they appear to be, that the lines are virtual images of the glowing tube (just as they would be images of slits if a slit were being used). With a fairly good idea of how these images are produced by the diffraction grating, show the class a really sophisticated diffraction grating — not of vertical parallel lines in one dimension, but of microscopic swirls of lines in two dimensions — a hologram, illuminated with a laser.

Interestingly enough, holography does not require a laser. As the text states, Dennis Gabor created the first hologram using light from a sodium vapor lamp. Holography requires monochromatic light from a point source. Gabor simply passed sodium light through a pinhole, which reduced intensity and required long exposures and sensitive film. The advantage of the laser for holograms is that a laser emits all its light in a point-source form. Lasers make holography much easier to do.

Although some layered holograms can be viewed with ordinary white light, like those on credit cards, they are nevertheless made with the coherent light of the laser.

29

Light Emission

Excitation
  Emission Spectra
Incandescence
  Absorption Spectra
Fluorescence
  Fluorescent Lamps
Phosphorescence
Lasers

This chapter begins by treating the Bohr model of the atom with simplified energy levels to explain light emission, whether by a gas discharge tube, incandescent or fluorescent lamp, phosphorescent mineral, or a laser.

Excitation between the various simplified energy levels of the Bohr model of the atom is used in this chapter to explain the emission of light. Note that this is quite a different model of light emission compared to the oscillator model we introduced in Chapters 25 and 26. Subtle oscillations of the electron shells underscore light being reflected or transmitted. Excitation is not subtle, and is a different process — electrons make transitions from one electron shell to another. There are two different models of behavior here. One suits the processes of reflection and transmission of light, and the other suits the way light is emitted from a light source to begin with. Neither of the two atomic models presented is intended to convey a picture of what atoms are "really like," but instead are simplified representations that are useful for conceptualizing how atoms behave. You may comment on the nature of a model in physics here; namely that a model is not "right" or "wrong", but "useful" or "nonuseful." No scientific models are carved in stone.

Students are quite familiar with glow-in-the-dark strips used as head gear or necklaces, popular in dance spots. Or glow-in-the-dark key rings, activated by light. For the record, these phosphorescent materials contain calcium sulfide, activated by bismuth, with additional traces of copper, silver, or lead. These materials are harmless, and very different from the old zinc sulphide materials impregnated with trace amounts of radium to supply alpha particles for stimulation.

This chapter is a necessary background for the following two chapters. If you are not going to lecture on the quantum physics of Chapters 30 and 31, then this chapter fits very well when sandwiched between Chapters 25 and 26. Then the nature of light (Chapter 25) is followed by how light is emitted. Color (Chapter 26) picks up the sequence. Another advantage is an earlier treatment of the laser, which is likely part of your demo equipment for Chapter 27.

SUGGESTED LECTURE PRESENTATION

Excitation Begin by holding a book above the lecture table and dropping it. Then hold it higher and drop it again. State that the potential energy you supplied to the book was converted to kinetic energy and then to sound energy. State that the higher you boost the book before dropping it, the louder the sound. State that a similar thing happens in the case of atoms. Parallel your book example and consider the case of an electron being boosted to a higher orbit in an atom. Just as a screen door that is pushed open against a spring snaps back and produces sound, the displaced electron snaps back to its ground state and produces light. It emits a throbbing spark of light we call a *photon*. Show that when it is boosted to higher levels, it emits a higher-frequency photon upon de-excitation. Introduce the relationship $E \sim f$ for the resulting photons. Discuss the variety of energy-level jumps for a simple atom.

> CHECK QUESTION: Two photons are emitted as a result of the transitions shown on the board. If one photon is red and the other blue, which is which? [Be sure to draw the shorter wavelength for the greater transition, from the second level to ground state, and the longer wavelength for the smaller transition from level one to ground.]

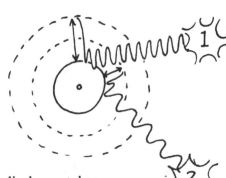

Emission Spectra

> DEMONSTRATION: Show the spectra of gas discharge tubes. Either use a large diffraction grating that you hold in front of the tube (I use one the size of a sheet of typing paper, Edmund Scientific Co.), or pass small gratings among the class, so the spectral lines can be observed.

Cite examples of the uses of spectrometers — how very minute quantities of materials are needed for chemical analysis — how tiny samples of ores are sparked in carbon arcs and the light directed through prisms or diffraction gratings to yield precise chemical composition — note their use in fields as diverse as chemistry and criminology.

Absorption Spectra Distinguish between emission and absorption spectra. Cite that a century ago, the chemical composition of the stars were thought to be forever beyond the knowledge of humankind — and now today we know as much about their composition as we do the earth's. (Figure 29.9, by the way, is exaggerated in that it shows an absorption line matching every emission line rather than the actual principle emission lines.)

Incandescence Emphasize the discreteness of the lines from atoms in the gaseous state. Then lead into the idea of excitation in an incandescent lamp, where the atoms are in the solid state. State how in the crowded condition the energy levels interact with one another and produce a distribution of frequencies rather than discrete frequencies that characterize the gaseous state. Sketch a bell-shaped curve and label the peak of the curve as the frequency proportional to the absolute temperature of the source. Be sure to clear up any misconceptions that $f \sim T$ means that the frequency of light is proportional to the temperature of light (light can impart temperature, but doesn't have a temperature of its own).

> CHECK QUESTION: Hold up an obviously broken light bulb and ask if it is presently emitting electromagnetic energy. [Sure is, as is everything —

its temperature is simply too low for the corresponding frequency to trigger our retinas.]

Get into the idea of the infrared part of the spectrum. Show in a sequence of radiation curves on the board how an increase in temperature brings the curve "sloshing over" into the lower frequency portion of the visible spectrum — hence the red hotness of a hot poker. Show how an increase in temperature brings the curve into the visible spectrum producing white light. Show why a hot poker does not become green hot, and how sharp the curve would have to be to produce green without sloshing into the other frequencies which result in white light. If you have discussed the treatment of overlapping distribution curves (page 98 in this manual), you might make reference to this and quip that only narrow-minded people would expect that a hot poker could glow green-hot.

Fluorescence   Show some fluorescent materials in the room light. Explain the role of photons in the room lighting that excite the molecules in the material that produces not only reflection, but emission — hence the term *day-glow* that sometimes describes fluorescent paints.

> CHECK QUESTION: Would higher-frequency light produce more glowing, and why? [Yep, more energy per photon!]

> DEMONSTRATION: Show fluorescent materials illuminated with a black light. Discuss the observations with the black light still on, and then extinguish the light so the room is totally dark. Ask what is happening (have some phosphorescent materials in your display).

Phosphorescence

> DEMONSTRATION: Call attention to the glowing of your phosphorescent materials while the lights are off. Compare this to swinging a screen door open when you walk out of the house and hearing it slam about a minute or so later. The screen door and the excited electrons become "stuck" for a while.

Cite common examples — watch and clock faces, light switches, even party jewelry. Acknowledge watch faces activated by radioactive minerals. Discuss also the phenomena of bioluminescence. It turns out that even the the deepest depths of the ocean there is a background of bioluminescence that is not understood. Photodetectors at great depths sense light when objects suddenly move in water.

Lasers   William J. Beaty of the Museum of Science in Boston has put together an informative set of notes, "Laser Misconceptions." Some of his points are the following: Laser light travels in straight lines like any other light. Clear up the possible misconception that laser light travels in wiggly paths as suggested by Figures 29.14 through 29.17. The common sine configuration represents the changing intensity of the electric field of light — a graph of intensity versus time or distance.

Another misconception is that laser light is parallel light. While it's true that many lasers are designed to emit thin non-spreading beams, it is wrong to suppose this is a characteristic of laser light. Those in your supermarket check-out stand, for example, fan out. A common HeNe classroom laser contain a converging lens, a "parallelizing lens," to correct for the spreading that exists within the beam. Without it, the beam would spread. So although laser light can be *made* extremely parallel, it is not a characteristic of laser light in general.

Laser light is not necessarily brighter than other types of light. Your classsroom laser puts out much less light than a flashlight bulb. A primary difference is that a laser provides a point source while an ordinary bulb is an extended source. Even weak light from a laser is concentrated by the lens of your eye to a blazing pinpoint on your retina. This is why even a weak laser is dangerous. Concentration is the factor, like the difference between looking at a frosted bulb and an unfrosted bulb of the same wattage. If a laser beam were of the same wattage of an ordinary house lamp, the beam would burn whatever it touched. A laser can concentrate light.

DEMONSTRATION: Give a laser show. Sprinkle chalk dust or smoke in the beam, show diffraction through a thin slit and so forth. An unforgettable presentation is that of Home Project 3 Chapter 19, page 355. Project a laser beam on a mirror fastened to a rubber membrane that is stretched over a radio loudspeaker (order a ready-made apparatus from Edmund Scientific Co.). Do this to music and fill the darkened room with a display of dancing lissajous patterns on the walls.

RUBBER MEMBRANE STRETCHED OVER SPEAKER
MIRROR
LASER
VIEWING AREA

30

Light Quanta

Birth of the Quantum Theory
Quantization and Planck's Constant
Photoelectric Effect
Wave-Particle Duality
Double-Slit Experiment
Particles as Waves: Electron Diffraction
Uncertainty Principle
Complementarity

This chapter is part of a three-chapter sequence — Chapters 29 - 31, and serves as a transition to the quantum nature of the atom in Part 7.

Unless you wish to lecture about the physicists who led us to our present understanding of light, and how the processes and developments leading to these findings were discovered and fashioned into the building blocks of quantum mechanics, the chapter can be assigned as reading and not treated during lecture time. If lecture time is used to support the chapter, demonstrate the photoelectric effect as described below. Perhaps the concept most interesting in the chapter to expand upon in lecture is the uncertainty principle.

An excellent source for the historical period spanned by the chapter is Barbara Cline's book, cited in the Suggested Reading at the end of the chapter on page 578. Heinz Pagels' book is also an excellent resource, cited on page 592.

SUGGESTED LECTURE PRESENTATION

Birth of the Quantum Theory   Begin by citing the flavor of physics at the turn of the century, that many in the physics community felt that the bulk of physics was in the can and only applications and engineering were left.   And then along came Einstein and Max Planck, who fell through cracks that turned out to be Grand Canyons! Continue with a historical perspective.

Quantization and Planck's Constant   You may or may not wish to discuss Planck's work with blackbody radiation and how it led to the notion that energy occurs in discrete amounts called quanta (it is not covered in the text). Acknowledge that the proportion E ~ f becomes an exact equation when the proportionality constant h is included (and that h is simply E/f).

Photoelectric Effect

DEMONSTRATION: Demonstrate the photoelectric effect by placing a freshly polished piece of zinc on an electroscope and illuminate it with an open carbon arc lamp (no glass lens). To focus the beam, use a quartz lens (to pass the UV). Show that a positively charged electroscope will not discharge when the light shines on the zinc plate. But that a negatively charged electroscope will quickly lose its charge, showing that the negative charges (electrons!) are ejected form the zinc surface by the light. Show the blockage of UV light by placing a piece of glass in the path of the light beam. This is evidenced by the stopping of the discharge process. If you have a quartz prism, pass the light through a slit, then through the prism, and onto the zinc. Show that the negatively charged electroscope discharges only when the portion of the spectrum beyond the violet end strikes the zinc plate.

Asking and Answering Questions   The answers one gets often depends on the way the question is asked. This is illustrated by the two monks who wished to smoke in the prayer room of a monestary. The first monk wrote a letter to his superior asking if it was permissible to smoke while praying. The answer was a resounding no. The second monk wrote a letter to his superior asking if it was permissible to pray while smoking. The answer was a resounding yes. In a sort of similar way, many of the perplexities of quantum physics have to do with the way questions are asked, and more particularly with what kind of questions are asked. For example, asking for the energy of a hydrogen atom in its first excited state has a definite answer, accurate to one part in 10^{12}. The answer to asking exactly when the electron makes its transition to the ground state, on the other hand, is probalistic. The probabilistic answers to such questions fosters the false notion that there are no exact answers at the quantum realm. Questions appropriate to the quantum realm are crisply and precisely answered by quantum mechanics.

Quantum Physics   Cite the behavior of light as being wavelike in traveling from place to place, but being particle like when incident upon matter, as evident in various **double slit experiments**. It travels like waves and lands like particles. Discuss the **wave-particle duality**, and the photon-by-photon buildup of the photograph of Figure 30.4. Like others, de Broglie was in the right place at the right time, for the notion of particles having wave properties was at hand. De Broglie showed Planck's constant again with his formula that relates the wavelength of a "matter wave" with its momentum. So matter, like light, has wave properties. When incident upon a target its matter nature is evident. We don't ordinarily notice the wave nature of matter only because the wavelength is so extremely small. The footnote on page 572 illustrates this. (Interestingly enough, de Broglie never did any physics after his one large contribution. He died in 1987.) Discuss the **uncertainty principle** and what it means and what it does not mean. End with Bohr's principle of **complementarity**.

31

The Atom and the Quantum

Discovery of the Atomic Nucleus
Atomic Spectra: Clues to Atomic Structure
Bohr Model of the Atom
Relative Sizes of Atoms
Explanation of Quantized Energy Levels: Electron Waves
Quantum Mechanics
Correspondence Principle

Although this short chapter begins Part 7, it is a continuation of Chapters 29 and 30. It is background for Chapters 32 and 33, but is not prerequisite to them. This chapter can, with some discussion of atomic spectra, stand on its own as a continuation of Chapter 10, *The Atomic Nature of Matter*. For a short course, Chapter 10 followed by most of this chapter (to the top of page 589) should work quite well.

This chapter presents a brief historical and conceptual treatment of the quantum mechanical model of the atom. I include this chapter as supplementary reading for students who are interested in this major area of physics that is more removed from their everyday environment. I do not lecture on this material and have no suggested lecture for this chapter.

You may wish to lecture about the physicists who took part in the developing of quantum mechanics. Barbara Cline's book, *The Questioners: Physicists and the Quantum Theory*, is a flavorful resource. Build from the Thompson plum-pudding model of the atom, to Rutherford's gold foil experiments, and to the Bohr model. Apply de Broglie waves to the electrons that surround the atomic nucleus, and tie this to the relative sizes of the atoms.

Quantum physics is concerned with the extremely small. Today's physicists, after all, are involved in exploring extremes: the outer limits of the fast and the slow, hot and cold, few and many, and big and small. In a light sense it can be said that everything in the middle is engineering.

The chapter discusses the character of quantum mechanics. There is some confusion in the minds of many people about the wave-particle duality. Much of this confusion is failing to see that light behaves as a wave when it travels in empty space, and lands like a particle when it hits something. It is mistaken to insist it must be both a particle and a wave at the same time. This is not the case, despite some writers who try to make this mysteriously profound. What something *is* and *what it does* are not the same. Another misconception fostered in popular and not-so-popular literature is that quantum theory is non-deterministic and that it is acausal. Solutions to the fundamental quantum equation are unique, continuous, and incorporate the principle of causality. Another misconception is that quantum theory reveals nature as a game of probability. Although some predictions about certain quantities are sometimes probabilistic, it doesn't follow that the predictions of quantum mechanics are necessarily uncertain. Quantum mechanics, in fact, leads to extremely accurate results (it predicts for example, the energy of the hydrogen atom in its ground state to one part in 10^{12}). Whether quantum mechanics gives definite or probabilistic answers to questions depends on the nature of the questions. For questions inappropriate to the quantum level, quantum mechanics gives probabilistic answers. For appropriate questions, its answers are definite. See more on this in the Reference Frame essay, *Ask a Foolish Question...by* Herman Feshback and Victor Weissdopf in the October 88 issue of *Physics Today*.

The chapter treats the matter-wave concept that gives a clearer picture of the electrons that "circle" the atomic nucleus. Instead of picturing them as tiny BBs whirling like planets, the matter-wave concept suggests we see them as smeared standing waves of energy — existing where the waves reinforce, and nonexisting where the waves cancel (Figures 31.7 and 31.8).

The philosophical implications of quantum mechanics is left to your lecture. At minimum you might warn your class that there are many people who have much to say about quantum physics who don't understand it. Quantum physics does not come in the neat package that Newtonian physics comes in, and is not all sewed up like other less complex bodies of knowledge. It is still an incomplete theory. It is a widely respected theory, however, and we should be wary of pseudoscientists who attempt to fit their own theories into the cracks of quantum mechanics, and ride on the back of its hard-earned reputation.

32

Atomic Nucleus and Radioactivity

X Rays and Radioactivity
Alpha, Beta, and Gamma Rays
The Nucleus
Isotopes
Why Atoms are Radioactive
Half-life
Radiation Detectors
Natural Transmutation of the Elements
Artificial Transmutation of the Elements
Radioactive Isotopes
Carbon Dating
Uranium Dating
Effects of Radiation on Humans

This chapter begins with X rays and presents a relatively extensive treatment of radioactivity and its applications. Formulas for decay reactions are illustrated with supporting sketches that enable better comprehension. The background for this material goes back to Chapter 10. This chapter is a prerequisite to Chapter 33.

On page 613 of the text it is stated that a couple of round-trip flights across country exposes one to as much radiation one receives in a normal chest X ray. More specifically, a dose of 2 millirems is typically received in flying across the United States in a jet. This is the same dose received annually from those old luminous dial wristwatches. Cosmic radiation at sea level imparts 45 millirems annually, and radiation from the earth's crust imparts about 80 millirems. Living in a concrete or brick house makes this figure slightly higher, for these materials contain more radioactive material than wood. The human body contains small amounts of carbon-14, potassium-40, and traces of uranium and thorium daughter products, which give an annual dose of 25 millirems. So the total natural background radiation annually is about 150 millirems. This makes up about 56% of the radiation the average person encounters, the rest being mainly medical and dental X rays.

The high-flying British-French SST, the Concorde, was equipped with radiation detectors that signaled the pilots when a level of 10 millirems per hour was reached (during a solar flare, for example). The pilots were required to decend to lower altitudes at 50 millirems per hour. According to a report by the British government after a year of Concorde operation, none of the alarms had ever gone off. Concorde pilots are limited to 500 hours flying time per year, compared to 1000 hours for crews on conventional aircraft.

Common smoke detectors in the home make use of the very low dose of about 2 microcuries of americium-241, used to make the air in the detector's ionization chamber electrically conductive. When smoke enters the chamber it inhibits the flow of electricity, which activates the alarm. The lives saved each year by these devices number in the thousands (which dwarfs the numbers seriously harmed by radiation).

A radiation sequence similar to that in Figure 32.13 is in **Practicing Physics**. An activity on half life is in the **Laboratory Manual**.

SUGGESTED LECTURE PRESENTATION

Begin by commenting on the little girl's statement about the warmth of the hot spring she is enjoying on page 581 — that radioactivity is nothing new and is as natural as hot springs and geysers. It in fact powers them. When electricity was harnessed in the last century, people were fearful of it and its effects on lifeforms. Now it is commonplace, for its dangers are well understood. We are at a similar stage with regard to anything called nuclear. Even the very beneficial medical science *nuclear magnetic resonance* (*NMR*) has undergone a name change to *magnetic resonant imaging* (*MRI*). Why? "I don't want *my* Aunt Minnie near any *nuclear* machine!"

Hundreds of thousands of Americans live in houses that have a yearly radiation dose from radon in the ground equal to the dose residents living in the vicinity of Chernobyl received in 1986 when one of its reactors exploded and released radioactive materials into the environment (Scientific American, May, 88). This is not to say it is unharmful to live in the vicinity of radon emission, but to say that radioactivity is not a modern problem and not a byproduct of science per se. It's been with us since day 1.

X Rays and Radioactivity Begin by comparing the emission of X rays with the emission of light, showing that X rays are emitted when the innermost electrons of heavy elements are excited. Then discuss medical and dental applications of X rays, citing the newer photographic films now available that permit very short exposures of low intensity, and therefore safer dosages. Cite also the fact that the eye is the part of the body most prone to radiation damage — something that seems to be ignored by many dentists when making exposures of the teeth (and inadvertently, the eyes). (Why not eye masks as well as chest masks?)

Alpha, Beta, and Gamma Rays Distinguish between alpha, beta, and gamma rays. If you've covered electricity and magnetism, ask if the rays could be separated by an electric field, rather than the magnetic field depicted in Figure 32.3.

The Nucleus Everybody is interested in quarks. Nobody has ever seen one, but its a fact they exist. Go quarks!

Isotopes Less exotic than quarks, but make the point that isotopes are associated with all atoms, not just radioactive ones. Distinguish between isotopes and ions. Start with the isotopes of hydrogen (Figure 32.5) and then discuss uranium (which will be important in the next chapter).

Why Atoms are Radioactive This continues from your discussion of the nucleus. Make the point that although neutrons provide a sort of nuclear cement, too many of them separate the protons and lead to instability. The nuclear fragments of fission (Chapter 33) are radioactive because of their preponderance of neutrons.

Half Life Talk of jumping half way to the wall, then half way again, then half way again and so on, and ask how many jumps will get you to the wall. Similarly with radioactivity. Of course, with a sample of radioactivity, there is a time when all the atoms undergo decay. But measuring decay rate in terms of this occurrence is a poor idea if only because of the small sample of atoms one deals with as the process nears the end of its course. Insurance companies can make accurate predictions of car accidents and the like with large numbers, but not so for small numbers. Dealing with radioactive half life at least insures half the large number of atoms you start with.

CHECK QUESTIONS: If the radioactive half-life of a certain isotope is one day, how much of the original isotope in a sample will still exist at the end of two days? Three days? Four days?

Radiation Detectors Discuss and compare the various detectors of radiation. Page 604 shows the bubble chamber, and the easy-to-reproduce tracks left by charged particles traveling through it (ask your class to venture a reason for the spiral shapes instead of the circular or helical shapes that a magnetic field would produce — of course the track is there only because of an interaction with the liquid hydrogen, friction of sorts). The conceptually nice bubble chamber is fading fast and arrays of fine wires in concert with fast computers have taken their place.

DEMONSTRATION: Show a cloud chamber in action.

Natural and Artificial Transmutation of Elements Introduce the symbolic way of writing atomic equations. Write some transmutation formulas on the board while your students follow along with their books opened to the periodic table, inside front cover. A repetition and explanation of the reactions shown on pages 605, 606 and 608 is in order, if you follow up with one or two new ones as check questions. Be sure that your class can comfortably write equations for alpha decay before having them write equations for beta decay, which are more complex because of the negative charge. Your treatment is the same for both natural and artificial transmutations.

Radioactive Isotopes Acknowledge the use of these in so many common devices. One is the ionization smoke detectors where particles of smoke are ionized as they drift by a beta emitter to complete an electric circuit that sounds the alarm. Ironically while many people fear anything associated with *nuclear* or *radioactivity*, these devices save thousands of lives each year.

Carbon Dating Pose the Check Question on page 612 as a lecture skit, after explaining the nitrogen-carbon-nitrogen cycle. The idea of the archeologist in the cave adds interest to the idea.

Effects of Radiations on Humans Radiation is not good for anybody, but we can't escape it. It is everywhere. However, we can take steps to avoid unnecessary radiation. Radiation, like everything else that is both damaging and little understood, is usually seen to be worse than it is. You can alleviate a sense of hopelessness about the dangers of radiation by pointing out that radiation is nothing new. It not only goes back before science and technology but before the earth came to be. It goes back to day 1. It is a part of nature that must be lived with. Good sense simply dictates that we avoid unnecessary concentrations of radiation.

NEXT-TIME QUESTION: With the aid of the periodic table, consider a decay-scheme diagram similar to the one shown on page 607, but beginning with U-235 and ending up with an isotope of lead. Use the following steps and identify each element in the series with its chemical symbol. What isotope does this produce? [Pb-207]

1.	Alpha	5.	Beta	9.	Beta
2.	Beta	6.	Alpha	10.	Alpha
3.	Alpha	7.	Alpha	11.	Beta
4.	Alpha	8.	Alpha	12.	Stable

33

Nuclear Fission and Fusion

Nuclear Fission
Nuclear Reactors
Plutonium
Breeder Reactors
Mass-Energy Equivalence
Nuclear Fusion
    Controlling Fusion
    Cold Nuclear Fusion
    Fusion Torch and Recycling

The material in this chapter is of great technological and sociological importance. Nuclear bombs are not avoided in the applications of nuclear energy, but the emphasis of the few applications discussed in the chapter is on the positive aspects of nuclear power and its potential for improving the world. Much of the public sentiment against nuclear power has to do with a distrust of what is generally not understood, and with the sentiments against centralized power, rather than with the technological pros and cons. In this climate, we have a responsibility to provide our students with an understanding of the basics physics of nuclear power. In your physics class, an appropriate slogan is "KNOW NUKES."

Note that in this text, the energy release from the opposite processes of fission and fusion is approached from the viewpoint of decreased mass rather than the customary treatment of increased binding energy. Hence the usual binding energy curve is "tipped upsidedown" in Figure 33.15, and shows the relationship of the mass per nucleon versus atomic number. I consider this way conceptually more appealing, for it shows that any reaction involving a decrease in mass releases energy in accordance with mass-energy equivalence.

Mass-energy can be measured in either joules or kilograms (or in ergs or grams). For example, the kinetic energy of a 2-gram beetle walking 1 cm/s = 1 erg, and the energy of the Hiroshima bomb = 1 gram. So we can express the same quantity in essentially different units.

Distinguish cold fusion via muons, as treated in this chapter, with the controversial 1989 Utah experiment of Fleishman and Pons. Very different!

One of my general lectures that makes sweeping generalizations about fusion power and an idealized description of a fusion torch is available on videotape. It goes into a speculative and entertaining scenario of a follow-up device to the fusion torch — a replicator, similar to that described by Arthur C. Clark in his 1963 book, *Profiles of the Future*. Contact a HarperCollins rep for information on this 45-minute videotape.

Nuclear reactions are featured in an exercise in **Practicing Physics.** An activity and an experiment on radioactivity is in the **Laboratory Manual**.

SUGGESTED LECTURE PRESENTATION

Nuclear Fission   Briefly discuss the world atmosphere back in the late 30s when fission was discovered in Germany, and how this information was communicated to American physicists who urged Einstein to write his famous letter urging President Roosevelt to consider its potential in warfare. The importance of the fission reaction was not only the release of enormous energy, but the ejected neutrons that could stimulate other fissions in a chain reaction. In the practice of writing equations from the previous chapter, write the reaction shown at the top of page 620 on the board and discuss its meaning. To give some idea as to the magnitude of the 200 000 000 eV of energy associated with one fission reaction, state that New York City is powered by water falling over Niagra Falls, and that the energy of one drop over the falls is 4 eV; the energy of a TNT molecule is 30 eV, the energy of a molecule of gasoline oxydizing is 30 eV. So 200 000 000 eV is impressive. Discuss the average 3 neutrons that are kicked out by the reaction and what a chain reaction is (Figure 33.2). Discuss critical mass, and a nuclear device, simplified in Figure 33.4.

Nuclear Reactors   A piece of uranium or any radioactive material is slightly warmer than ambient temperature because of the thermal activity prodded by radioactive decay. Fission reactions are major nuclear proddings, and the material becomes quite hot — hot enough to boil water and then some. Make clear that a nuclear reactor of any kind is no more than a means to heat water to steam and generate electricity as a fossil fuel plant does. The principle difference is the fuel used to heat the water. You could quip that nuclear fuel is closer to the nature of the earth than fossil fuels, whose energies come from the sun.

Discuss the mechanics of a reactor via Figure 33.11.

Plutonium   Show the production of plutonium via the equation suggested by Figure 33.9. Make this two steps, from U-238 + n   Np-239. Then by beta decay Np-239 to Pu-239. Neptunium's half live of 2.3 days quickly produces plutonium, with a half life of 24 000 years. Acknowledge that all reactors produce plutonium.

Breeder Reactors   Reactors designed to maximize the production of plutonium are the breeder reactors. Make clear that they don't make something from nothing, but merely convert a nonfissionable isotope of uranium (U-238) to a fissionable isotope of plutonium (Pr-239).

Mass-Energy Equivalence   It's helpful if students have studied relativity at this point, but a brief discussion of what $E_o = mc^2$ says and what it doesn't say (pages 667 to 669) should suffice. This is the most important part of your lecture — the *why* of nuclear power.

Begin by supposing that one could journey into fantasy and compare the masses of different atoms by grabbing their nuclei with bare hands and shaking the nuclei back and forth. Show with hand motion, holding an imaginary giant nucleus, how the difference might appear in shaking a hydrogen atom and a lead atom. State that if you were to plot the results of this investigation for all the elements, that the relationship between mass and atomic number would look like Figure 33.14, (which you draw on the board). Ask if this plot is a "big deal?" The answer is "no," it simply shows that mass increases with the number of nucleons in the nucleus. No surprise.

Distinguish between the mass of a nucleus and the mass of the nucleons that make up a nucleus. Ask what a curve of mass/nucleon versus atomic number would look like — that is, if you divided the mass of each nucleus by the number of nucleons composing it, and compared the value for different atoms. If all nucleons had the same

163

mass in every atomic configuration, then of course the graph would be a horizontal line. But the masses of nucleons differ. The interrelationship between mass and energy is apparent here, for the nucleons have "mass-energy", which is manifest partly in the "congealed" part which is the material matter of the nucleons, and the other part which we call binding energy. The most energetically bound nucleus has the least mass/nucleon (iron). Go into the nucleon shaking routine again and demonstrate how the nucleons become easier to shake as you progress from hydrogen to iron. Do this by progressing from the student's left to right the full length of your lecture table. Indicate how they become harder to shake as you progress beyond iron to uranium. Then draw the curve that represents your findings, and you have Figure 33.15 on the board. Announce that this is the most important graph in the book!

From the curve you can show that any nuclear reaction that produces products with less mass than before reaction, will give off energy, and any reaction in which the mass of the products is increased will require energy. Further discussion will show how the opposite processes of fission and fusion release energy.

> CHECK QUESTIONS: Will the process of fission or fusion release energy from atoms of lead? Gold? Carbon? Neon? (Be careful in selecting atoms too near atomic number 26 in this exercise — for example, elements slightly beyond 26 when fissioned will have more massive products, that extend "up the hydrogen hill"; elements near 26 when fused will combine to elements "up the uranium hill". Acknowledging this point, however, may only serve to complicate the picture — unless, of course, a student brings it up in class.)

State how the graph can be viewed as an pair of "energy hills," that to progress "down" the hill is a reaction with less mass per nucleon and therefore a gain in energy.

Nuclear Fusion   By way of the energy hill idea, there are two hills to go down. Going from hydrogen down to iron is even steeper — more mass "defect" in combining light nuclei than splitting heavy ones. This combining atomic nuclei is nuclear fusion — the energy releasing process of the sun and the stars.

> CHECK QUESTION: Will the process of fission or fusion release energy from the nucleus of iron? [Neither! Iron is the nuclear sink; either process results in "going up the hill," gaining rather than losing mass.]

Discuss the latest developments in *inertial confinement fusion*, which includes not only fusion induced by lasers, but also by electron beams and ion beams. Explain how in each case a small fuel pellet is "ignited" to yield a thermonuclear microexplosion, and that the greatest problem to overcome other than obtaining significant energies is the precise timing of laser firings. (As of this writing the Shiva and Nova lasers at Lawrence Livermore Labs have both achieved fusion burns, but not sustained burns. Problems have had to do with characteristics of the fuel pellets and the stability of the supporting optics. Sustained fusion by lasers is presently a 21st Century hope.)

Cold Nuclear Fusion   Another and exciting entry to the hopes of fusion power (which should not be confused with the 1989 University of Utah experiments)! Fusion by muonic atoms is so conceptually simple — the barrier of electrostatic repulsion in plasma fusion is simply not there. Impressive!   For more on this see the Scientific American article in the July 1987 issue.

Fusion Torch and Recycling   A discussion of the prospects of fusion power is most fascinating. With all the inputs students get from the prophets of doom, it is well to balance some of this negativity with some of our positive prospects. Abundant energy from controlled fusion is one such positive prospect, which should concern not only physicists, but economists, political scientists, sociologists, ecologists, psychologists, and the everyday person on the street. Particularly exciting is the prospect of the fusion torch, which may provide a means of recycling material and alleviate the scarcity of raw material — not to mention the sink it could provide for wastes and pollutants. Ideally, all unwanted wastes could be dumped in the fusion torch and vaporized. Atoms could be separated into respective bins by being beamed through giant mass spectrographs. Point out that the fusion torch may never come to be — but not because technology won't progress to such a point, but because it most likely will progress further. If the past is any guide, something even better will make this 1970's idea obsolete. Whether or not the fusion torch is around the corner, the more important questions to consider are how this or comparable achievements will affect the life of people. How will people interact with one another in a world of relatively abundant energy and material? Admittedly, abundant energy and material will not solve all the major problems, but it will mark an end to the scarcity that has always been a foundation of the governance of past and the present civilization — a scarcity that has shaped the institutions governing the respective civilizations. The institutions of tomorrow's world will surely be unlike those we have known to date.

This is a time of transition — an exciting time to be alive! Particularly for those who are participating in the transition — for those who have not lost nerve and retreated from knowledge into irrationality in its many generally-respected forms. Ask how many of your students would prefer living in the past?

34

Special Theory of Relativity

The ideas discussed in this chapter are perhaps the most exciting in the book. But they are difficult to comprehend. Regardless of how clearly and logically this material is presented, students will find that they do not "understand" it in a manner that satisfies them. This is understandable for so brief an exposure to a part of reality untouched by conscious experience. The intention of this chapter is to develop enough insight into relativity to stimulate further student interest and inquiry.

Time is one of those concepts we are all familiar with yet are hard pressed to define. A simple yet less than satisfying way to look at it is like our definition of space; that which we measure with a measuring stick — and time, that which we measure with a clock. Or we may quip, time is nature's way of seeing to it that everything doesn't happen all at once! (I heard this last statement attributed to somebody at an AAPT meeting a few years ago, but I forget who.)

Note the important significance of "The Twin Trip" section in the text, in that it completely bypasses the equations for time dilation and the relativistic Doppler effect. The reciprocity of relativistic Doppler frequencies for approach and recession stems only from Einstein's 1st and 2nd postulates and is established without the use of a single mathematical formula. This is abbreviated in the footnote on page 658 and is detailed in the 4-step classroom presentation in the following suggested lecture. [This reciprocal relationship does not hold for sound, where the "moving" frame is not equivalent to the "rest" (relative to air) frame. If the ratio of frequency received to frequency sent for hearing in the rest frame is 2, the ratio for hearing in the moving frame is 3/2 (clearly not 2!). For sound, the speed as well as the frequency depends on the motion of the receiver.] From this and the simple flash-counting sequence, time dilation follows without the use of any mathematical formulas. The results of the twin-trip flash sequence agree with Einstein's time dilation equation. So this treatment is completely independent to the time dilation equation and the relativistic Doppler equation! (Who says that good physics can't be presented without high-powered math?)

If your class is in a more mathematical mood, you may wish to show an alternative approach to The Twin Trip and consider straightforward time dilation plus corrections for the changing positions of the emitting or receiving body between flashes. Instead of bypassing the time dilation equation, use it to show that at $0.6c$, 6-minute flash intervals in the emitting frame compute to be 7 1/2-minute flash intervals in the receiving frame. The flashes would *appear* at 7 1/2-minute intervals if the ship were moving crosswise, neither approaching or receding, such that each flash travels essentially the same distance to the receiver. In our case the ship doesn't travel crosswise, but recedes from and then approaches the receiver — so corrections must be made in the time interval due to the extra distance the light travels when the spaceship is receding and the lesser distance the light travels when the ship is approaching. This turns out to be 4 1/2 minutes;

$$[\Delta t = (\text{extra distance})/c = (0.6c \times 7\ 1/2\ \text{min})/c = 4\ 1/2\ \text{min}]$$

So when receding, the flashes are seen at 7 1/2 + 4 1/2 = 12-min intervals; when approaching, the flashes are seen at 7 1/2 - 4 1/2 = 3-min intervals. The results of this method are the same as those of the 4-step conceptual presentation in the following suggested lecture.

My 12-minute animated film, *Relativistic Time Dilation*, amplifies the section on The Twin Trip. It is part of the video tape of relativity in the Conceptual Physics Alive! series. Contact a Harper Collins representive for availability.

Some physics types object to the notion of a relativistic mass, and maintain that it is not mass that increases at relatistic speeds, but momentum. Changes in momentum, after all, is what is measured in the laboratory. This book adheres to the conceptually simpler view of mass increasing.

There is an exercise on relativistic clocks in **Practicing Physics**.

Not surprisingly, there are no activities or experiments on special relativity in the **Laboratory Manual**.

Because of the interest in physics that relativity generates, this chapter may be treated earlier in the course — even to begin your course.

SUGGESTED LECTURE PRESENTATION

After discussing Einstein and a broad overview of what special relativity is and is not, point out somewhere along the line that the theory of relativity is grounded in *experiment*, and in its development it explained some very perplexing experimental facts (constancy of the speed of light, muon decay, solar energy, the nature of mass, etc.). It is not, as some people think, only the speculations of one man's way of thinking.

Motion Is Relative Ask your class to pretend they are in a parking lot playing ball with someone driving toward them and away from them in an open vehicle. A pitcher in the vehicle tosses a ball at them, always with the same pitching speed — no variation. Ask for the relative speed of catching a ball when the car approaches, and when it recedes. They know there will be a difference. Ask how they would react if the speeds of the ball in catching were the same, whether the thrower was moving toward them, at rest, or moving away from them. This would be most perplexing. Now discuss the null result of the Michelson-Morley experiment.

Michelson-Morley Experiment Treat the Michelson-Morley experiment very briefly, and I suggest you do not go into the mechanics of the interferometer. Instead direct your students' mental energies to the broad ideas of special relativity. Explain what it means to say the velocity of light is invariant.

First Postulate The laws of physics are the same in all uniformly moving reference frames. A bee inside a fast-moving jet plane executes the same flying maneuvers regardless of the speed of the plane. If you drop a coin to the floor of the moving plane, it will fall as if the plane were at rest. Physical experiments behave the same in all uniformly moving frames. This leads, most importantly, to the development of special relativity, to the speed of light that is seen to be the same for all observers. There is no violation of common sense in this first postulate. It rules out any effect of uniform motion on any experiment, however. For any observed effect violates this postulate and the foundation of relativity.

Second Postulate Stand still and toss a piece of chalk up and down, catching it as you would when flipping a coin. Ask the class to suppose that in so doing that all measurements show the chalk to have a constant average speed. Call this constant speed c for short. That is, both they and you see only one average speed for the tossed chalk. Then proceed to walk at a fairly brisk pace across the room and again toss the chalk. State that from your frame of reference you again measure the same speed. Ask if the speed looked any different to them. They should respond that the chalk was moving faster this time. Ask them to suppose that their measurement yielded the same previous value. They may be a bit perplexed, which again is similar to the perplexed state of physicists at the turn of the century. On the board, write with uniformly sized letters

$$c = \frac{\text{SPACE}}{\text{TIME}}$$

This is the speed as seen by you in your frame of reference. State that from the frame of reference of the class, the space covered by the tossed chalk appeared to be greater, so write the word SPACE in correspondingly larger letters. Underline it. State that if they see the same speed, that is, the same ratio of space to time, then such can be accounted for if the time is also measured to be greater. Then write the enlarged word TIME beneath the underline, equating it to c.

Analogy: Just as all observers will measure the same ratio of circumference to diameter for all sizes of circles, all observers will measure the same ratio of space to time for electromagnetic waves in free space.

Simultaneity Show by way of Figures 34.5, 34.6, and the footnoted diagrams on page 649 that an interesting result of the constancy of the speed of light in all reference frames is the non-simultaneity of events in one frame that are simultaneous in another. Contrast this to classical non-simultaneity, like different observers hearing gun blasts at different time intervals.

Space-Time An interesting way to look at how space and time are related to the speed of light is to think of all things moving through space-time at a constant speed. When movement is maximum through space, movement in time is minimum. When movement in space is minimum, movement in time is maximum. For example, something at rest relative to us moves not at all in space and moves in time at the maximum rate of 24 hours per day. When something approaches the speed of light relative to us, it moves at its near maximum speed in space, and moves near zero in time — it doesn't age.

Time Dilation   Jacob Bronowski spoke of an interesting way to look at time dilation that goes something like this. Einstein is riding in a street car in a direction away from a huge clock in the village square. The clock reads 12 noon. To say it reads 12 noon is to say that light reflecting from the clock that moves in the direction of Einstein's line of sight carries the information 12 noon. If Einstein suddenly moves his head to the side, the light carrying the information continues past, presumably out into space. Out there an observer later will receive the light and say, "Oh, it's 12 noon on earth now." But it isn't. Einstein and the distant observer will see 12-noon at different times. Then Einstein wondered, if the street car travels faster, say as fast as light travels, then it will keep up with the light that says 12-noon. Traveling at the speed of light, then, tells one that it is always 12-noon at the village square. Time on the square is frozen! How about at speeds less than the speed of light? A little thought will show that time will not be frozen, but will be slowed down. Hence time dilation with motion.

Relate the analogy of your prior chalk-tossing sequence to the light clock discussed on page 646 and in Figures 34.10 and 34.11 and in the footnote on page 652.

The Twin Trip   You have a choice of a short treatment of this or a longer more detailed treatment. The short treatment begins without fanfare and as a matter of fact presents the half rate of flashes seen when a ship approaches (Figure 34.15) and the doubled rate seen when the ship recedes (Figure 34.16). The fact that the half rate and doubled rate are reciprocals is not developed. For the vast majority of my students this is fine. More sophisticated students may be uneasy with this and wish to see this reciprocal relationship developed. This is the longer treatment. This longer treatment is shown by the 4 steps below. For the shorter treatment, jump ahead to paragraph 2, with the * on page 171.

We will in effect bypass the derivation of the relativistic doppler effect, namely,

$$f = f_0 \sqrt{\frac{1 + v/c}{1 - v/c}}$$

with the following four-step conceptual presentation:

Step 1: Consider a person standing on earth directing brief flashes of light at 3-min intervals to a distant planet at rest relative to the earth. Some time will elapse before the first of these flashes reaches the planet, but since there is no relative motion between the sender and receiver, successive flashes will be observed at the distant planet at 3-min intervals. While you are making these remarks, make a sketch on the board of Fig. 1.

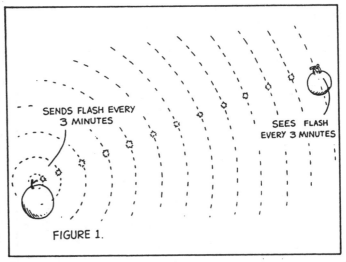

SENDS FLASH EVERY 3 MINUTES

SEES FLASH EVERY 3 MINUTES

FIGURE 1.

Step 2: How frequently would these flashes encounter an observer in a fast-moving space-ship traveling between the earth and the planet? Although the speed of the flashes would be measured by the spaceship to be *c*, the frequency of flashes would be greater or less than the emitting frequency depending on whether the ship were receding or approaching the light source. After supporting this idea with some examples of the Doppler effect (car horns, running into versus away from a slanting rain, etc.) make the supposition that the spaceship recedes form the light source at a speed great enough for the frequency of light flashes to decrease by half— so they're seen from the ship only half as often, at 6-min intervals. By now your chalkboard sketch looks like Fig. 2.

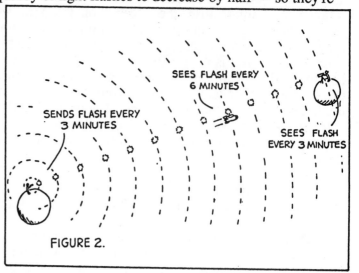

FIGURE 2.

Step 3: Suppose further that each time a flash reaches the ship, a triggering device activates a beacon on the ship that sends its own flash of light toward the distant planet. According to a clock in the spaceship then, this flash is emitted every 6 min. Since the flashes from earth and the flashes emitted by the space-ship travel at the same speed c, both sets of flashes travel together, and an observer on the distant planet sees not only the earth flashes at 3-min intervals, but the spaceship flashes at 3-min intervals as well (Fig. 3). At this point you have established that 6-min intervals on the approaching spaceship are seen as 3-min intervals on the stationary planet.

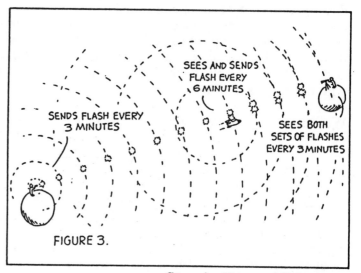

FIGURE 3.

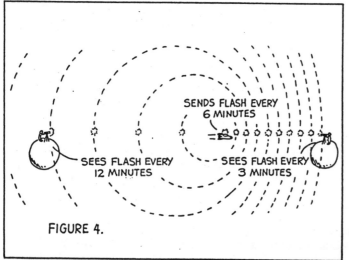

FIGURE 4.

Step 4: To establish that the 6-min flashes emitted by the spaceship are seen at 12-min intervals from the earth, go back to your earlier supposition that 3-min intervals on earth are seen as 6-min intervals from the frame of reference of the receding ship. Ask your class: If instead of emitting a flash every 3-min, the person on earth emits aflash every 6-min, then how often would these flashes be seen from the receding ship? And then ask if the situation would be any different if the ship and earth were interchanged — if the ship were at rest and emitted flashes every 6 min to a receding earth? After a suitable response erase from your chalk-board drawing all the flashes emitted form the earth. Replace the earth-twin's light source with a telescope while asking how often the 6-min flashes emitted by the moving spaceship are seen from earth. Class response should show that you have established the reciprocity of frequencies for the relativistic Doppler effect without a single equation. This is summarized in Fig. 4.

Note that you have employed Einstein's postulates in the last two steps, that is, the second postulate in Step 3 (constancy of the speed of light) and the first postulate in Step 4 (equivalence of the earth and ship frames of reference).

Whether you have established this reciprocity from the Doppler equation or from the preceding four steps, you are now ready to present the twin trip and demonstrate time dilation while also presenting a resolution to the so-called twin paradox.

*With a sketch of Fig. 4 above in an upper corner of your board, proceed to make a rendition of textbook Figure 34.17 on the main part of your board. You'll draw only one picture of the earth and let your eraser be the ship which you move away from earth (to the right as the top part of the figure, *a*, suggests). State the ship sends 10 flashes at 6-min intervals. At the 10th flash 1 hour has passed for the ship. Ask how these 6-min intervals appear to earth observers? [at 12 min apart]. What time is it on earth when the 10th flash is received? [Two hours later!] The ship quickly turns around and continues homeward, again sending 10 flashes at 6-min intervals. When the 10th flash is emitted, another hour passes for the ship and its total trip time is 2 hours. But ask how often the incoming flashes occurred to earth types. [at 3-min intervals] Ten incoming 3-min flashes take only 30 min, earth time. So from the earth frame of reference the spaceship took a grand total of 2 1/2 hours.

During your discussion, summarize this on the board as the lettering of Figure 34.18.

Depending on lecture time, switch frames of reference and repeat the similar sequence suggested by Figures 34.19 and 34.20 for the case where the flashes are emitted from earth and viewed by the moving ship. Same results.

Space Travel Speculate on the idea of "century hopping," the future version of to-days "jet hopping." In this scenario future space travelers may take relatively short trips of a few years or less and return in decades, or even centuries. This is, of course, pending the solution to two present problems: rocket engines and sufficient fuel supplies for prolonged voyages, and a means of shielding the radiation that would be produced by impact of interstellar matter.

The Centrifuge Follow this up with this interesting but fictitious example to show that one needn't go far in space for significant time dilation: Suppose that one could be whirled in a giant centrifuge up to relativistic speeds without physical injury. Of course one would be crushed to death in such a case, but pretend that somehow one is physically unaffected by the crushing centripetal forces (the fictitiousness of this ex-ample). Then cite how one taking a "ride" in such a centrifuge might be strapped in his seat and told to press a button on the seat when he or she wishes the ride termi-nated. And suppose that after being whirled about at rim speeds near the speed of light the occupant decides that 10 minutes is enough. So he or she presses the button, sig-naling those outside to bring the machine to a halt. After the machine is halted, those outside open the door, peer in, and ask, "Good gosh, what have you been doing in there for the past 3 weeks!" In the laboratory frame of reference, 3 weeks would have elapsed during a ten-minute interval in the rotating centrifuge. Motion in space, rather than space itself is the key factor.

Length Contraction   Hold up a meter stick, horizontally, and state that if your students made accurate measurements of its length, their measurements would agree with your own. Everyone would measure it as 1 meter long. People at the back of the room would have to compensate for its appearing smaller due to distance, but nevertheless, they would agree it is 1 meter long. But now walk across the room holding the meter stick like a spear. State that your measurements and those of your students would differ. If you were to travel at 87% the speed of light, relative to the class, they would measure the stick to be half as long, 0.5 m. At 99.5% the speed of light, they would see it as only 10 cm long. At greater speeds, it would be even shorter. At the speed of light it would contract to zero length. Write the length-contraction formula on the board:

$$L = L_0 \sqrt{1 - (v^2/c^2)}$$

State that contraction takes place only in the direction of motion. The stick moving in spear fashion appears shorter but it doesn't appear thinner.

Contraction is shown in Figure 34.22, and in fun in the facing photo of my grandson Manuel and his dog.

Mass Increase   Write the equation $KE = 1/2\, mv^2$ on the board. State that there is no reason why one cannot increase without limit the amount of energy that is given to a particle. But there is a speed limit, so ask where the energy goes when the speed limit is approached. Then discuss how the energy is manifest not as speed, but as mass...and that this happens not only at speeds near the speed of light, but for everyday speeds as well. Point out the practical insignificance of these tiny differences, and that only for speeds near c are the differences appreciable.

You might write the equation for relativistic mass on the board and give examples of mass increase for different relative speeds. A good example is the mass increase of electrons and protons in the linear accelerator at Stanford University, where speeds greater than $0.99c$ are attained within the first meter, and most of the energy given to the charged particles during the remaining journey goes into mass increase — the particles therefore strike their targets with masses thousands of times their rest mass. But if you traveled along with the charged particles, you would note no mass increase in the particles themselves (the v in the relativistic mass equation would be zero), but you'd measure a mass increase in the atoms of the "approaching" target. Cite how mass increase must be compensated for in the design of circular accelerators such as cyclotrons, bevatrons, and the like, and how such compensation is not required for a linear accelerator (except for the bending magnets at its end).

Discuss the notion that mass, every bit as much as energy, is delivered by the power utilities through the copper wires that run from the power plants to the consumers. This is discussed on page 667.

On the 4 1/2 million tons of matter that is converted to radiant energy by the sun every second: that tonnage is carried by the radiant energy through space, so when we speak of matter being "converted" to energy, we are merely converting units — the units of mass with their corresponding units of energy. Because of the equivalence of mass and energy, in any reaction that takes into account the whole system, the total amount of mass does not change, nor does the total amount of energy.

Optional side point: From the expression $W = \int F \cdot ds$, the work done in setting a body in motion when taking into account the relativistic expression for mass yields

$$W = (m - m_0) c^2.$$

That is, the kinetic energy equals the increase in mass over the rest mass, multiplied by c^2, the famous Einstein relation between mass and energy. When the velocity is small compared to c, the expression above reduces to the familiar $1/2\ mv^2$. Discuss the celebrated $E_o = mc^2$, noting that from a long view, the significance of the twentieth century will be most likely seen as a major turning point with the discovery of this relationship. It may be interesting to speculate what the equation of the 21st century might be.

The Correspondence Principle Show your students that when small speeds are involved, the relativity formulas reduce to the everyday observation that time, length, and the masses of things do not appear any different when moving. That's because the differences are too tiny to detect.

35

General Theory of Relativity

Principle of Equivalence
Bending of Light by Gravity
Gravity and Time: Gravitational Red Shift
Gravity and Space: Motion of Mercury
Gravity, Space, and a New Geometry
Gravitational Waves
Newtonian and Einsteinian Gravitation

The three most important theories of physics in the 20th century are the special theory of relativity (1905), the general theory of relativity (1915), and the theory of quantum mechanics (1926). The first and third theories have been focal points of interest and research since their inceptions, yet the second, general relativity, has been largely ignored by physicists — until recently. New interest stems from many of the new astronomical phenomena discovered in recent years — pulsars, quasars, compact x-ray sources, and speculations of black holes, all of which have indicated the existence of very strong gravitational fields that could be described only by general relativity. The move is now on to a quantum theory of gravitation that will agree with general relativity for macroscopic objects.

One important point to make is that relativity doesn't mean that everything is relative, but rather that no matter how you view a situation, the physical outcome is the same. There is a general misconception about this. Point out that in special and general relativity that fundamental truths of nature look the *same* from every point of view — not different from different points of view!

We measure velocities with rods and clocks; rods for space, and clocks for time. In our local environment, rods and clocks are no different when in different locations. In a larger environment in accord with general relativity, however, we find that space and time are "warped". Rods and clocks at appreciably different distances from the center of the earth are affected differently. Accordingly, gravitation can be seen as the effects of a curved space-time such that the motion of objects subject to what we call the gravitational force is simply the result of objects moving freely through curved space-time.

John Mallinckrodt of Claremont College asks his class the following question: If relative *motion* can alter the measurements made by rods and clocks, might it also be possible for different *locations* (in space and time) to alter such measurements? Then he compares the observations of two observers at rest to each other — one just inside a window on a second floor of an apartment building, and the other on the sidewalk below. Both observers use rods and clocks to make their measurements. Consider a refrigerator accidentally pushed off the roof of the building. The first observer (by the window) uses her rods and clocks to measure the time it takes for the refrigerator to travel the short distance between the top and bottom of her window. From her measurements she infers a velocity. The second observer on the sidewalk does the same

174

with his rods and clocks just before the frig hits the ground. They of course measure entirely different velocities. The guy on the ground measures a larger downward velocity than the woman in the window and, when they compare notes, conclude that the refrigerator was accelerating downward. John asks someone in class to play the role of Isaac Newton and explain this observation — that a *force* acted on the falling refrigerator. Quite incredible back then (and to many theoreticians now!) that the earth somehow exerts a force on the refrigerator without even touching it! Is it any less preposterous an idea to suppose the rods and closks used by the observers were affected differently by their differing distances from the center of the earth? (Out of fairness to Isaac, you should point out that he himself found the idea of a graviatational force exerted through the void of space to be a particularly absurd idea.)

An oldie but goody student reference for general relativity is *Physical Foundations of General Relativity*, by D.W. Sciami, a Doubleday Science Study Series (S-58) paperback (1969).

I do not have a suggested lecture presentation for this chapter, and welcome ideas from you that I can incorporate into future printings of this manual.

Appendix IV
Exponential Growth and Doubling Time

This material makes a fine lecture, for the material is not only very important, but is fascinating — and very wide in scope. It can nicely fit at the end of Chapter 15, where the last sentence of the chapter (page 284) suggests reading Appendix IV. It can also be coupled to a discussion of radioactive half life as treated in Chapter 32. Or it can be treated in any break — following an exam, perhaps, or on any day that lends itself to a departure from chapter material.

This material is adapted from papers written by Al Bartlett. Consider showing the 1984 version of his 50 minute videotape, "The Forgotten Fundamentals of the Energy Crisis," which comes in 3 tape formats for merely the cost and copying of the tape (Dr. Bartlett receives no royalty). Available from: Academic Media Services, Box 379, University of Colorado, Boulder, CO 80309. For more information on this call Al Bartlett, (303) 492 7341.

The concept of growth rate can be expressed in simple steps: Step 1: (new amount) = (old amount) + k times (old amount). Step 2: (new amount) becomes (old amount). Step 3: Keep repeating. That's it. The mathematics is just arithmetic. Use positive k for growth, and negative k for decay.

A beginning application is simple 10% annual interest on each dollar in a savings account. At the end of the 1st year, $A = 1 + 0.10(1)$; 2nd year, $A = 1.10 + 0.10(1.10)$; 3rd year, $A = 1.21 + 0.10(1.21)$; and so on. Suppose your savings are silver dollars and the bank charges 10% annual storage fee.

Year	INTEREST Change	INTEREST Amount	RENTAL Change	RENTAL Amount
0		1.00		1.00
1	+0.100	1.10	-0.100	0.90
2	+0.110	1.21	-0.090	0.81
3	+0.121	1.33	-0.081	0.73
4	+0.133	1.46	-0.073	0.66
5	+0.146	1.61	-0.066	0.59
6	+0.161	1.77	-0.059	0.53
7	+0.177	1.95	-0.053	0.48
8	+0.195	2.14	-0.048	0.43
9	+0.214	2.36	-0.043	0.39
10	+0.236	2.59	-0.039	0.35
20	+0.612	6.73	-0.014	0.12

Note that in 7 years at a 10% rate the amount just about doubles for positive k and just about halves for negative k.

It is customary to use the decay halving time (half life) of processes such as radio-active decay as a property of the decaying elements. There is nothing special about doubling-halving time. Tripling-thirding or 3/2ing-2/3ing, or any factor and its reciprocal could be used. As the number of time intervals increases, the process approaches continuity, which leads to the exponential e^{kt}.

The formula for doubling time in the text appears without derivation, which is likely beyond the scope of a non-science physics class. Its derivation is as follows: Exponential growth may be described by the equation

$$A = A_o e^{kt}$$

where k is the rate of increase of the quantity A_o. We can re-express this for a time T when $A = 2A_o$,

$$2A_o = A_o e^{kT}$$

If we take the natural logarithm of each side we get

$$\ln 2 = kT \text{ where } T = \frac{\ln 2}{k} = \frac{0.693}{k}$$

If k is expressed in percent, then

$$T = \frac{69.3}{\%} \sim \frac{70}{\%}$$

When percentage figures are given for things such as interest rates, population growth, or consumption of non-renewable resources, conversion to doubling time greatly enhances the meaning of these figures.

An update on population growth: Population growth of the 12 most populous nations, in decreasing order of population, as of 1990, shown by doubling time in years and annual percent was: China 49, 1.4%; India 33, 2.1%; ex-USSR 80, 0.9%; USA 92, 0.8%; Indonesia 38, 1.8A%; Brazil 36, 1.9%; Japan 175, 0.4%; Nigeria 24, 2.9%; Bangladesh 28, 2.5%; Pakistan 23, 3.0%; Mexico 29, 2.4%; Germany 7000, 0.0% (from *Engineering & Science*, Spring 1992.)

Examinations

I usually give two or three 30-question multiple-choice "midterms" exams and a 50-question multiple choice final exam in my course. Or I give 15-double-question multiple choice exams for midterms. The double-response questions have the advantage of providing students a consistency check that minimizes goofs. Most students have adequate time to finish each exam. To encourage thinking rather than memorization, I give exams with open book.

Multiple-choice exams are not the only way to fly. You could give a balance of multiple-choice, sentence completion, simple calculations, or short essay questions. If you're into increasing your supply of questions, do as Rog Lucido and Alan Pepper do—have your students make up their own questions, say one per week. As we all know, making up meaningful multiple-choice questions with credible wrong answers is not an easy task. This student input will provide you not only with a fresh supply of questions, but also supply you with a supply of credible wrong answers (often from their "correct" answers!).

I have a "retake policy", where students can take as many as three similar retake exams during out-of-class time and average their score each try. This relieves anxiety and encourages many students to take the course who wouldn't otherwise. But it's a lot of work, and I am fortunate to have teaching assistants to help with this task. My colleague, Chelcie Liu, instead uses an additional hour of lecture time following the full period of exam discussion to give an optional retake. He then uses the higher score. This is easier, scheduling and otherwise, but consumes an extra lecture period per exam. I think it is important to provide some early means of allowing students to improve their scores if they fall beneath their expectations the first time. I also recommend you provide your students with sample practice exams. Practice exams for each part of the text are show on the following pages, 179—186. Block out the answers at the bottom, photocopy, and distribute to your class. Class discussion of these during a class period before the exam is helpful.

Before my classes got too large and before I depended on multiple-choice questions, I used to astonish my classes by distributing final examinations on the first day of class. A sample essay final is shown on page 187. I tell students they are responsible for only 5 of the 20 questions that span the course material, which gives them a whole semester to think and formulate good short-essay answers. At final exam day I pick 4 questions and then tell them to pick the 5th. This policy defines specific and obtainable objectives for the students, lessens anxiety, and encourages a more positive attitude. This kind of essay final makes an excellent compliment to multiple-choice midterm exams.

More than 1600 multiple-choice examination questions, mainly single-answer type, but some double-answer type, are in the Test Bank—both in book form and on computer discs. Questions are keyed to the text by chapter and topic, and come in three levels of difficulty. Some have optional art work. Note that most questions test for understanding rather than recall, and therefore lend themselves to the open-book approach.

Sample MECHANICS Exam

Write the BEST answer to each of the following only in the small box. No penalty for guessing. Good Energy!

1. The acceleration of a bowling ball rolling along a smooth horizontal bowling alley is
   a. zero.   b. about 10 m/s^2.   c. constant.

2. You stand at the top of a cliff and throw a rock downward, and another rock horizontally at the same speed. The rock that stays in the air for the longest time is the one thrown
   a. downward.   b. horizontally.   c. both take the same time.

3. If an object moves along a straight-line path, then it *must* be
   a. accelerating.   b. acted on by a force.   c. both of these.   d. none of these.

4. A heavy rock and a light rock in free fall have the same acceleration. The *reason* the heavy rock does not have more acceleration is because
   a. the force of gravity on each is the same.
   b. there is no air resistance.
   c. the inertia of both rocks is the same.
   d. all of these.   e. none of these.

5. A ball rolls down a curved ramp as shown. As its speed increases, its rate of gaining speed
   a. increases.   b. decreases.   c. remains unchanged.

6. Apply the equation $Ft = \Delta mv$ to the case of a person falling on a wooden floor. If v is the speed of the person as she strikes the floor, then m is the
   a. mass of the person.   b. mass of the floor.   c. both.   d. none of these.

7. Looking at the seesaw you can see that compared to the weight of the boy, the weight of the board is
   a. more   b. less   c. the same   d. there's no way to tell

8. A pair of tennis balls fall through the air from a tall building. One is regular and the other is filled with lead pellets. The ball to reach the ground first is the
   a. regular ball   b. lead-filled ball   c. is the same for both

9. The same pair of tennis balls (regular and lead filled) fall from a tall building. Air resistance just before they hit is actually greater for the
   a. regular ball   b. lead-filled ball   c. is the same for both

10. When a bullet is fired from a rifle, the force that accelerates the bullet is equal in magnitude to the force that makes the rifle recoil. But compared to the rifle, the bullet has a greater
    a. inertia   b. potential energy.   c. kinetic energy.   d. momentum.

11. The reason for the answer to the preceding question has to do with the fact that the force on the bullet acts over
    a. the same time.   b. a longer time.   c. a longer distance.   d. none of these.

12. Which pulls with the greater force on the earth's oceans?
    a. moon.   b. sun.   c. both the same.

1a, 2b, 3d, 4e, 5b, 6a, 7a, 8b, 9b, 10c, 11c, 12b.

Sample PROPERTIES OF MATTER Exam

Write the BEST answer to each of the following only in the small box. No penalty for guessing. Good Energy!

1. What makes one element distinct from another is the number of
   a. protons in its nucleus.
   b. neutrons in its nucleus.
   c. electrons in its nucleus.
   d. total particles in its nucleus.

2. In the atomic nucleus of a certain element are 26 protons and 28 neutrons. The ATOMIC NUMBER of the element is
   a. 26. b. 27. c. 28. d. 54. e. none of these.

3. Which is bigger in size? A kilogram of aluminum or a kilogram of lead.
   a. aluminum b. lead c. the same.

4. Consider two oranges, one with twice the diameter of the other. How much heavier is the larger orange?
   a. twice. b. four times. c. eight times. d. sixteen times e. none of these.

5. Consider the same two oranges, one with twice the diameter of the other. How much more skin does the larger orange have?
   a. twice. b. four times. c. eight times. d. sixteen times. e. none of these.

6. Three bowling balls are suspended at various depths in the water as shown. Buoyant force is greatest on ball
   a. A. b. B. c. C. d. same on each.

7. Compared to an empty ship, a ship with a cargo of styrofoam floats
   a. deeper in the water.
   b. higher in the water.
   c. with no change in level.

8. The greatest amount of water is displaced by a rock when it
   a. floats in a light pie pan. b. is submerged. c. ...same either way.

9. Two life preservers have identical volumes, but one is filled with styrofoam while the other is filled with sand. When the two life preservers are fully submerged, the buoyant force is greater on the one filled with
   a. styrofoam.
   b. sand.
   c. same on each as long as their volumes are the same.

10. As a weighted air-filled balloon sinks deeper and deeper into water, the buoyant force on it
    a. increases. b. decreases. c. remains essentially the same.

11. Squeeze an air-filled balloon to half size and the pressure inside
    a. remains the same. b. halves. c. doubles. d. none of these.

12. As a helium-filled balloon rises in the air, it becomes
    a. lighter. b. less dense. c. non buoyant. d. all of these e. none of these.

1a, 2a, 3a, 4c, 5b, 6d, 7a, 8a, 9c, 10b, 11c, 12b.

Sample HEAT Exam

Write the BEST answer to each of the following only in the small box. No penalty for guessing. Good Energy!

1. In a mixture of hydrogen gas, oxygen gas, and nitrogen gas, the molecules with the greatest average speed are those of
   a. hydrogen.
   b. oxygen.
   c. nitrogen.
   d. ...all will have the same average speed at the same temperature.

2. The reason that the white-hot sparks that strike your face from a 4th-of-July-type sparkler don't harm you is because
   a. they have a low temperature.
   b. the energy per molecule is very low.
   c. the energy per molecule is high, but little energy is transferred because of relatively few molecules in the spark.

3. As a piece of metal with a hole in it cools, the diameter of the hole
   a. increases.   b. decreases.   c. remains the same size.

4. If water had a higher specific heat, in cold weather, ponds would be
   a. less likely to freeze.
   b. more likely to freeze.
   c. neither more nor less likely to freeze.

5. Consider a sample of water at 2°C. It the temperature is increased slightly, say by one degree, the volume of water
   a. increases.   b. decreases.   c. remains unchanged.

6. The temperature of water at the bottom of a deep ice-covered lake is
   a. slightly below freezing temperature.
   b. itself at the temperature of freezing.
   c. somewhat above freezing temperature.

7. The principle reason one can walk barefoot on red-hot wooden coals without burning the feet has to do with
   a. low temperature of the coals.
   b. low thermal conductivity of the coals.
   c. mind-over-matter techniques.

8. If the slower-moving molecules in a liquid were more likely to undergo evaporation, then evaporation would make the remaining liquid
   a. warmer.   b. cooler.   c. no warmer or cooler than without evaporation.

9. Melting ice actually
   a. tends to warm the surroundings.
   b. tends to cool the surroundings.
   c. has no effect on the temperature of the surroundings.

10. Consider a piece of metal that has a temperature of 5°C. If it is heated until it has twice the internal energy, its temperature will be
    a. 10°C.   b. 273°C.   c. 278°C.   d. 283°C.   e. 556°C.

1a, 2c, 3b, 4a, 5b, 6c, 7b, 8a, 9b, 10d.

Sample SOUND Exam

Write the BEST answer to each of the following only in the small box. No penalty for guessing. Good Energy!

1. A portion of water oscillates up and down two complete cycles in one second as a water wave passes by. The wave's wavelength is 5 meters. What is the wave's speed?
   a. 2m/s. b. 5 m/s. c. 10 m/s. d. 15 m/s. e. none of these.

2. A 60-vibration per second wave travels 30 meters in one second. Its frequency is
   a. 30 hertz and it travels at 60 m/s.
   b. 60 hertz and it travels at 30 m/s.
   c. neither of these.

3. A mass on the end of a spring bobs up and down one complete cycle every two seconds. Its frequency is
   a. 0.5 Hz. b. 2 Hz. c. neither of these.

4. When a source of sound approaches you, you detect an increase in its
   a. speed. b. wavelength. c. frequency. d. all of these.

5. True or false: A sonic boom is typically produced when an aircraft goes from subsonic to the supersonic speed.
   a. true. b. false.

6. The speed of sound in air depends on
   a. its frequency.
   b. its wavelength.
   c. air temperature.
   d. all of these.
   e. none of these.

7. A singer holds a high note and shatters a distant crystal wine glass. This phenomenon best demonstrates
   a. forced vibrations.
   b. the Doppler Effect.
   c. interference
   d. resonance.

8. To set a tuning fork of 400 Hz into resonance, it is best to use another of
   a. 200 Hz. b. 400 Hz. c. 800 Hz. d. any of these three.

9. About how many octaves are present between 100 Hz and 1600 Hz?
   a. 4. b. 5. c. 6. d. 7. e. 8.

10. True or false: Any radio wave travel s faster under all conditions than any sound wave.
    a. true. b. false.

1c, 2b, 3a, 4c, 5b, 6c, 7d, 8b, 9a, 10a.

Sample ELECTRICITY & MAGNETISM Exam

Write the BEST answer to each of the following only in the small box. No penalty for guessing.
Good Energy!

1. Protons and electrons
    a. repel each other.   b. attract each other.   c. do not interact.

2. Particle A interacts with particle B, which has twice the charge of particle A.
    Compared to the force on particle A, the force on particle B is
    a. four times as much.
    b. two times as much
    c. the same.
    d. half as much.
    e. none of these.

3. When you touch a negative Van de Graaff generator, your standing hair is
    a. negative also. b. positive.

4. Two charged particles held close to each other are released. As the particles
    move, the velocity of each increases. Therefore the particles have
    a. the same sign of charge. b. opposite signs of charge. c. not enough
    information is given.

5. You can touch and discharge a 10,000-volt Van de Graaff generator with little
    harm because although the voltage is high, there is relatively little
    a. resistance. b. energy. c. grounding d. all of these. e. none of these.

6. The current through a 12-ohm hairdryer connected to 120-V is
    a. 1 A. b. 10 A. c. 12 A   d. 120 A.   e. none of these.

7. Double the voltage that operates a hair dryer and the current within tends to
    a. halve. b. remain the same. c. double. d. quadruple.

8. A woman experiences an electrical shock with a faulty hairdryer. The
    electrons making the shock come from the
    a. woman's body.
    b. ground
    c. power plant
    d. hairdryer.
    e. electric field in the air.

9. As more lamps are connected to a series circuit, the overall current in the
    power source
    a. increases.   b. decreases.   c. stays the same.

10. As more lamps are connected to a parallel circuit, the overall current in the
    power source
    a. increases. b. decreases.   c. stays the same.

11. Change the magnetic field in a closed loop of wire and you induce in the loop a
    a. voltage. b. current. c. electric field. d. all these. e. none of these.

12. A step-up transformer increases
    a. power.   b. energy.   c. both of these. d. neither of these.

1b, 2c, 3a, 4c, 5b, 6b, 7c, 8a, 9b, 10a, 11d, 12d.

Sample LIGHT Exam

Write the BEST answer to each of the following only in the small box. No penalty for guessing. Good Energy!

1. Which of the following does not fit in the same family?
   a. light wave. b. radio wave. c. sound wave. d. microwave. e. X-ray.

2. If the resonant frequency of the outer electron shells in atoms in a particular material match the frequency of green light, the material will be
   a. transparent to green light. b. opaque to green light.

3. If water naturally absorbed blue and violet light rather than infrared, water would appear
   a. green-blue, as it presently appears.
   b. a more intense green-blue.
   c. orange-yellowish.
   d. black.
   e. to have no color at all.

4. The sky is blue because air molecules in the sky act as tiny
   a. mirrors that reflect primarily blue light.
   b. oscillators that scatter high-frequency light.
   c. incandescant blue-hot sources.
   d. prisms.
   e. none of these.

5. The average speed of light is greatest in
   a. red glass. b. yellow glass. c. green glass. d. blue glass. e. all the same.

6. If different colors of light had the same speed in matter, there would be no
   a. rainbows. b. dispersion by prisms. c. colors from diamonds. d. all of these.

7. When light is refracted there is a change in its
   a. frequency. b. wavelength. c. both of these. d. none of these.

8. Lenses work because in different materials light has different
   a. wavelengths. b. frequencies. c. speeds. d. energies. e. none of these.

9. A fish outside water will see better if it has goggles that are
   a. tinted green-blue. b. flat. c. filled with water. d. none of these.

10. Waves diffract most when their wavelengths are
    a. long. b. short. c. same each way.

11. A hologram best illustrates
    a. resonance. b. interference. c. laser light. d. a new photography.

12. Which photons have the most energy of those listed below?
    a. red. b. white. c. blue. d. all the same.

1b, 2b, 3c, 4b, 5a, 6d, 7b, 8c, 9c, 10a, 11b, 12c.

Sample ATOMIC & NUCLEAR PHYSICS Exam

Write the BEST answer to each of the following only in the small box. No penalty for guessing. Good Energy!

1. Which of the following forms an interference pattern when directed toward two suitably-spaced thin slits?
a. light. b. sound. c. electrons. d. all of these. e. none of these.

2. An electron and a baseball move at the same speed. Which has the shorter de-Broglie wavelength?
a. electron. b. baseball. c. both the same.

3. Electrical forces within the atomic nucleus tend to
a. hold it together. b. push it apart. c. neither of these.

4. Which of these experiences the greatest electrical force in an electric field?
a. alpha particle. b. beta particle. c. gamma ray. d. none of these.

5. The radioactive half life of a certain isotope is 1 day. At the end of 3 days the amount remaining is
a. 1/2. b. 1/4. c. 1/8. d. 1/16. e. none of these.

6. When U-238 emits an alpha particle, the nucleus left behind has
a. 90 protons. b. 91 protons. c. 92 protons. d. 93 protons. e. 94 protons.

7. When U-239 emits a beta particle, the nucleus left behind has
a. 90 protons. b. 91 protons. c. 92 protons. d. 93 protons. e. 94 protons.

8. When U-235 undergoes fission, the pair of nuclei that result have a total of
a. less than 92 protons. b. 92 protons. c. more than 92 protons.

9. A nuclear proton has a greater mass in
a. helium. b. iron. c. uranium. d. same in each.

10. If an iron nucleus undergoes fission, the masses of its nucleons
a. increase. b. decrease. c. neither increase or decrease.

11. If an iron nucleus undergoes fusion, the masses of its nucleons
a. increase. b. decrease. c. neither increase or decrease.

12. The type of ray that originates in the cosmos is the
a. alpha ray. b. beta ray. c. cosmic ray. d. hoo ray!

1d, 2b, 3b, 4a, 5c, 6a, 7d, 8b, 9a, 10a, 11a, 12c.

Sample RELATIVITY Exam

Write the BEST answer to each of the following only in the small box. No penalty for guessing. Good Energy!

1. Which equation is the triumph of the theory of Special Relativity?
   a. $E_o = ma^2$. b. $E_o = mb^2$. c. $E_o = mca^2$. d. $E_o = md^2$. e. $E_o = me^2$.

2. Relativistic equations for time, length, and mass hold true for
   a. speeds near the speed of light.
   b. everyday low speeds.
   c. both of these.
   d. none of these.

3. According to special relativity, if you measure your pulse while traveling a very high speeds, you would notice that your pulse rate would be
   a. increased. b. decreased. c. no different.

4. When a light source approaches you, your measurements of it will show an increase in its
   a. speed. b. wavelength. c. frequency. d. all of these. e. none of these.

5. Because of relativistic effects, the masses of the electrons that are fired against the inside surface of a TV tube are
   a. slightly greater. b. slightly less. c. unchanged.

6. A spear has a rest mass of 1 kilogram. When properly thrown past you your instruments show it to have a mass of 2 kilograms. Your instruments also show the speed of the spear to be
   a. 0.5c. b. 0.75c. c. 0.87c. d. 0.99c. e. none of these.

7. Since there is an upper limit on the speed of a particle, there is also an upper limit on its
   a. momentum. b. kinetic energy. c. temperature. d. all of these. e. none of these.

8. Compared to special relativity, general relativity is more concerned with
   a. acceleration. b. gravitation. c. space-time geometry. d. all of these. e. none of these.

9. From a general relativistic point of view, compared to a watch at the earth's poles, a watch at the earth's equator should run
   a. faster. b. slower. c. at the same rate.

10. From a general relativistic point of view, a person on the ground floor of a skyscraper ages
    a. faster than a person on the top floor.
    b. slower than a person on the top floor.
    c. at the same rate as a person on the top floor.

11. If the orbit of Mercury were perfectly circular, its rate of precession would be
    a. larger. b. smaller. c. no different that it is now. d. zero.

12. An astronaut falling into a black hole would see the universe
    a. red shifted. b. blue shifted.

1c, 2c, 3c, 4c, 5a, 6c, 7e, 8d, 9a, 10b, 11d, 12b.

Final Exam

Answer in detail, using examples and diagrams to make your points clear. Keep your answers to less than a page for each question.

1. "Inertia is that property of all matter that causes it to resist being moved." Is there anything wrong with this statement, and if not, why not, and if so, why so?

2. Distinguish between mass and weight. Why, for example, does a heavy object accelerate no more than a light object in free fall?

3. Give at least two examples of an object or collection of objects that have some (not zero) kinetic energy, but a net momentum of zero.

4. The force of gravity pulls apples off trees and they fall. The same force extends to the moon—so why doesn't the moon fall also?

5. What accounts for the fact that there are two ocean tides per day?

6. What evidence can you cite to support the atomic theory of matter?

7. Discuss the principles that account for the flight of both lighter-than-air and heavier-than-air aircraft?

8. How does a suction cup work?

9. Why does warm air rise?

10. Why is it that deep bodies of water, such as Lake Tahoe in California, do not freeze over even in the coldest of winters?

11. What is a sonic boom and how is it produced?

12. What does it mean to say the electrical outlets in your home are rated at 110 volts?

13. Explain how an electircal transformer operates.

14. Distinguish between light waves and sound waves.

15. What is the evidence for the claim that the stars are composed of the same elements found on earth?

16. Why is the sky blue and the sunsets orange?

17. What produces the spectrum of colors of gasoline on a wet street?

18. Distinguish between nuclear fission and nuclear fusion.

19. How is radioactivity used to determine the ages of ancient organic and inorganic objects?

20. What would be unusual about your observations of occupants in a space ship traveling at relativistic speeds. Assume you can clearly see them make any measurements you like.

CONCEPTUAL Physics PRACTICE SHEET

Chapter 3: Nonlinear Motion
Velocity Vectors

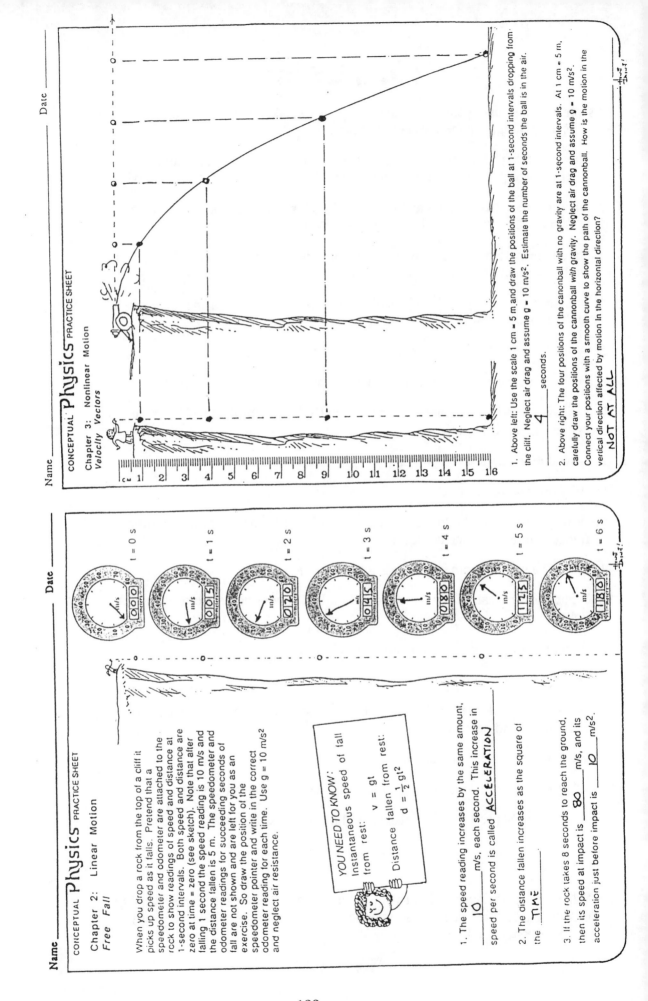

1. Above left: Use the scale 1 cm = 5 m, and draw the positions of the ball at 1-second intervals dropping from the cliff. Neglect air drag and assume g = 10 m/s². Estimate the number of seconds the ball is in the air.
4 seconds.

2. Above right: The four positions of the cannonball with no gravity are at 1-second intervals. At 1 cm = 5 m, carefully draw the positions of the cannonball *with* gravity. Neglect air drag and assume g = 10 m/s². Connect your positions with a smooth curve to show the path of the cannonball. How is the motion in the vertical direction affected by motion in the horizontal direction?
NOT AT ALL

CONCEPTUAL Physics PRACTICE SHEET

Chapter 2: Linear Motion
Free Fall

When you drop a rock from the top of a cliff it picks up speed as it falls. Pretend that a speedometer and odometer are attached to the rock to show readings of speed and distance at 1-second intervals. Both speed and distance are zero at time = zero (see sketch). Note that after falling 1 second the speed reading is 10 m/s and the distance fallen is 5 m. The speedometer and odometer readings for succeeding seconds of fall are not shown and are left for you as an exercise. So draw the position of the speedometer pointer and write in the correct odometer reading for each time. Use g = 10 m/s² and neglect air resistance.

YOU NEED TO KNOW:
Instantaneous speed of fall from rest:
$$v = gt$$
Distance fallen from rest:
$$d = \frac{1}{2}gt^2$$

1. The speed reading increases by the same amount, **10** m/s, each second. This increase in speed per second is called **ACCELERATION**

2. The distance fallen increases as the square of the **TIME**

3. If the rock takes 8 seconds to reach the ground, then its speed at impact is **80** m/s, and its acceleration just before impact is **10** m/s².

t = 0 s
t = 1 s
t = 2 s
t = 3 s
t = 4 s
t = 5 s
t = 6 s

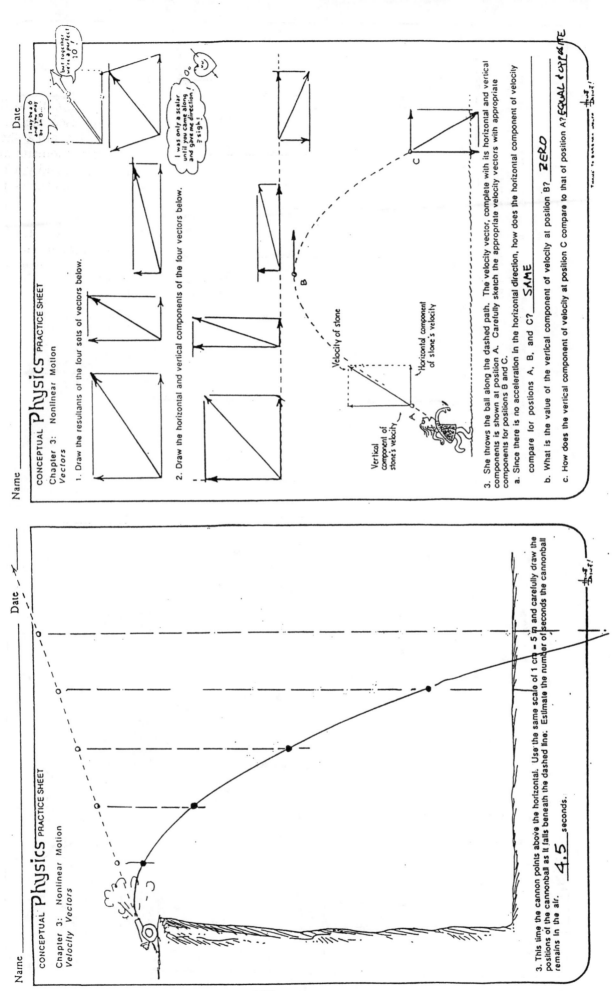

CONCEPTUAL **Physics** PRACTICE SHEET

Chapter 3: Nonlinear Motion
Velocity Vectors

3. This time the cannon points above the horizontal. Use the same scale of 1 cm = 5 m and carefully draw the positions of the cannonball as it falls beneath the dashed line. Estimate the number of seconds the cannonball remains in the air. __4.5__ seconds.

CONCEPTUAL **Physics** PRACTICE SHEET

Chapter 3: Nonlinear Motion
Vectors

1. Draw the resultants of the four sets of vectors below.

2. Draw the horizontal and vertical components of the four vectors below.

I was only a scalar until you came along and gave me direction! ?sigh!

but together we're a pulse! 10!

I may be a 6 and you may be an 8...

Velocity of stone

Vertical component of stone's velocity

Horizontal component of stone's velocity

3. She throws the ball along the dashed path. The velocity vector, complete with its horizontal and vertical components is shown at position A. Carefully sketch the appropriate velocity vectors with appropriate components for positions B and C.

a. Since there is no acceleration in the horizontal direction, how does the horizontal component of velocity compare for positions A, B, and C? __SAME__

b. What is the value of the vertical component of velocity at position B? __ZERO__

c. How does the vertical component of velocity at position C compare to that of position A? __EQUAL & OPPOSITE__

189

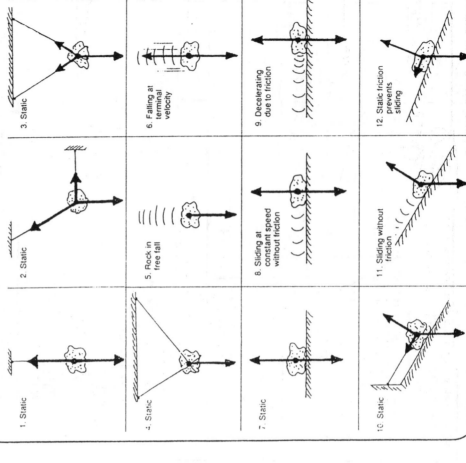

CONCEPTUAL Physics PRACTICE SHEET

Chapter 4: Newton's Laws of Motion
Vector Diagrams

In each case, a rock is acted on by one or more forces. Draw an accurate vector diagram showing all forces *acting on the rock*, and no other forces. Use a ruler, and do it in pencil so you can correct mistakes. The first two are done as examples.

1. Static

2. Static

3. Static

4. Static

5. Rock in free fall

6. Falling at terminal velocity

7. Static

8. Sliding at constant speed without friction

9. Decelerating due to friction

10. Static

11. Sliding without friction

12. Static friction prevents sliding

CONCEPTUAL Physics PRACTICE SHEET

Chapter 4: Newton's Laws of Motion
Force and Velocity Vectors

1. Draw sample vectors to represent all the *forces* that act on the ball in the positions shown above (*after* it leaves the thrower's hand). Include air drag.

2. Draw sample *bold vectors* to represent the *velocity* of the ball in the positions shown above. With lighter vectors, show the horizontal and vertical components of velocity at each position.

HORIZONTAL COMPONENTS ALL SAME AT ALL POSITIONS

3. All forces on the bowling ball, weight down and support of alley up, are shown by vectors at its center (a) before it strikes the pin. Draw vectors of all the forces that act *on* the ball (b) when it strikes the pin, and (c) after it strikes the pin.

a.   b.   c.

4. A block slides down an inclined plane at constant velocity. Draw vectors to show all the forces that act on the sliding block.

or

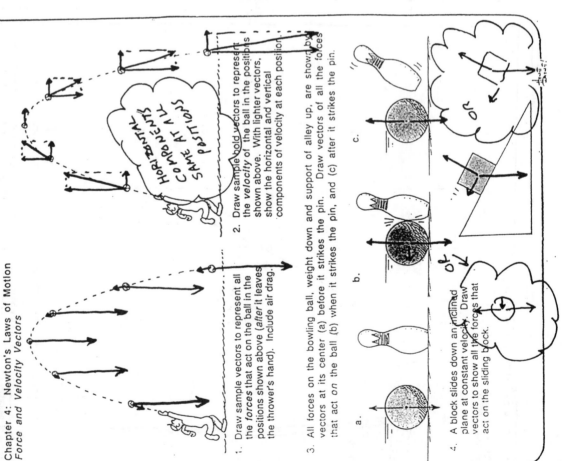

CONCEPTUAL Physics PRACTICE SHEET

Chapter 4: Newton's Laws of Motion
Statics

Little Nellie Newton aspires to be a gymnast and hangs from a variety of positions as shown. Since she is not accelerating, the net force on her is zero. This means the upward pull of the rope(s) equals the downward pull of gravity. She weighs 300 N. Show the scale readings for each case.

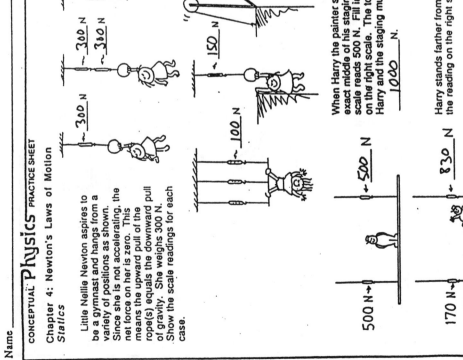

300 N

300 N   300 N

150 N

150 N

100 N

300 N

When Harry the painter stands in the exact middle of his staging, the left scale reads 500 N. Fill in the reading on the right scale. The total weight of Harry and the staging must be **1000** N.

500 N →   ← 500 N

Harry stands farther from the left. Fill in the reading on the right scale.

170 N →   830 N

Harry continues to horse around. Fill in the reading on the right scale.

0 N →   1000 N

CONCEPTUAL Physics PRACTICE SHEET

Chapter 4: Newton's Laws of Motion
Newton's 2nd Law

Bronco Brown skydives and parachutes from a stationary helicopter. Various stages of fall are shown in positions a through f. Using Newton's 2nd law,

$$a = \frac{F_{net}}{m} = \frac{W - R}{m}$$

find his acceleration at each position (mark your answers in the blanks to the right). You need to know that Bronco's mass m is 100 kg so his weight is a constant 1000 N. Air resistance R varies with speed and cross-sectional area as shown.

a   R = 0   W = 1000 N   a = 10 m/s²

b   R = 400 N   W = 1000 N   a = 6 m/s²

c   R = 1000 N   W = 1000 N   a = 0 m/s²

d   R = 1200 N   W = 1000 N   a = -2 m/s²

e   R = 2000 N   W = 1000 N   a = -10 m/s²

f   R = 1000 N   W = 1000 N   a = 0 m/s²

Circle the correct answer.

1. When Bronco's speed is least, his acceleration is (least)(most).

2. In which position(s) does Bronco experience a downward acceleration?
(a)(b)(c)(d)(e)(f)

3. In which position(s) does Bronco experience an upward acceleration?
(a)(b)(c)(d)(e)(f)

4. When Bronco experiences an upward acceleration, his velocity is (still downward)(upward also).

5. In which position(s) is Bronco's velocity constant?
(a)(b)(c)(d)(e)(f)

6. In which position(s) does Bronco experience terminal velocity?
(a)(b)(c)(d)(e)(f)

7. In which position(s) is terminal velocity greatest?
(a)(b)(c)(d)(e)(f)

8. If Bronco were heavier, his terminal velocity would be (greater)(less)(the same).

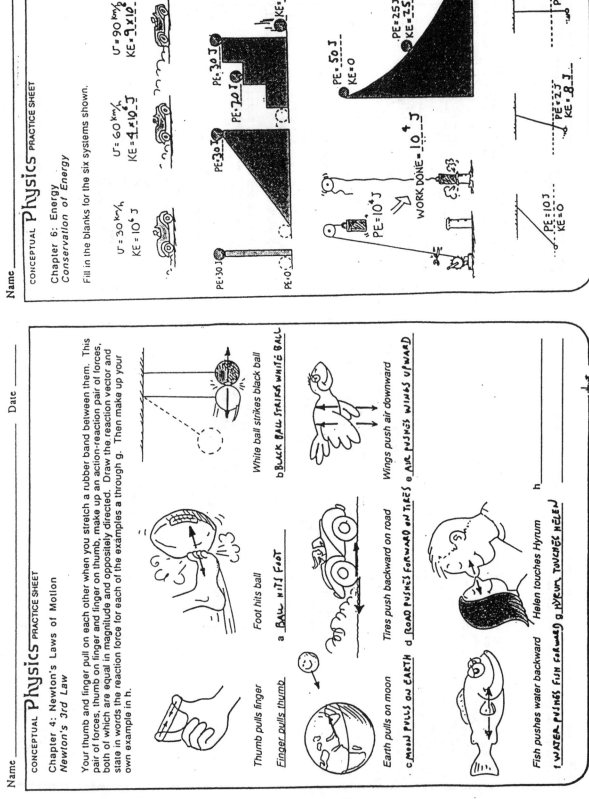

CONCEPTUAL **Physics** PRACTICE SHEET

Chapter 6: Energy
Conservation of Energy

Fill in the blanks for the six systems shown.

PE = 15000 J
KE = 0

PE = 11250 J
KE = 3750 J

PE = 7500 J
KE = 7500 J

PE = 3750 J
KE = 11250 J

PE = 0 J
KE = 15000 J

$v = 30 \frac{km}{h}$
KE = 10^6 J
PE = 30 J

$v = 60 \frac{km}{h}$
KE = 4×10^6 J
PE = 20 J

$v = 90 \frac{km}{h}$
KE = 9×10^6 J
KE = 30 J

PE = 30 J

PE = 20 J
PE = 0 J

PE = 50 J
KE = 0

PE = 25 J
KE = 25 J

PE = 0
KE = 50 J

PE = 10^4 J
WORK DONE = 10^4 J

PE = 10 J
KE = 0

PE = 2 J
KE = 8 J

PE = 0
KE = 10 J

PE = 10 J
KE = 0 J

CONCEPTUAL **Physics** PRACTICE SHEET

Chapter 4: Newton's Laws of Motion
Newton's 3rd Law

Your thumb and finger pull on each other when you stretch a rubber band between them. This pair of forces, thumb on finger and finger on thumb, make up an action-reaction pair of forces, both of which are equal in magnitude and oppositely directed. Draw the reaction vector and state in words the reaction force for each of the examples a through g. Then make up your own example in h.

Thumb pulls finger

Finger pulls thumb

Foot hits ball

a BALL HITS FOOT

White ball strikes black ball

b BLACK BALL STRIKES WHITE BALL

Earth pulls on moon

c MOON PULLS ON EARTH

Tires push backward on road

d ROAD PUSHES FORWARD ON TIRES

Wings push air downward

e AIR PUSHES WINGS UPWARD

Helen touches Hyrum

g HYRUM TOUCHES HELEN

Fish pushes water backward

f WATER PUSHES FISH FORWARD

h _____

CONCEPTUAL Physics PRACTICE SHEET

Chapter 7: Rotational Motion
Torques

A mobile is an interesting application of torques. Shown below are five horizontal arms (made of stiff wires) with fixed 1- and 2-kg masses attached. String can be attached in any of the loops, lettered A through R. Your task is to determine where strings should be attached so that when the whole system is suspended from the spring scale at the top, it will hang as a proper mobile with each arm suspended horizontally.

Work from the bottom up and circle the loops where the strings should be attached. For example, a little thought will show that the bottom arm should be suspended from loop B. Circle loop B to show that the bottom end of the string is tied there. Draw a line to the loop above where the top of this same string should be attached (D, E, F, or G) and work your way upward. Show the reading on the scale when it supports the completed mobile. Neglect the masses of the stiff wires and strings, which are small compared to the 1- and 2-kg masses.

or 117.6 N

12 kg

R

N

O

K

G

P

M

L

J

2

2

H

E

D

A

C

1

2

2

1

STRING

#1-a-1

CONCEPTUAL Physics PRACTICE SHEET

Chapter 7: Rotational Motion
Centripetal Force

Newton's 2nd law, a = F/m, tells us that net force and its corresponding acceleration are always in the same direction. (Both force and acceleration are vector quantities). But force and acceleration are not always in the direction of velocity (another vector). When any force or acceleration is at right angles to the velocity, then we call the force centripetal force and the acceleration centripetal acceleration.

1. You're in a car at a traffic light. The light turns green and the driver "steps on the gas." In which direction does (a) your body lurch? __BACKWARD__ (b) the car accelerate? __FORWARD__ (c) the force on the car act? __FORWARD__

The sketch shows the top view of the car. Note the directions of the velocity and acceleration vectors.

2. You're driving along and approach a stop sign. The driver steps on the brakes. In which direction does (a) your body lurch? __FORWARD__ (b) the car accelerate? __BACKWARD__ (c) the force on the car act? __BACKWARD__

The sketch shows the top view of the car. Draw vectors for velocity and acceleration.

3. You continue driving, and round a sharp curve to the left at constant speed. In which direction does your body lean? __RIGHT__ In which direction is the acceleration of the car? __LEFT__ In which direction does the force on the car act? __LEFT__ In general, how are the direction of lurch and direction of acceleration and force related? (same direction or opposite?) __OPPOSITE DIRECTIONS__

Draw vectors for velocity and acceleration of the car.

4. The whirling stone's direction of motion keeps changing. If it moves faster, does its direction also change faster? __YES__ Does this indicate 'a' and 'v' are directly related, or inversely related? __DIRECTLY__ Consider whirling the stone on a shorter string (smaller radius). For a given speed, does the stone change its direction at a greater or a lesser rate? __GREATER__ Are 'a' and 'r' therefore directly related, or inversely related? __INVERSELY__

Try some unit analysis and place units m/s for v, and m for r in the following equations to see which is the likely valid equation (which gives a in units m/s2).

$$a = v \cdot r; \quad a = \frac{v}{r}; \quad a = \frac{v^2}{r}$$

$$a = \frac{v}{r^2}; \quad a = \frac{v}{r}; \quad a = \frac{v^2}{r}$$

$$a = \frac{v^2}{r}$$

#7-1

CONCEPTUAL Physics PRACTICE SHEET

Chapter 8: Gravity
Gravitational Force

1. The spaceship is attracted to both the planet and its moon. The planet has 4 times the mass of the moon. The force of attraction to the planet is shown by the vector.

a. Carefully sketch another vector to show its attraction to the moon. Then sketch the resultant force.

b. Calculate or estimate the location between the planet and its moon (along the dotted line) where gravitational forces cancel. Make a sketch of the spaceship there.

2. Consider a planet of uniform density with a straight tunnel that extends from its north pole, through its center, to its south pole. An object at the surface weighs 1 ton.

a. Fill in the gravitational force on the object when it is half way to the center, then at the center.

1 TON→

b. Describe the motion you would experience if you fell into the tunnel.
SIMPLE HARMONIC (To + FRo)

3. An object weighs 1 ton at the surface of a planet, just before it gravitationally collapses.

a. Fill in the weights of the object at the planet's shrinking surface at the radial values shown.

1 TON → ⇒ R/10 ←4 TON ⇒ R/10 ←100 TON R/10 ←.1.TON

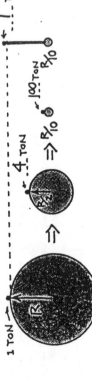

b. When the planet has collapsed to $1/10$ its initial radius, a ladder is erected that puts the object as far from its center as the object was originally. Fill in its weight at this position.

194

CONCEPTUAL Physics PRACTICE SHEET

Chapter 9: Satellite Motion
Circular Orbit

DIRECTION OF V COULD AS WELL BE COUNTERCLOCKWISE

Figure A

1. Figure A shows four positions of a satellite in circular orbit. At each position draw a vector to represent the gravitational force that acts on the satellite. Then label the force vectors F.

2. Are all four F vectors the same length? Why or why not? YES, BECAUSE EQUAL DISTANCES FROM PLANET

3. Draw a vector to represent the velocity of the satellite at each of the four positions. Then label the velocity vectors V.

4. Are all four V vectors the same length? Why or why not? YES; CONSTANT SPEED IN CIRCULAR ORBIT BECAUSE F⊥ TO V; NO COMPONENT OF F ALONG PATH TO CHANGE V.

5. What is the angle between your F and V vectors? 90°

6. Is there any component of F along V? NO

7. What does this say about the work done by the force of gravity on a satellite in circular orbit? NO WORK DONE BECAUSE NO COMPONENT OF FORCE ALONG PATH

Elliptical Orbit

BE CAREFUL NOT TO DRAW F ↓ PERPENDICULAR!!!!!! NO!

Figure B

1. Figure B shows four positions of a satellite in elliptical orbit. At each position draw a vector to represent the gravitational force that acts on the satellite. Then lable the force vectors F.

2. Are all four F vectors the same length? Why or why not? NO BECAUSE DISTANCES TO PLANET VARY

3. Draw a vector to represent the velocity of the satellite at each of the four positions. Then lable the velocity vectors V.

4. Are all four V vectors the same length? Why or why not? NO — YELOCITY DECREASES IN GOING AWAY AND INCREASES IN APPROACHING PLANET

5. Compare the angle between your F and V vectors to that for circular orbit. IN CIRCULAR ORBIT F IS EVERYWHERE 90 TO V; IN ELLIPTICAL ORBIT ANGLE VARIES

6. Is there any component of F along V? YES

7. What does this say about the work done by gravity on a satellite in an elliptical orbit? WORK IS DONE TO DECREASE KE GOING AWAY AND TO INCREASE KE IN APPROACHING

CONCEPTUAL Physics PRACTICE SHEET

Chapter 9: Satellite Motion
Mechanics Overview

1. The sketch shows the elliptical path described by a satellite about the earth. In which of the marked positions, A - D, (put S for "same everywhere") does the satellite experience the maximum

a. gravitational force? __A__

b. speed? __A__

c. velocity? __A__

d. momentum? __A__

e. kinetic energy? __A__

f. gravitational potential energy? __C__

g. total energy (KE + PE)? __S__

h. acceleration? __A__

i. angular momentum? __S__

2. Answer the above questions for a satellite in circular orbit.

a. __S__ b. __S__ c. __S__ d. __S__ e. __S__ f. __S__ g. __S__ h. __S__ i. __S__

3. In which position(s) is there momentarily no work done on the satellite by the force of gravity? Why? __A + C BECAUSE NO FORCE COMPONENTS IN DIRECTION OF MOTION__

4. Work changes energy. Let the equation for work, $W = Fd$, guide your thinking on these: Defend your answers in terms of $W = Fd$.

a. In which position will a several-minutes thrust of rocket engines do the most work on the satellite and give it the greatest change in kinetic energy? __A BECAUSE d WILL BE GREATER DURING THRUST (DURING THRUST F MOVES GREATEST d)__

b. In which position will a several-minutes thrust of rocket engines do the most work on the exhaust gases and give the *exhaust gases* the greatest change in kinetic energy? __C WHERE SATELLITE IS SLOWEST__

c. In which position will a several-minutes thrust of rocket engines give the satellite the least boost in kinetic energy? __C BECAUSE RELATIVE TO PLANET MOST OF THE ENERGY IS GIVEN TO EXHAUST GASES__

CONCEPTUAL Physics PRACTICE SHEET

Chapter 11: Solids
Scaling

1. Consider a cube 1 cm x 1 cm x 1 cm (about the size of a sugar cube). Its volume is 1 cm³. The surface area of one of its faces is 1 cm². The total surface area of the cube is 6 cm² because it has 6 sides. Now consider a second cube, scaled up by a factor of 2 so it is 2 cm x 2 cm x 2 cm.

a. What is the total surface area of each cube?

1st cube __6__ cm²; 2nd cube __24__ cm²

b. What is the volume of each cube?

1st cube __1__ cm³; 2nd cube __8__ cm³

c. Compare the ratio of surface area to volume for each cube.

1st cube: $\dfrac{\text{surface area}}{\text{volume}} = \dfrac{6}{1}$; 2nd cube: $\dfrac{\text{surface area}}{\text{volume}} = 3\left(\dfrac{24}{8}\right)$

2. Now consider a third cube, scaled up by a factor of 3 so it is 3 cm x 3 cm x 3 cm.

a. What is its total surface area? __54__ cm²

b. What is its volume? __27__ cm³

c. What is its ratio of surface area to volume?

$\dfrac{\text{surface area}}{\text{volume}} = 2\left(\dfrac{54}{27}\right)$

3. When the size of a cube is scaled up by a certain factor (2 and then 3 for the above examples), the area increases as the __SQUARE__ of the factor, and the volume increases as the __CUBE__ of the factor.

4. Does the ratio of surface area to volume increase or decrease as things are scaled up? __RATIO DECREASES__

5. Does the rule for the scaling up of cubes apply also to other shapes? __YES__ Would your answers have been different if we started with a sphere of diameter 1 cm and scaled it up to a sphere of diameter 2 cm, and then 3 cm? __NO; SAME RATIOS__

6. The effects of scaling are beneficial to some creaters and detrimental to others. Check either beneficial (B) or detrimental (D) for each of the following:

a. an insect falling from a tree __B__   b. an elephant falling from the same tree __D__

c. a small fish trying to flee a big fish __D__   d. a big fish chasing a small fish __B__

e. a hungry mouse __D__   f. an insect that falls in the water __D__

CONCEPTUAL **Physics** PRACTICE SHEET

Chapter 12: Liquids
Archimedes' Principle

1. Consider a balloon filled with 1 liter of water (1000 cm³) in equilibrium in a container of water as shown.

WATER DOES NOT SINK IN WATER!

a. What is the mass of the 1 liter of water? __1__ kg

b. What is the weight of the 1 liter of water? __9.8__ N   1000 cm³

c. What is the weight of water displaced by the balloon? __9.8__ N

d. What is the buoyant force on the balloon? __9.8__ N

e. Sketch a pair of vectors in the figure: one for the weight of the balloon and the other for the buoyant force that acts on it. How do the size and directions of the vectors compare? __SAME__

2. As a thought experiment, pretend you could remove the water from the balloon but still have it remain the same size of 1 liter. Inside the balloon is a perfect vacuum.

a. What is the mass and weight of the liter of nothing? __0__ kg, and __0__ N

b. What is the buoyant force on the liter-sized balloon of nothing? __9.8__ N

c. In what direction would the massless balloon be accelerated? __up__

3. Continue this thought experiment by pretending the balloon is replaced by a 0.5 kg block of wood (1000 cm³) that is exactly the same volume (1000 cm³). You hold the wood in the same submerged position beneath the surface of the water.

a. What volume of water is displaced by the wood? __1000__ cm³

b. What is the weight of water displaced by the wood? __9.8__ N   1000 cm³

c. What is the buoyant force on the wood? __9.8__ N

d. What is the net force exerted on the wood?   __4.9__ N
$F_{net} = BF - W = 9.8 - 4.9 = 4.9 N$ ↗

e. When released, in what direction does the wood accelerate? __up__

4. Repeat parts a through e in the previous question for a 5-kg rock of the same volume. Assume the rock is suspended by a string in the container of water.

a. __1000__ cm³   b. __9.8__ N   c. __9.8__ N   d. __39.2__ N   e. __down__

CONCEPTUAL **Physics** PRACTICE SHEET

Chapter 14: Temperature, Heat, and Expansion
Expansion

$\Delta \ell = \frac{1}{10^5} \ell_o \Delta T$

1 Steel expands by about 1 part in 100,000 for each 1°C increase in temperature.

a. How much longer will a piece of steel 1000 mm long (1 meter) be when its temperature is increased by 10 °C? __0.1 mm__

$\Delta \ell = \frac{1}{10^5} \ell_o \Delta T = \frac{10^3 mm}{10^5} \cdot 10 \cdot 1 = \frac{10^4}{10^5} = 10^{-1} mm$

b. How much longer will a piece of steel 1000 m long (1 kilometer) be when its temperature is increased by 10 °C? __0.1 m = 10 cm__

c. You place yourself between a wall and the end of a 1-m steel rod when the opposite end is securely fastened as shown. No harm comes to you if the temperature of the rod is increased a few degrees. Discuss the consequences of doing this with a rod many meters long?

__$\Delta \ell$ IS SMALL WHEN ℓ_o IS SMALL; BUT $\Delta \ell$ CAN BE FATAL) LARGE (MUST OF YOUR BODY WIDTH) FOR LARGE__

2. The Eiffel Tower in Paris is 298 meters high. On a cold winter night it is shorter than on a hot summer day. What is its change in height for a 30°C temperature difference?

$\Delta \ell = \frac{2 \cdot 10^2 m}{10^5} \times 30 = 0.09 m = 90 cm$

3. Consider a gap in a piece of metal. Does the gap become wider or narrower when the metal is heated? [Consider the piece of metal made up of 11 blocks — if the blocks are individually heated, each is slightly larger. Make a sketch of them, slightly enlarged, beside the sketch shown.]

__GAP IS WIDER (BY SAME AMOUNT AS IF IT WERE METAL)__

Δr

4. The equatorial radius of the earth is about 6370 km. Consider a 40,000-km long steel pipe that forms a giant ring that fits snugly around the equator of the earth. Suppose people all along its length breathe on it so as to raise its temperature 1°C. The pipe gets longer. It is also no longer snug. How high does it stand above the ground? (Hint: Concentrate on the radial distance.)

$\Delta r = \frac{6370 \, Km}{10^5} \cdot 1°C = 0.0637 \, Km = 63.7 \, m \, !$

CONCEPTUAL **Physics** PRACTICE SHEET

Chapter 15: Heat Transfer
Calorimetry

1. You apply heat to 1 L of water and raise its temperature by 10°C. If you add the same quantity of heat to 2 L of water, how much will the temperature rise? To 3 L of water? *Record your answers on the blanks in the drawing at the right.*

$\Delta T = 10°C$ $\Delta T = 5°\underline{4}$ $\Delta T = 3.3°\underline{g}$

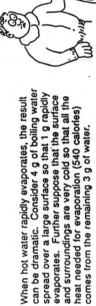

2. A large bucket contains 1 L of 20°C water.

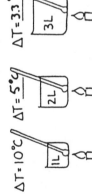

   a. What will be the temperature of the mixture when 1 L of 20°C water is added?

     <u>Still 20°c</u>

   b. What will be the temperature of the mixture when 1 L of 40°C water is added?

     <u>30°C</u>

   c. If 2 L of 40°C water were added, would the temperature of the mixture be greater or less than 30°C?

     <u>GREATER</u>

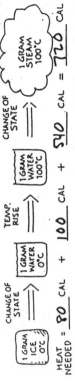

$Q = mc\,\Delta T$

$Q_{gain} = Q_{lost}$

$1\cdot1(40-T) = 1\cdot1(T-20)$

$T = 30°C$

$2(40-T) = 1\cdot(T-20)$

$T = 33.3°C$

3. A red-hot iron kilogram mass is put into 1 L of cool water. Mark each of the following statements true (T) of false (F). (Ignore heat transfer to the container.)

   a. The increase in the water temperature is equal to the decrease in the iron's temperature. <u>F</u>

   b. The quantity of heat gained by the water is equal to the quantity of heat lost by the iron. <u>T</u>

   c. The iron and the water will both reach the same temperature. <u>T</u>

   d. The final temperature of the iron and water is about halfway between the initial temperatures of each. <u>F</u>

4. *True or False:* When Queen Elizabeth throws the last sip of her tea over Queen Mary's rail, the ocean gets a little warmer. <u>T (UNLESS IT WAS ICE TEA!)</u>

CONCEPTUAL **Physics** PRACTICE SHEET

Chapter 16: Change of State
Energy Changes

Transfer of energy occurs when matter changes state. For H_2O, 80 calories are required to melt 1 gram of 0° ice, 1 calorie is required to change the temperature of 1 gram of water by 1 C°, and 540 calories are required to change 1 gram of 100°C water to steam.

1. Fill in the number of calories at each step below for changing 1 g of ice to 100°C steam.

$$\text{HEAT NEEDED} = \underline{80}\text{ CAL} + \underline{100}\text{ CAL} + \underline{540}\text{ CAL} = \underline{720}\text{ CAL}$$

2. A 50-g sample of 0°C ice is placed in a styrofoam cup that contains 200 g of water at 20°C.

   a. How many calories are needed to melt the ice? $50 \times 80 = \underline{4000}$

   b. By how much would the temperature of the water change if it supplied this much heat to the ice? $\underline{4000}{\big/}\underline{200} = \underline{20°c}$

   c. What will be the final temperature of the mixture? (Disregard any heat transfer by the container or surrounding air.) <u>0°C</u>

3. When hot water rapidly evaporates, the result can be dramatic. Consider 4 g of boiling water spread over a large surface so that 1 g rapidly evaporates. Further suppose that the surface and surroundings are very cold so that all the heat needed for evaporation (540 calories) comes from the remaining 3 g of water.

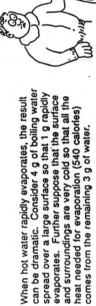

   a. How many calories are transferred from each gram of remaining water? $\underline{\tfrac{540}{3} = 180}$

   b. How many calories must be transferred to cool each gram of 100°C water to 0°C? <u>100</u>

   c. How many calories must be taken from each gram of 0°C water to change it to 0°C ice? <u>80</u>

   d. What happens to the remaining 3 g of boiling water when the 1 g rapidly evaporates?

     <u>SUBTRACTION OF 180 CALORIE PER GRAM CHANGES IT TO ICE</u>

CONCEPTUAL Physics PRACTICE SHEET

Chapter 18: Vibrations and Waves
Shock Waves

The cone-shaped shock wave produced by a supersonic aircraft is made up of overlapping spherical waves of sound. Sketches a, b, c, d, and e at the right show the "animated" growth of only one of the many spherical sound waves (shown as an expanding circle in the two-dimensional sketches). The circle originates when the aircraft is at position a. As the circle of sound grows, the aircraft moves farther to the right. The overlapping of many other circles, not shown, produce the V shape.

You can tell how fast the aircraft is traveling compared to the speed of sound. Note in sketch e that in the same time that sound travels from O to A, the aircraft travels from O to B. A simple check with a ruler will show distance OB is twice OA. So the aircraft is traveling __Twice__ as fast as sound.

Inspect sketches b, c, and d. In these positions, has the aircraft also traveled twice as far as sound in the same time (yes or no)? __YES__

If the aircraft traveled at a greater speed, how would the angle of the shock wave compare (wider, narrower, or the same)? __NARROWER__

Use a ruler to estimate the speeds of the aircraft that produce the shock waves below.

The first aircraft travels about __1.7__ the speed of sound.
The second aircraft travels about __4.3__ the speed of sound.

Draw your own circle (centered anywhere on the dashed line) and estimate the speed of the aircraft to produce the shock wave below.

On the other side of this sheet, draw the shock wave made by an aircraft that travels 5 times the speed of sound.

4.3 cm
1.7 cm

4.5 cm
1.5 cm

3 × SPEED OF SOUND

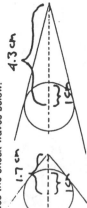

AIR CIRCLE
1/5 of mile circle
$U_s = \frac{U_s}{U_a}$
$U_a = \frac{U_{same}}{\sin \theta}$
$\sin \theta = \frac{U_s}{U_a}$

CONCEPTUAL Physics PRACTICE SHEET

Chapter 21: Electrostatics
Electric Potential

Just as PE transforms to KE for a mass lifted against the gravitation field (left), the electric PE of an electric charge transforms to other forms of energy when it changes location in an electric field (right). In both cases, how does the KE acquired compare to the decrease in PE? __SAME__

A force compresses the spring. The work done in compression is the product of the average force and the distance moved. $W = Fd$. This work increases the PE of the spring.

Complete the statements.

A force pushes the charge (call it a test charge) closer to the charged sphere. The work done in moving the test charge is the product of the average __FORCE__ and the __DISTANCE__ moved. $W = Fd$. This work __INCREASES__ the PE of the test charge.

If the test charge is released, it will be repelled and fly past the starting point. Its gain in KE at this point is __EQUAL__ to its decrease in PE.

At any point, a greater amount of test charge means a greater amount of PE. But not a greater amount of PE *per amount* of charge. The quantities PE (measured in joules) and PE/charge (measured in volts) are different concepts.

By definition: Electric Potential = PE/charge. 1 volt = 1 joule/1 coulomb. So 1 C of charge with a PE of 1 J has an electric potential of 1 V. And 2 C of charge with a PE of 2 J has an electric potential of __1__ V.

If a conductor connected to the terminal of a battery has an electric potential of 12 V, then each coulomb of charge on the conductor has a PE of __12__ J.

You do very little work in rubbing a balloon on your hair to charge it. The PE of several thousand billion electrons (about one-millionth coulomb [10^{-6}C]) transferred may be a thousanth of a joule [10^{-3}J]. Impressively, however, the electric potential of the balloon is about

$$\frac{1000 \text{ VI} \leftarrow 10^{-3} \text{J}}{10^{-6} \text{C}}$$

$\frac{1J}{1C} = 1V$
$\frac{2J}{2C}$ volts

Why is contact with a balloon charged to thousands of volts not as dangerous as contact with household 110 V? HOUSEHOLD CIRCUIT TRANSFERS MANY COULOMBS AND MUCH ENERGY

... A BALLOON TRANSFERS VERY LITTLE OF BOTH. —Bruce!

CONCEPTUAL Physics PRACTICE SHEET

Chapter 22: Electric Circuits
Series Circuits

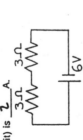

1. The simple circuit is a 6-V battery that pushes charge through a single lamp that has a resistance of 3 Ω. According to Ohm's law, the current in the lamp (and therefore the whole circuit) is __2__ A.

2. If a second identical lamp is added, the 6-V battery must push charge through a total resistance of __6__ Ω. The current in the circuit is then __1__ A.

3. If a third identical lamp is added in series, the total resistance of the circuit (neglecting any internal resistance in the battery) is __9__ Ω.

4. The current through all three lamps in series is __⅔__ A. The current through each individual lamp is __⅔__ A.

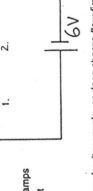

5. Does current in the lamps occur simultaneously, or does charge flow first through one lamp, then the other, and finally the last, in turn? SIMULTANEOUSLY (~ SPEED OF LIGHT)

6. Does current flow *through* a resistor, or *across* a resistor? THROUGH   Is voltage established *through* a resistor, or *across* a resistor? ACROSS

7. The voltage across all three lamps in series is 6 V. The voltage (or commonly, *voltage drop*) across each individual lamp is __2__ V.

8. Suppose a wire connects points *a* and *b* in the circuit. The voltage drop across lamp 1 is now __3__ V, across lamp 2 is __3__ V, and across lamp 3 is __0__ V. So the current through lamp 1 is now __1__ A, through lamp 2 is __1__ A, and through lamp 3 is __1__ A. The current in the battery (neglecting internal battery resistance) is __1__ A.

9. Which circuit dissipates more power, the 3-lamp circuit or the 2-lamp circuit? (Another way of asking this is which circuit would glow brightest; which would be best seen on a dark night from a great distance?) Defend your answer.
FOR 3 LAMPS P=IV = ⅔ ·6 = 4 W   FOR 2 LAMPS P=IV =1·6 = 6 W
∴ 2-LAMP CIRCUIT IS BRIGHTEST.

CONCEPTUAL Physics PRACTICE SHEET

Chapter 22: Electric Circuits
Parallel Circuits

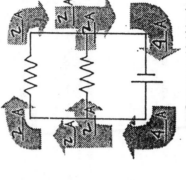

THE SUM OF THE CURRENTS IN THE TWO BRANCH PATHS EQUALS THE CURRENT BOTH BEFORE AND AFTER IT DIVIDES!

1. In the circuit shown to the left there is a voltage drop of 6 V across each 3-Ω lamp. By Ohm's law, the current in each lamp is __2__ A. The current through the battery is the sum of the currents in the lamps, __4__ A.

2. Fill in the current in the eight blank spaces in the view of the same circuit shown again at the right.

3. Suppose a third identical lamp is added in parallel to the circuit. Sketch a schematic diagram of the 3-lamp circuit in the space at the left.

4. For the three identical lamps in parallel, the voltage drop across each lamp is __6__ V. The current through each lamp is __2__ A. The current through the battery is now __6__ A. Is the circuit resistance now greater or less than before the third lamp was added? Explain.
LESS; MORE PATHS BETWEEN BATTERY TERMINALS

5. Which circuit dissipates more power, the 3-lamp circuit or the 2-lamp circuit? (Another way of asking this is which circuit would glow brightest; which would be best seen on a dark night from a great distance?) Defend your answer and compare this to the similar case for 2- and 3-lamp series circuits.
FOR THE 3 LAMPS, P=IV = 6·6 = 36 W   FOR 2 LAMPS P=IV=4·6 = 24 W
3-LAMP CIRCUIT IS BRIGHTEST; MORE CURRENT (BECAUSE OF LESS R) FOR SAME VOLTAGE
(OPPOSITE TO SERIES CIRCUIT)

CONCEPTUAL Physics PRACTICE SHEET

Chapter 24: Electromagnetic Induction
Transformer

A changing magnetic field is produced in a coil of wire when a bar magnet is plunged in and out of the coil. This induces an electric pressure in the coil called __VOLTAGE__

If the number of loops in the coil are increased, the induced voltage is __INCREASED__

The physical movement of a bar magnet is one way to produce a changing magnetic field. Another is to use a stationary electromagnet powered with __ALTERNATING__ current.

The square iron core (right) becomes an electromagnet when current flows through the primary loop. This magnetic field is enclosed by the secondary loop. If the current is ac, it induces an alternating magnetic field that induces voltage in the secondary loop. In (a) the voltage induced in the secondary equals the input voltage. (b) An extra secondary encloses the same changing magnetic field and voltage is induced in it also. (c) The induced voltages combine when the two secondaries are combined. Write in the induced voltage where indicated.

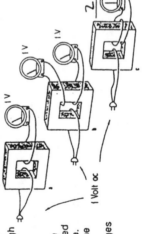

1 Volt ac

1V   1V   1V

2V

200 TURNS   1000 TURNS

Consider a more practical transformer with a 200-turn primary and a 1000-turn secondary (left). Suppose the primary is connected to a 120-volt alternating source, and the secondary is connected to an electrical device with a resistance of 600 ohms.

What will be the voltage output of the secondary? $5 \cdot 120 = $ __600__ V

What current will flow in the secondary circuit? $\frac{600}{600} = 1$ __1__ A

Knowing the voltage and current, what will be the power in the secondary? $P_{in} = $ __600__ W

Neglecting small heat losses, and knowing that energy is conserved, what will be the power in the primary? __600__ W

What is the current drawn by the primary? $I = \frac{P}{V} = \frac{600}{120} = 5$ A __5__ A

From this we see that the voltage is stepped up in the secondary, and compared to the current in the primary, is the current stepped up or down? __Down__

Can a transformer step up voltage? __YES__

Can a transformer step up current? __YES__

Can a transformer step up energy and or power? __No !__

200

CONCEPTUAL Physics PRACTICE SHEET

Chapter 25: Properties of Light
Pinhole Image Formation

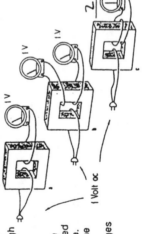

Take notice of the round spots of light on the shady ground beneath trees. These are *sunballs*, and are actually images of the sun. They are cast by openings between leaves in the trees that act as pinholes. The diameter of a sunball depends on its distance from the small opening that produces it. Large sunballs, several centimeters in diameter or so, are cast by openings that are relatively high above the ground, while small ones are produced by closer "pinholes." The interesting point is that the ratio of the diameter of the sunball to its distance from the pinhole is the same as the ratio of the sun's diameter to its distance from the pinhole. Knowing this ratio tells us the diameter of the sun. That's what this practice sheet is about. Instead of finding sunballs under the shade of trees, make your own easier-to-measure sunballs.

150,000,000 km

We know that the sun is approximately 150,000,000 km from the pinhole, so careful measurement of this ratio tells us the diameter of the sun.

Poke a small hole in a piece of cardboard (like with a sharp pencil). Hold the cardboard in the sunlight and note the circular image that is cast. This is an image of the sun. Note that its size does not depend on the size of the hole in the cardboard, but only on its distance. The greater the distance between image and cardboard, the larger the sunball. Position the cardboard so the image is about 1 or 2 cm in diameter (or so it exactly covers a nickel, dime, or something that can be accurately measured). Carefully measure the distance to the small hole in the cardboard. Complete the following:

$$\frac{\text{Diameter of sunball}}{\text{Distance to pinhole}} = \frac{1}{108}$$

With this ratio, estimate the diameter of the sun. Show your work below.

$$\frac{D_{sun}}{150\,000\,000\ km} = \frac{1}{108}$$

$$D_{sun} = \frac{1}{108} \cdot 150\,000\,000\ km = 140\,000\ km$$

WHAT SHAPE DO SUNBALLS HAVE DURING A PARTIAL ECLIPSE OF THE SUN?

CONCEPTUAL Physics PRACTICE SHEET

Chapter 27: Reflection and Refraction
Refraction

1. A pair of toy cart wheels that can spin independently of one another are rolled from a smooth surface onto two plots of grass as shown. The surface is slightly inclined so that after slowing down in the grass the wheels speed up again when emerging on the smooth surface. Complete each sketch showing some positions of the wheels inside the plots and on the other side. Clearly indicate their paths and directions of travel.

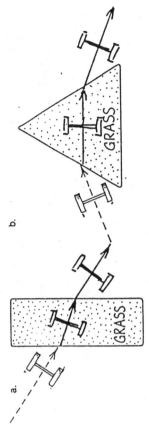

a.

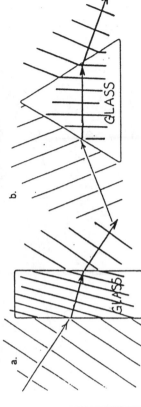

b.

2. Waves of sunlight and a light ray are shown shining on the two glass blocks. The speed of the waves decreases inside the glass blocks and returns to original speed upon emerging. Complete each sketch showing the positions of the waves inside and outside the glass blocks. Clearly indicate the path and direction of travel of the ray in each case.

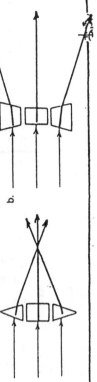

a.

b.

3. Show how light rays bend when they pass though the arrangements of glass blocks.

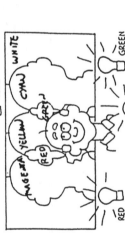

a.

b.

CONCEPTUAL Physics PRACTICE SHEET

Chapter 26: Color

The sketch to the right shows the shadow of an instructor in front of a white screen in a dark room. The light source is red, so the screen looks red and the shadow looks black. Color the sketch, or label the colors with pen or pencil.

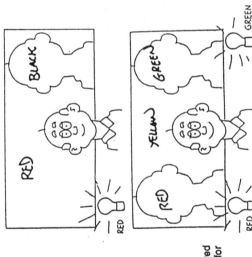

A green lamp is added and makes a second shadow. The shadow cast by the red lamp is no longer black, but is illuminated by green light. So it is green. Color or mark it green. The shadow cast by the green lamp is not black because it is illuminated by the red lamp. Indicate its color. Do the same for the background, which receives a mixture of red and green light.

A blue lamp is added and three shadows appear. Indicate the appropriate colors of the shadows and the background.

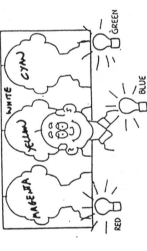

The lamps are placed closer together so the shadows overlap. Indicate the colors of all screen areas.

CONCEPTUAL Physics PRACTICE SHEET

Chapter 27: Reflection and Refraction
Ray Diagrams for Lenses

The arrows represent an object in front of a lens. The relative size and location of the image can be found by constructing a ray diagram. Three of many rays are shown by the dashed lines in the diagram above. Note they are (1) a ray parallel to the principal axis that passes through the focal point after passing through the lens; (2) A ray through the center of the lens that does not change direction; and (3) A ray through the focal point in front of the lens that emerges parallel to the principal axis after passing through the lens. The position of the image occurs where these rays intersect. Use any two of these rays to locate the image for each case below.

CONCEPTUAL Physics PRACTICE SHEET

Chapter 28: Light Waves
Interference Patterns

The illustration is a schematic depiction of coherent monochromatic light incident upon a thin slit at O that diffracts to thin slits M and N where it emerges to form an interference pattern on a screen S. Carefully count the number of wavelengths along the following paths between the double slits and the screen.

a LIGHT
b DARK
c LIGHT
DARK
LIGHT

Number of wavelengths between slit M and point a = **10½**

Number of wavelengths between slit N and point a = **11½**

Number of wavelengths between slit M and point b = **16**

Number of wavelengths between slit N and point b = **10½**

Number of wavelengths between slit M and point c = **10**

Number of wavelengths between slit N and point c = **10**

When the number of wavelengths along each path is the same or differs by one or more whole wavelengths, is interference is constructive or destructive? **CONSTRUCTIVE**

When the number of wavelengths differs by a half wavelength (or odd multiples of a half wavelength) is interference constructive or destructive? **DESTRUCTIVE**

If the light used were higher in frequency, would the fringes of light and dark areas be more widely or more closely spaced? **CLOSER**

If the spacing between slits were reduced, would the fringes of light and dark areas be more widely or more closely spaced? **WIDER**

If a greater number of equally-spaced slits, instead of two slits, were illuminated, would an interference pattern, still be produced? (Give an example.)
YES, AS IN A DIFFRACTION GRATING

CONCEPTUAL Physics PRACTICE SHEET

Chapter 32: Atomic Nucleus and Radioactivity
Natural Transmutation

Draw in a decay-scheme diagram below, similar to the one on page 603 of your text. In this case you begin at the upper right with U-235 and end up with a different isotope of lead. Use the table at the left and identify each element in the series by its chemical symbol.

Step	Particle Emitted
1	Alpha
2	Beta
3	Alpha
4	Alpha
5	Beta
6	Alpha
7	Alpha
8	Alpha
9	Beta
10	Alpha
11	Beta
12	Stable

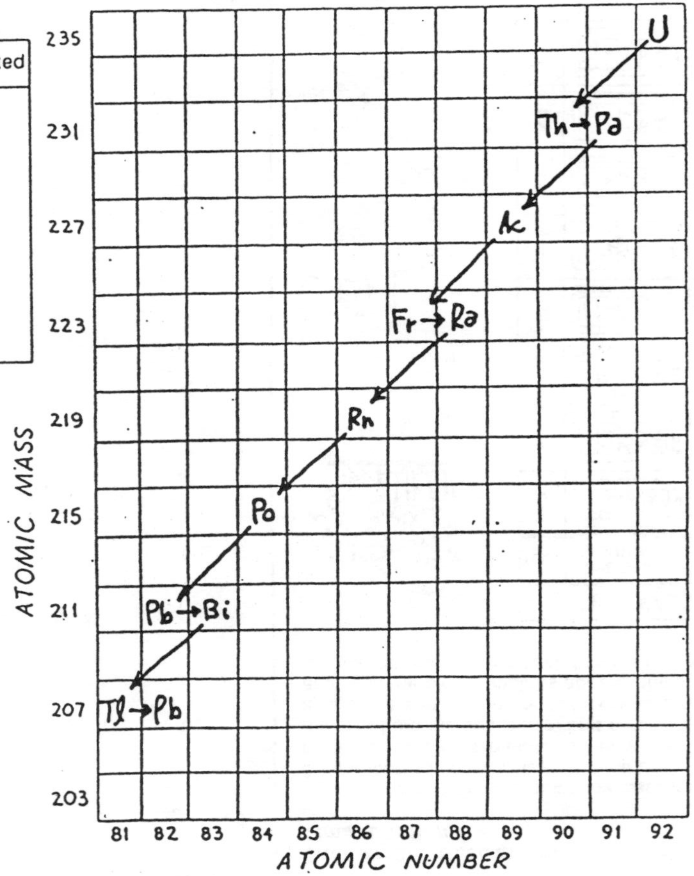

ATOMIC MASS (vertical axis: 235, 231, 227, 223, 219, 215, 211, 207, 203)
ATOMIC NUMBER (horizontal axis: 81 82 83 84 85 86 87 88 89 90 91 92)

Decay path labels: U, Th→Pa, Ac, Fr→Pa, Rn, Po, Pb→Bi, Tl→Pb

What isotope is the final product? $^{207}_{82}Pb$ (LEAD 207)

CONCEPTUAL Physics PRACTICE SHEET

Chapter 32: Atomic Nucleus and Radioactivity
Nuclear Reactions

Complete these nuclear reactions.

THORIUM LATE; I OVERTHLEPT!

1. $^{230}_{90}Th \longrightarrow ^{226}_{88}Ra + ^{4}_{2}He$

2. $^{218}_{85}At \longrightarrow ^{214}_{83}Bi + ^{4}_{2}He$

3. $^{14}_{6}C \longrightarrow ^{0}_{-1}e + ^{14}_{7}N$

4. $^{80}_{35}Br \longrightarrow ^{80}_{36}Kr + ^{0}_{-1}e$

5. $^{214}_{83}Bi \longrightarrow ^{4}_{2}He + ^{210}_{81}Tl$

6. $^{212}_{83}Bi \longrightarrow ^{0}_{-1}e + ^{212}_{84}Po$

NUCLEAR PHYSICS--- IT'S THE SAME TO ME WITH THE FIRST TWO LETTERS INTERCHANGED!

7. $^{80}_{35}Br \longrightarrow ^{0}_{-1}e + ^{80}_{36}Kr$

8. $^{80}_{35}Br \longrightarrow ^{0}_{+1}e + ^{80}_{34}Se$

9. $^{1}_{1}H + ^{7}_{3}Li \longrightarrow ^{4}_{2}He + ^{4}_{2}He$

10. $^{2}_{1}H + ^{3}_{1}H \longrightarrow ^{4}_{2}He + ^{1}_{0}n$

KNOW NUKES!

CONCEPTUAL **Physics** PRACTICE SHEET

Chapter 34: Special Theory of Relativity
Time Dilation

Chapter 34 in your textbook discusses *The Twin Trip*, in which a traveling twin takes a 2-hour journey while a stay-at-home brother records the passage of 2 1/2 hours. Quite remarkable! Times in both frames of reference are marked by flashes of light, sent each 6 minutes from the spaceship, and received on earth at 12-minute intervals for the ship going away, and 3-minute intervals for the ship returning. Read this section in the book carefully, and fill in the clock readings aboard the spaceship when each flash is emitted, and the clock reading on earth when each flash is received.

SHIP LEAVING EARTH

FLASH	TIME ON SHIP WHEN FLASH SENT	TIME ON EARTH WHEN FLASH SEEN
0	12:00	12:00
1	12:06	12:12
2	12:12	12:24
3	12:18	12:36
4	12:24	12:48
5	12:30	1:00
6	12:36	1:12
7	12:42	1:24
8	12:48	1:36
9	12:54	1:48
10	1:00	2:00

SHIP APPROACHING EARTH

FLASH	TIME ON SHIP WHEN FLASH SENT	TIME ON EARTH WHEN FLASH SEEN
11	1:06	2:03
12	1:12	2:06
13	1:18	2:09
14	1:24	2:12
15	1:30	2:15
16	1:36	2:18
17	1:42	2:21
18	1:48	2:24
19	1:54	2:27
20	2:00	2:30

THIS CHECKS: FOR v = 0.6c
$$t = \frac{2h}{\sqrt{1-(\frac{v}{c})^2}} = 2.5 \text{ hr}$$

1 | About Science

Answers

CONCEPTUAL **Physics** 7th EDITION

1. Aristotle's hypothesis was partially correct, for material that makes up the plant comes partly from the soil, but mainly from the air and water. An experiment would be to weigh a pot of soil with a small seedling, then weigh the potted plant later after it has grown. The fact that the grown plant will weigh more is evidence that the plant is composed of more material than the soil offers. By keeping a record of the weight of water used to water the plant, and covering the soil with plastic wrap to minimize evaporation losses, the weight of the grown plant can be compared to the weight of water it absorbs. How can the weight of air taken in by the plant be estimated?

2. To publicly change your mind about your ideas is a sign of strength rather than a sign of weakness. It takes more courage to change your ideas when confronted with counter evidence than to hold fast to your ideas. If a young person's ideas and view of the world are no different after a lifetime of varied experience, then that person was either miraculously blessed with unusual wisdom at an early age, or learned nothing. The latter situation is more likely. Education is learning that which you don't yet know about. It would be arrogant to think you know it all in the later stages of your education, and stupid to think so at the beginning of your education.

3. The examples are endless. Knowledge of electricity, for example, has proven to be extremely useful. The number of people who have been harmed by electricity who understood it are far fewer than the number of people who are harmed by it that don't understand it. A fear of electricity is much more harmful than useful to one's general health and attitude.

4. The ratio of pole's shadow to pole's height should be the same as the ratio of distance between Alexandria and Syene to the earth's radius.

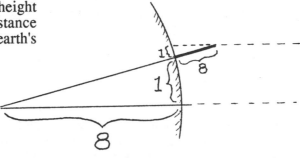

5. The sun's radius is about 7×10^8 m, and distance between earth and moon is approximately 4×10^8 m. So the sun's radius is much larger, nearly twice. The earth and moon at their present distance from each other would easily fit inside the sun. The sun is *really* big!

1-1

2 | Linear Motion

Answers

1. Aristotle would interpret the slowing down and stopping of the ball as only natural. He would claim that since no one was pushing the ball it should return to its proper state of rest. Galileo's interpretation of the same event would be entirely different. To him the slowing down of the ball would be attributed to resistance (friction) that the table offers to the ball. In the absence of table resistance and air resistance the ball would roll "indefinitely."

2. Galileo had no adequate time pieces, so he used inclined planes to effectively lower the acceleration so he could more easily investigate it. The relationships seen at small angles are the same when the incline is vertical, when the acceleration is a full g.

3. A golf ball normally has the greater average speed during the times it is moving in a game, followed by a baseball, then a football.

4. The speeds of both are exactly the same, but the velocities are not. Velocity includes direction, and since the directions of the airplanes are opposite, their velocities are opposite. The velocities would be equal only if both speed and direction were the same.

5. False. Charlie may drive his car around the block at constant speed, but not at constant velocity, because he must change his direction at the corners.

6. An object moving in a circular path at constant speed is a simple example of constant acceleration at constant speed, because it is changing direction (velocity) at a constant rate. Any object that changes direction while traveling at constant speed, changes velocity (direction is a part of velocity). Thus, it is not possible for an ob-ject to accelerate and move at constant velocity at the same time. Constant velocity means no change in motion, speed or direction — which means no acceleration.

7. The acceleration of an object is in a direction opposite to its velocity when velocity is decreasing, i.e., a ball rising, or a car braking to a stop.

8. You would not have to lean to compensate for uniform motion. You would lean only to compensate for *changes* in motion — for accelerated motion. If the car is moving with constant acceleration, velocity would be changing constantly and you would lean into the direction of the acceleration. If the car gains in speed, you'd lean forward; if braking, you'd lean backward; if rounding a curve, you'd lean into the curve. Once this leaning posture is assumed, however, no further adjustment would be necessary as long as the acceleration doesn't change.

9. Only on hill B does the acceleration decrease with time, for the hill becomes less steep as motion progresses. When the hill levels off, acceleration will be zero. On hill A, acceleration is constant. On hill C, acceleration increases as the hill becomes steeper.

10. The acceleration is zero, for no change in velocity occurs. Whenever the change in velocity is zero, the acceleration is zero. If the velocity is "steady," "constant," or "uniform," the change in velocity is zero. Remember the definition of acceleration!

11. The acceleration of free fall at the end of the 5th, 10th, or any number of seconds will be g. Its *velocity* has different values at different times, but since it is free from the effects of air resistance, its *acceleration* remains a constant g.

12. Since acceleration = 10 m/s^2, speed would increase 10 m/s each second. (See Table 2.2, page 29.) (Using 9.8 m/s^2 changes these values by 2%.)

13. Distances would be successively larger and larger since the average speed each second is larger. (See Table 2.3, page 31.)

14. Whether up or down, the rate of change of speed with respect to time is 10 m/s^2 (or 9.8 m/s^2), so each second while going up the speed decreases by 10 m/s (or 9.8 m/s). Coming down, the speed increases 10 m/s (or 9.8 m/s) each second. So when air resistance can be neglected, the time going up equals the time coming down (like running movie film backward.)

15. Both will strike the ground below at the same speed. That's because the ball thrown upward will have the same initial speed when it returns to its starting position — the same as the ball thrown downward.

16. If air resistance is not a factor, its acceleration is the same 9.8 m/s^2 regardless of its initial velocity. Thrown downward, its velocity will be greater, but not its acceleration.

17. Its acceleration would actually be less if the air resistance it encounters at high speed retards its motion. (We will treat this concept in detail in Chapter 4.)

18. If it were not for the slowing effect of the air, raindrops would strike the ground with the speed of high-speed bullets!

19.

Time (in seconds)	Velocity (in meters/second)	Distance (in meters)
0	0	0
1	10	5
2	20	20
3	30	45
4	40	80
5	50	125
6	60	180
7	70	245
8	80	320
9	90	405
10	100	500

30. How you respond may or may not agree with the author's response: There are few pure examples in physics, for most real situations involve a combination of effects. There is usually a "first order" effect that is basic to the situation, but then there are 2nd, 3rd, and even 4th or more order effects that interact also. If we begin our study of some concept by considering all effects together before we have studied their contributions separately, understanding is likely to be difficult. To have a better understanding of what is going on, we strip a situation of all but the first order effect, and then examine that. When that is well in hand, then we proceed to investigate the other effects for a fuller understanding.

Chapter 2 Problem Solutions

1. $v = \dfrac{d}{t} = \dfrac{100m}{10s} = \textbf{10 m/s}$.

By unit analysis: $10\dfrac{m}{s} \times \dfrac{1mi}{1609m} \times \dfrac{3600s}{1hr} = \textbf{22.4 mi/hr}$. (Note how units guide conversion!)

2. $a = \dfrac{change\ in\ velocity}{time\ interval} = \dfrac{-100\ km/h}{10s} = \textbf{-10 km/h·s}$. (The vehicle decelerates at 10 km/h·s.)

3. Since it starts going up at 30 m/s and loses 10 m/s each second, its time going up is 3 seconds. Its time returning is also 3 seconds, so it's in the air for a total of **6 seconds**. Distance up (or down) is $1/2\ gt^2 = 5 \times 3^2 = \textbf{45 m}$. Or from $d = vt$, where average velocity is $(30 + 0)/2 = 15$ m/s, and time is 3 seconds, we also get $d = 15$ m/s x 3 s = 45 m.

4. (a) The velocity of the ball at the top of its vertical trajectory is instantaneously **zero**.
   (b) One second before reaching its top, its velocity is **10 m/s**.
   (c) The amount of change in velocity is **10 m/s** during this 1-second interval (or any other 1-second interval).
   (d) One second after reaching its top its velocity is **-10 m/s** — equal in magnitude but oppositely directed to its value 1 second before reaching the top.
   (e) The amount of change in velocity during this (or any) 1-second interval is **10 m/s**.
   (f) In 2 seconds, the amount of change in velocity is **20 m/s**.
   (g) The acceleration of the ball is **10 m/s²** before reaching the top, when reaching the top, and after reaching the top. In all cases acceleration is downward, toward the earth.

5. Using $g = 10$ m/s², we see that $v = gt = (10$ m/s²$)(10$ s$) = \textbf{100 m/s}$;
   $v = \dfrac{(v_{beginning} + v_{final})}{2} = \dfrac{(0 + 100)}{2} = \textbf{50 m/s, downward}$.
   We can get "how far" from either $d = vt = (50$ m/s$)(10$ s$) = \textbf{500 m}$,
   or equivalently, $d = 1/2\ gt^2 = 5\ (10)^2 = 500$ m.
   (Physics is nice...we get the same distance using either formula!)

6. $v = gt = (10$ m/s²$)(8$ s$) = \textbf{80 m/s}$.
   The average speed of fall is 40 m/s, so $d = vt = (40$ m/s$)(8$ s$) = \textbf{320 m}$;
   or $d = 1/2\ gt^2 = 5\ (8^2) = 320$ m.

7. $a = \dfrac{change\ in\ velocity}{time\ interval} = \dfrac{[50m/s - 0]}{10s} = \textbf{5 m/s}^2$.

8. How fast: at $a = 20$ m/s², $v = at = (20$ m/s²$)(1$ s$) = \textbf{20 m/s}$.
   How far: $d = 1/2\ at^2 = 1/2\ (20$ m/s²$)(1$ s$)^2 = \textbf{10 m}$.
   Note these values make sense, for they are simply **twice** those if the acceleration were half as much, 10 m/s².

9. From $d = 1/2\ gt^2 = 5\ t^2$, $t = \sqrt{d/5} = \sqrt{(0.6)/5} = 0.35$ s. Double for a hang time of **0.7 s**.

10. Time up = 0.5 s; so $d = 1/2\ gt^2 = 5\ t^2 = 5(0.5)^2 = \textbf{1.25 m}$.

3 | Nonlinear Motion

Answers

1. Your swimming speed would be the same as that of the river for a 45°-45°-90° triangle described by the width, your distance downsteam, and the diagonal path you follow. Since your distance downstream is less than the width of the river, you swim faster than the river flows.

2. The streaks are slanted on the window of a moving car because the rain has not only a vertical component of motion, but a horizontal component of motion equal to the speed of the car. At 45° the horizontal and vertical components are equal, so the car travels at the speed of the falling rain. (Because of air resistance, raindrops normally have a constant speed by the time they reach the ground.)

3. The thrown ball maintains its horizontal component of motion while in air, and normally would return to the moving car. But since the car slows while the ball continues in its motion, the ball will land in front of its thrown position.

4. As seen from the side of the road (the rest frame of reference), the ball moves sideways with the same speed as the bus while it falls vertically. It is like the path of the ball rolled off the table in Figure 3.9. So although the path appears as a straight vertical line from the frame of reference of the moving bus, it appears as a parabola from the side of the road.

5. The path of the falling object will be a parabola as seen by an observer off to the side on the ground. You, however, will see the object fall straight down along a vertical path beneath you. You'll be directly above the point of impact. In the case of air resistance, where the airplane maintains constant velocity via its engines while airdrag decreases the horizontal component of velocity for the falling object, impact will be somewhere behind the airplane.

6. When air resistance is negligible, the downward component of motion for a projectile is identical to that of free fall.

7. When air resistance is negligible, there is no acceleration in the horizontal direction of motion. So the horizontal component of motion is the same all along the rock's trajectory.

8. Where air resistance is negligible, a projectile will fall 4.9 m below an initial straight-line path in one second.

9. The stone will drop a vertical distance of 4.9 m whether it is simply dropped, or tossed horizontally outward. If you toss the stone horizontally and estimate the time it takes to strike the ground, you can estimate the height from the relationship $d = 4.9t^2$. (Or $d = 5t^2$.)

10. For very slow-moving bullets, the dropping distance is comparable to the horizontal range, and the resulting parabola is easily noticed (the curved path of a bullet tossed sideways by hand, for example). For highspeed bullets, the same drop occurs in the same time, but the horizontal distance traveled is so large that the trajectory is "stretched out" and hardly seems to curve at all. But it does curve. All bullets will drop equal distances in equal times, whatever their speed. (It is interesting to note that air resistance plays only a small role, since the air resistance acting *downward* is practically the same for a slow-moving or fast-moving bullet.)

11. Hold the hose at 45° (see Figure 3.15) — slightly less if you're holding it high off the ground. [Incidentally, there is a simple rule for estimating how much less than 45° to project

when the landing spot is below the launching elevation, like downhill. Simply subtract *half* the angle of the "incline" from 45°. For example, if the landing spot is 10° below the launch point, project at 45° - (10°/2) = 40° for maximum horizontal displacement. If the landing spot is above the launching point, say uphill, then add half the angle of "incline" above the launch point to 45°. So if your projectile is to land uphill by 10°, launch it at 50°. This rule holds for maximum *horizontal* distance from launch point to landing point when air resistance is not important.]

12. The monkey is hit as the dart and monkey meet in mid air. For a fast-moving dart, their meeting place is closer to the monkey's starting point than for a slower-moving dart. The dart and monkey fall equal vertical distances — the monkey below the tree, and the dart below the line of sight — because they both fall with equal accelerations for equal times.

13. Any vertically projected object has zero speed at the top of its trajectory. But if it is fired at an angle, only its vertical component of velocity is zero and the velocity of the projectile at the top is equal to its horizontal component of velocity. This would be 100 m/s when the 141-m/s projectile is fired at 45°.

14. The catching and pitching speeds will be the same (Figure 3.17). If air resistance is a factor, the catching speed will be less than 20 m/s.

15. Hang time depends only on your vertical component of motion. If you can increase this vertical component from a running position rather than from a dead stop, then hang time is also increased. In any case, hang time depends only on the vertical component.

16. The hang time will be the same, in accord with the answer to the preceding exercise. Hang time depends only on height, not on horizontal distance moved across a level floor.

17. An 8-km/s horizontally moving projectile does not strike the earth's surface because it falls a distance of 4.9 m beneath an 8-km tangent line each second, exactly as much as the earth curves. So the projectile falls around the earth rather than into it and becomes an earth satellite.

18. Because the moon is smaller, the curvature of a satellite in circular orbit is less, which means less speed. And because gravity is weaker on the moon, the satellite wouldn't curve as much as on earth, which means even less speed. (A satellite in close moon orbit travels only 0.2 the speed of a satellite in close orbit about the earth.)

19. The moon's tangential velocity is what keeps the moon coasting around the earth rather than crashing into it. If its tangential velocity were reduced to zero, then it would fall straight into the earth!

20. According to $v = r \omega$, if the RPMs (ω) are doubled, the speed is doubled. Then if r is also doubled, the speed doubles again and the ladybug moves with four times its initial speed.

21. According to $v = r \omega$, the outer part (larger r) of the record travels faster, so the needle rides faster at the beginning of a recording. If fidelity increases with speed, the highest fidelity occurs for cuts at the beginning of the record.

22. Large diameter tires mean you travel farther with each revolution of the tire. So you'll be moving faster than your speedometer indicates. (A speedometer actually measures the RPMs of the wheels and displays this as mi/h or km/h. The conversion from RPMs to the mi/h or km/h reading assumes the wheels are a certain size.) Oversize wheels give too low a reading, because they really travel farther per revolution than the speedometer indicates; and undersize wheels give too high a reading because the wheels do not go as far per revolution.

Chapter 3 Problem Solutions

1. Ground velocity will be **141 km/h at 45°** from the direction of the wind, for your path makes the diagonal of a 45°-45°-90° triangle. ($v = \sqrt{[100^2 + 100^2]} = 141$)

2. The bullet will be in the air for 2 seconds (Table 2.3, page 31), and will travel a horizontal distance of 250 m/s x 2 s = **500 m**.

3. In 30 seconds the airplane will travel a horizontal distance of **8400 m** (as seen from $d = vt$ = 280 m/s x 30 s = 8400 m). The falling engine will travel the **same horizontal distance** in the same time if air resistance is neglected. (In a more practical case, air resistance is overcome for the plane by its engines, but not for the falling engine which we assume is no longer operating, so its speed is reduced by air drag and it covers less than 8400 horizontal meters.)

4. John and Tracy's horizontal jumping velocity will be the horizontal distance traveled divided by the time of the jump. The horizontal distance will be a minimum of 20 m, but what will be the time? Aha, the same time it would take John and Tracy to fall straight down! From Table 2.3 we see such a fall would take 4 seconds. Or we can find the time from

$$d_{down} = 5\ t^2, \text{ where rearrangement gives } t = \sqrt{\frac{d}{5}} = \sqrt{\frac{80}{5}} = 4 \text{ s.}$$

So to travel 20 m horizontally in this time means John and Tracy should jump horizontally at

$$v_{horizontal} = \frac{d_{horizontal}}{t} = \frac{20 \text{ m}}{4 \text{ s}} = \textbf{5 m/s.}$$

But a velocity of 5 m/s would put them at the edge of the pool, so they should jump a little faster. If we knew the length of the pool, we could calculate how much faster without hitting the far end of the pool.

5. Hang time depends only on the vertical distance attained. From $d = 5t^2$, the time for ascending 1.2 m is $t = \sqrt{d/5} = \sqrt{(1.2)/5} = 0.49$ s. Double this for total time ascending and decending and we get a hang time of **1 s**.

6. Since the bicycle moves 2 m with each turn of the wheel, and the wheel turns once each second, the linear speed of the bicycle is **2 m/s**.

7. The linear speed, more correctly, "tangential speed" $v = distance/time$, will be the circumference of the ferris wheel divided by the time for one revolution, 30 s. From geometry,

Circumference = $2\pi r = 2(3.14)(10 \text{ m}) = 62.8$ m.

So the linear speed $v = \dfrac{62.8 \text{ m}}{30 \text{ s}} = \textbf{2.1 m/s.}$

4 | Newton's Laws of Motion

Answers

1. The less massive the camera, the more "recoil" it will experience when the shutter is released. The more massive a tripod, the less it will tend to move in response to extraneous forces.

2. When carrying a heavy load there is more mass involved; more tendency to remain moving. If a load in your hand is moving toward a wall, its tendency is to remain moving when contact is made. This tends to squash your hand if its between the load and the wall — an unfortunate example of Newton's lst law in action.

3. A massive cleaver is more effective in chopping vegetables because its greater mass contributes to greater tendency to keep moving as the cleaver chops through the vegetables.

4. The inertia of a whole roll resists the large acceleration of a sharp jerk and only a single piece tears. If a towel is pulled slowly, a small acceleration is demanded of the roll and it unwinds. This is similar to the hanging ball and string shown in Figure 4.1.

5. An object in motion tends to stay in motion, hence the discs tend to compress upon each other just as the hammer head is compress-ed onto the handle in Figure 4.1. This compression results in people being slightly shorter at the end of the day than in the morning. The discs tend to separate while sleeping in a prone position, so you regain your full height by morning. This is easily noticed if you find a point you can almost reach up to in the eve-ning, and then find it is easily reached in the morning. Try it and see!

6. A stone will fall vertically if released from rest. If the stone is dropped from the top of the mast of a moving ship, the horizontal motion is not changed when the stone it dropped. Like Exercise 5 in Chapter 3, the path of the stone will be parabolic as seen from a frame of reference at rest on shore. If air resistance is not a factor, and the ship doesn't accelerate while the stone falls, it will move as far horizontally as the ship moves in the same time, and hit the same place below that it would hit if the ship were at anchor. From the frame of reference of the moving ship, the stone falls in a vertical straight line path.

7. A body in motion tends to remain in motion, so you move with the moving earth whether or not your feet are in contact with it. When you jump, your horizontal motion matches that of the earth, you travel with it. Hence the wall does not slam into you.

8. This is similar to Exercise 5. If the ball is shot while the train is moving at constant velocity (constant speed in a straight line), its horizontal motion before, during, and after being fired is the same as that of the train; so the ball falls back into the chimney as it would have if the train were at rest. If the train accelerates, the ball will miss, because the ball's horizontal speed will match the train speed as the ball is fired — but the train continues to gain speed while the ball is in the air, so the chimney has advanced in front of the ball by the time it falls back to the train (or it falls in front of the chimney if the acceleration is negative — slowing down). On a circular track, the ball would also miss the chimney, for the ball will move along a tangent to the track while the train turns away from this tangent. So the ball returns to the chimney in the first case, and misses in the second and third cases because of the *change* in motion (acceleration).

9. Although the amount of air space the car occupies changes (its volume), neither the mass nor the weight of a junked car change when it is crushed.

10. Ten kilograms weighs 98 N on the earth (weight = mg = 10 kg x 9.8 m/s^2 = 98 N). On the moon the weight would be 1/6 of 98 N = 16.3 N. The mass would be 10 kg everywhere.

11. Mass in kilograms is weight in pounds divided by 2.2 (if we are at the earth's surface). One's weight in newtons is found by multiplying one's weight in pounds by 9.8/2.2. For example, if you weigh 100 pounds, your mass is 100/2.2 = 45.45 kg. Your weight in newtons is 100 (9.8/2.2) = 445.5 N. Once mass is determined, find weight by using the defining relationship, Wt = *mg*.

12. To see why the acceleration gains as a rocket burns its fuel, look at the equation $a = F/m$. As fuel is burned, the mass of the rocket becomes less. As *m* decreases, *a* increases! There is simply less mass to be accelerated as fuel is consumed.

13. If an object has no acceleration, we can conclude that no *net* force acts on it. There may be any number of impressed forces, but if the object does not accelerate their resultant will be zero.

14. No, an object cannot round a curve in the absence of a force. When any object moves in a curved path it is accelerated, requiring a force.

15. When standing on a floor, the floor pushes upward against your feet with a force equal to that of your weight. This upward force (called the *normal force*) and your weight are oppositely directed, and since they both act on the same body, you, they cancel to produce a net force on you of zero — hence, you are not accelerated. (Be careful here, the normal force is not the reaction to your weight — your weight is the world pulling on you, and reaction to this is you pulling on the world. See the next exercise.)

16. The scale will read half her weight. [In this way, the net force (upward pull of left rope + upward pull of right rope - weight) = 0.]

17. In the left figure, Harry is supported by two strands of rope that share his weight (like the little girl in the previous exercise). So each strand supports only 250 N, below the breaking point. Total force up supplied by ropes equals weight acting downward, giving a net force of zero and no acceleration. In the right figure, Harry is now supported by one strand, which for Harry's well-being requires that the tension be 500 N. Since this is above the breaking point of the rope, it breaks. The net force on Harry is then only his weight, giving him a downward acceleration of *g*. The sudden return to zero acceleration changes his vacation plans.

18. The forces must be equal and opposite because they are the only forces acting on the person, who obviously is not accelerating. Note that the pair of forces do *not* comprise an action-reaction pair, however, for they act on the *same* body. The downward force, the man's weight, *earth pulls down on man*; has the reaction *man pulls up on earth*, not the floor pushing up on his feet. And the upward force of the floor on the man's feet has the reaction of man's feet on the floor, not the interaction between the man and earth. [If you find this confusing, you may take solace in the fact that Newton himself had trouble applying his 3rd law to certain situations. Apply the rule, A on B; B on A, as in Figure 4.20.]

19. The scale will read 100 N, the same it would read if one of the ends were tied to a wall instead of tied to the 100-N hanging weight. Although the net force on the system is zero, the tension in the rope within the system is 100 N, as shown on the scale reading.

20. If an object is not moving, its acceleration is zero. This tells us the net force is zero, so we know that another force of equal magnitude must oppose the force we know about.

21. When you drive at constant velocity, the zero net force on the car is the resultant of the driving force that your engine supplies against the friction drag force. You continue to apply a driving force to offset the drag force that would otherwise slow the car.

22. High-speed meteorites grazing the earth's atmosphere burn up because of friction against the air.

23. A soaring balloon moves with the air; no air blows past the balloon, nor does the balloon move through the air. The balloon is "at one" with the air. Hence there is no sensation of air resistance.

24. When held at rest the upward support force equals the weight of the apple and the net force is zero. When released, the upward support force is no longer there and the net force is the weight of the apple, 1 N. (If the apple falls fast enough for air resistance, then the net force will be less than 1 N, and eventually reach zero if the apple falls fast enough for the air resistance to build up to 1 N.)

25. A stick of dynamite nor anything contains force. We will see later that a stick of dynamite contains "energy," which is capable of producing forces when an interaction of some kind occurs.

26. If the dog wags its tail (action), the tail will in turn wag the dog (reaction). How noticeable this is depends on the relative masses of the dog and the tail being wagged!

27. When the barbell is accelerated upward, the force exerted by the athlete is greater than the weight of the barbell (the barbell, in turn, pushes with greater force against the athlete). When acceleration is downward, the force supplied by the athlete is less.

28. In accord with Newton's 3rd law, when you pull up on your bootstraps, your bootstraps pull down on you. Suppose, for example, that you pulled your boots upward, away from the scale with a force of 200 N. Would the scale read 200 N less? No, because your bootstraps would pull you downward with 200 N, which would be transmitted through your legs to compensate for the 200 N loss. In any event, only two forces act on the weighing scale — the weight of your mass pushing down, and the normal support force of the scale pushing up. Your mass, and hence your weight, does not change by pulling up on your bootstraps.

29. When you pull up on the handle bars, the handle bars in turn pull down on you. This downward force is transmitted to the pedals.

30. In accord with Newton's 3rd law, if the earth exerts a force of 1000 N on the satellite, the satellite will exert an oppositely directed 1000 N of force on the earth. Or better, the earth and the satellite pull on each other with 1000 N of force.

31. In accord with Newton's 3rd law, if the earth pulls down on your body, your body will pull up equally on the earth.

32. The strongman can exert only equal forces on both cars, just as your push against a wall equals the push of the wall on you. Like-wise for two walls, or two freight cars. Since their masses are equal, they will undergo equal accelerations and move equally.

33. Like the preceding exercise, the force on each cart will be the same. But since the masses are different, the accelerations will differ. The twice-as-massive cart will undergo only half the acceleration of the less massive cart. The less massive cart will spring apart with twice the speed of the more massive cart.

34. The friction is 200 N, which cancels your 200-N push to yield the zero net force that accounts for the constant velocity (zero acceleration). Although the friction force is equal and oppositely directed to the applied force, the two do *not* make an action-reaction pair of forces.

That's because both forces *do* act on the same object — the crate. The reaction to your push on the crate is the crate's push back on you. The reaction to the friction of the floor on the crate is the friction of the crate acting on the floor.

35. In accord with Newton's 3rd law, the force on each will be of the same magnitude. But the effect of the force (acceleration) will be different for each because of the different mass. The more massive truck undergoes less change in motion than the Volks.

36. The forces on each are the same in magnitude, and their masses are the same, so their accelerations will be the same. They will slide equal distances of 6 meters to the midpoint.

37. The twice-as-massive person will undergo half the acceleration and slide half as far as the less massive person — that is, 4 m for the more massive person, and 8 m for the less massive person [so their combined sliding distance equals the 12 m].

38. The forces do not cancel because they act on different things — one acts on the horse, and the other acts on the wagon. It's true that the wagon pulls back on the horse, and this prevents the horse from running as fast as it could without the attached wagon. But the force acting on the wagon (the pull by the horse minus friction) divided by the mass of the wagon, produces the acceleration of the wagon. Toaccelerate, the horse must push against the ground with more force than it exerts on the wagon.

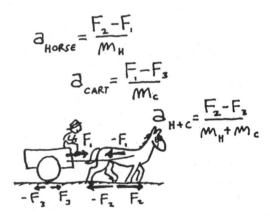

$$a_{HORSE} = \frac{F_2 - F_1}{m_H}$$

$$a_{CART} = \frac{F_1 - F_3}{m_C}$$

$$a_{H+C} = \frac{F_2 - F_3}{m_H + m_C}$$

39. A Cadillac and a Volkswagen will roll down a hill with equal accelerations for the same reason they will fall with equal accelerations. The ratios of components of weight to mass for each on the same incline are the same, just as the ratios of weights to mass for freefall are the same. (We neglect here the effects of friction and rotational effects of the wheels and so forth.)

40. Just before a falling body attains terminal velocity, there is still a downward acceleration because weight is still greater than air resistance. When the air resistance builds up to equal the weight, terminal velocity is reached. Then weight is equal and opposite to the force of air resistance.

41. The terminal velocity attained by the dropped tennis ball is the same whether dropped from 50 stories or 20 stories. Once terminal velocity is reached, falling extra distance does not affect the speed with which it hits the ground.

42. As an object falls faster through the air, air resistance increases which effectively diminishes the net force (weight - air resistance), which in turn reduces the acceleration. So as velocity increases, acceleration decreases!

43. Air resistance is not really negligible for so high a drop, so the heavier ball does strike the ground first. [This idea is shown in Figure 4.17.] But although a twice-as-heavy ball strikes first, it doesn't fall twice as fast as Aristotle's followers believed.

44. The heavier tennis ball will strike the ground first for the same reason the heavier parachutist in Figure 4.16 strikes the ground first. Note that although the air resistance on the heavier ball is small compared to the weight of the ball, it is greater than the air resistance that acts on the other ball. Why? Because the heavier ball falls faster and encounters more air in any instant.

45. The acceleration at the top or anywhere else in free fall is 9.8 m/s^2, downward. The velocity of the rock is momentarily zero, but the rate of change of velocity is still there. Or better, by Newton's 2nd law, the force of gravity acts at the top as elsewhere; divide this net force by the mass and you have the acceleration of free fall. That is, $a = F_{net}/m = mg/m = g$.

46. Air resistance decreases the velocity of a moving object. Hence the ball hits the ground with less speed in air than in a vacuum. The effect is easy to see for a feather projected upward by a sling shot. No way will it return to its starting point with its initial speed.

47. The ball rises in less time than it falls. By exaggerating the circumstance and considering the feather example in the preceding answer, the time for the feather to flutter from its maximum altitude is clearly longer than the time it took to attain that altitude. The same is true for the not-so-obvious case of the ball.

48. The path of the falling bullet curves more and more toward the vertical because the vertical component of its velocity increases and becomes very large compared to the horizontal component of velocity. The horizontal component of velocity dimin-ishes because of air resistance, but so long as it is greater than zero, the resultant of horizontal and vertical velocities can approach the vertical but never reach it.

Chapter 4 Problem Solutions

1. The acceleration of each is the **same**: $a = F/m = 2$ N/ 2 kg = 1 N/1 kg = **1 m/s^2**.
   [Incidentally, from the definition that 1 N = 1 kg·m/s^2, you can see that 1 N/kg is the same as 1 m/s^2.]

2. For the jumbo jet: $a = F/m = 4(30,000N)/30,000$ kg = **4 m/s^2**.

3. The wall pushes with the same amount of force, **30 N**. Acceleration $= \dfrac{F}{m} = \dfrac{30N}{60kg} = $ **0.5 m/s^2**.

4. Frictional force $= ma = (50kg)(5m/s^2) = $ **250 N**.

5 | Momentum

Answers

1. Supertankers are so massive, that even at modest speeds their motional inertia, or *momenta*, are enormous. This means enormous impulses are needed for changing motion. How can large impulses be produced with modest forces? By applying modest forces over long periods of time. Hence the force of the water resistance over the time it takes to coast 25 kilometers sufficiently reduces the momentum.

2. When you are brought to a halt in a moving car, an impulse, the product of force and time, reduces your momentum. During a collision, padded dashboards increase the time of impact while reducing the force of impact. The impulse equals your change in momentum.

3. This is another illustration of the previous exercise. The time during which momentum decreases is lengthened, thereby decreasing the jolting force of the rope.

4. The wing exerts a downward impulse on air it encounters, and produces a downward change in the momentum of oncoming air. The air at the same time exerts an upward impulse on the wing, which produces lift.

5. The impulse required to stop the momentum of a heavy truck is considerably more than the impulse required to stop a skateboard moving with the same speed. The force required to stop either, however, depends on the time during which it is applied. Stopping the skateboard in a split second results in a certain force. Apply less than this amount of force on the moving truck and given enough time, the truck will come to a halt.

6. The momentum of recoil of the world is 10 units of momentum. Again, this is not apparent because the mass of the earth is so enormous that its recoil velocity is imperceptible. (If the masses of earth and person were equal, both would move at equal speeds in opposite directions).

7. The momentum of the falling apple is transferred to the earth. Interestingly enough, when the apple is released, both the earth and the apple move toward each other with equal and oppositely directed momenta. Because of the earths enormous mass, its motion is imperceptible. When the apple and earth hit each other, their momenta are brought to a halt — zero, the same value as before.

8. Impact with a boxing glove extends the time during which momentum of the fist is reduced, and lessens the force. A punch with a bare fist involves less time and therefore more force.

9. When a boxer hits his opponent, the opponent contributes to the impulse that changes the momentum of the punch. When punches miss, no impulse is supplied by the opponent — all effort that goes into reducing the momentum of the punches is supplied by the boxer himself. This tires the boxer. This is very evident to a boxer who can punch a heavy bag in the gym for hours and not tire, but who finds by contrast that a few minutes in the ring with an opponent is a tiring experience.

10. Without this slack, a locomotive might simply sit still and spin its wheels. The loose coupling enables a longer time for bringing the entire train up to momentum, requiring less force of the locomotive wheels against the track. In this way, the overall required impulse is broken into a series of smaller impulses. This loose coupling is very important for braking as well.

11. The internal force of the brake brings the wheel to rest. But the wheel, after all, is attached to the tire which makes contact with the road surface. It is the force of the road on the slowly-rotating or nonrotating tires that stops the car.

12. To get to shore, the person may throw clothing. The momentum of the clothing will be accompanied by the thrower's oppositely-directed momentum. In this way, one can recoil towards shore. (One can also blow, like a jet or a rocket.)

13. If no momentum is imparted to the ball, no oppositely directed momentum will be imparted to the thrower. Going through the motions of throwing has no net effect. If at the beginning of the throw we begin recoiling backward, at the end of the throw where we pull backward on the ball to keep it from leaving, we recoil forward. No net momentum change means no net recoil.

14. The previous two exercises provide such examples. Momentum changes are always accompanied by equal and opposite impulses, which include equal and opposite forces. If we exert a force on something we throw, there is an equal and opposite force exerted on us. In such interactions we can equally as well explain them in terms of Newton's 3rd law, or in terms of momentum conservation. Either way may be considered fundamental.

15. Both recoiling carts have the same amount of momentum. So the cart with twice the mass will have half the speed of the less massive cart. That is, $2m(v/2) = mv$.

16. Momentum is not conserved for the ball itself, because an impulse is exerted on it (gravitational force x time). So the ball gains momentum. It is in the *absence* of an external force that momentum doesn't change. If the whole earth and the rolling ball are taken together as a system, then the gravitational interaction between the earth and the ball are internal forces and no external impulse acts. Then the momentum of the ball is accompanied by an equal and opposite momentum of the earth, which results in no change in momentum.

17. The large momentum of the spurting water is met by a recoil that makes the hose difficult to hold, just as a shotgun is difficult to hold when it fires birdshot.

18. The gun would recoil with a speed ten times greater than the muzzle velocity. Firing such a gun in the conventional way would not be a good idea!

19. The velocities of the bullet and recoiling rifle are not equal and opposite. The net velocity before and after firing are very different, and are therefore not conserved. If the masses of the bullet and rifle are the same, however, then in this special case the velocities will be conserved.

20. We can look at rocket propulsion via Newton's third law or via momentum conservation. Just as a rocket exerts a force on its exhaust gases, the gases exert a reaction force on the rocket. So we can say a rocket is propelled by the force, or the impulse, given to it by the exhaust gases. Momentum given to the exhaust gases is countered with an equal and opposite momentum given to the rocket. This propulsion is more effective in the absence of an atmosphere because there is no air resistance to deal with.

21. The craft moves to the right. This is because there are two impulses that act on the craft: one is that of the wind against the sail, and the other is that of the fan re-coiling from the wind it produces. These impulses are oppositely directed, but are they equal in magnitude? No, because of bouncing. The wind bounces from the sail and produces a greater impulse than if it merely stopped. This greater impulse on the sail produces a net impulse in the forward direction, toward the right. We can see this in terms of forces as well. Note in the sketch on the next page there are two force pairs to consider: (1) the fan-air force pair, and (2) the air-sail

force pair. Because of bouncing, the air-sail pair is greater. Solid vectors show forces exerted on the craft; dashed vectors show forces exerted on the air. The net force on the craft is forward, to the right.

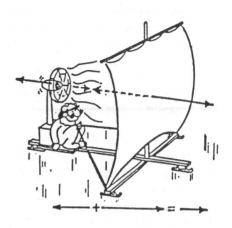

22. If the air is brought to a halt by the sail, then the impulse against the sail will be equal and opposite to the impulse on the fan. There will be no net impulse and no change in momentum. The boat will remain motionless. Bouncing counts!

23. Removing the sail and turning the fan around is the best means of propelling the boat! Then maximum impulse is exerted on the craft. [Such propellor-driven boats are used where the water is very shallow, like in the Florida Everglades.]

24. By Newton's 3rd law, the force on the bug is equal in magnitude and opposite in direction to the force on the car windshield. The rest is logic: Since the time of impact is the same for both, the amount of impulse is the same for both, which means they both undergo the same change in momentum. The change in momentum of the bug is evident because of its large change in speed. The same change in momentum of the considerably more massive car is not evident, for the change in speed is correspondingly very small. Nevertheless, the magnitude of $m\Delta V$ for the bug is equal to $M\Delta v$ for the car!

25. The magnitude of force, impulse, and change in momentum will be the same for each. The Volkswagen undergoes the greater acceleration because its mass is less.

26. Cars brought to a rapid halt constitute a change in momentum, and a corresponding impulse. But greater momentum change occurs if the cars bounce, with correspondingly greater impules and therefore greater damage. Less damage results if the cars stick upon impact than if they bounce apart.

27. We assume the equal strengths of the astronauts means that each throws with the same speed. Since the masses are equal, when the first throws the second, both the first and second move away from each other at equal speeds. Say the thrown astronaut moves to the right with velocity V, and the first recoils with velocity $-V$. When the third makes the catch, both she and the second move to the right at velocity $V/2$ (twice the mass moving at half the speed, like the freight cars in Figure 5-10). When the third makes her throw, she recoils at velocity V (the same speed she imparts to the thrown astronaut) which is added to the $V/2$ she acquired in the catch. So her velocity is $V + V/2 = 3V/2$, to the right — too fast to stay in the game. Why? Because the velocity of the second astronaut is $V/2 - V = -V/2$, to the left — too slow to catch up with the first astronaut who is still moving at $-V$. the game is over. Both the first and the third got to throw the second astronaut only once!

28. Yes, you exert an impulse on a ball that your throw. You also exert an impulse on the ball when you catch it. Since you change its momentum by the same amount in both cases, the impulse you exert in both cases is the same. To catch the ball and then throw it back again at the same speed requires twice as much impulse. On a skateboard, you'd recoil and gain momentum when throwing the ball, you'd also gain the same momentum by catching the ball, and you'd gain twice the momentum if you did both — catch and then throw the ball at its initial speed in the opposite direction.

29. The impulse will be greater if his hand is made to bounce, because there is a greater change in the momentum of his hand and arm, accompanied by a greater impulse. The force he exerts on the bricks is equal and opposite to the force of the bricks on his hand. Fortunately, his hand is resilient and toughened by long practice.

30. Impulse is greater for reflection, which is in effect, bouncing. The vanes therefore recoil more from the silvered sides. The vanes in the sketch therefore rotate clockwise as viewed from above. (This rotation is superseded by a counter rotation when air is present, which is the case for most radiometers. The black surface absorbs radiation and is heated, which warms the nearby air. The surface is pushed away from the warmed air resulting in a recoil that spins the vanes counterclockwise.)

31. Their masses are the same; half speed for the coupled particles means equal masses for the colliding and the target particles. This is like the freight cars of equal mass shown in Figure 5.10.

32. If a ball does not hit straight on, then the target ball flies off at an angle (to the left, say) and has a component of momentum sideways to the initial momentum of the moving ball. To offset this, the striking ball cannot be simply brought to rest, but must fly off in the other direction (say, the right). It will do this in such a way that its sideways component of momentum is equal and opposite to that of the target ball. This means the total sideways momentum is zero — what it was before collision. (See how the sideways components of momentum cancel to zero in Figure 5.15.)

Chapter 5 Problem Solutions

1. From $Ft = \Delta mv$, $F = \dfrac{\Delta mv}{t} = \dfrac{(1000)(20)}{10} = $ **2000 N.**

2. The answer is 4 km/h. Let m be the mass of the freight car, and $4m$ the mass of the diesel engine, and v the speed after both have coupled together. Before collision, the total momentum is due only to the diesel engine, $4m(5 \text{ km/h})$, because the momentum of the freight car is 0. After collision, the combined mass is $(4m + m)$, and combined momentum is $(4m + m)v$. By the conservation of momentum equation:

$$\text{Momentum}_{before} = \text{momentum}_{after}$$
$$4m(5 \text{ km/h}) + 0 = (4m + m)v$$
$$v = \frac{(20m \cdot \text{km/h})}{5m} = \textbf{4 km/h.}$$

3. $\qquad \text{Momentum}_{before} = \text{momentum}_{after}$
$$(5\text{kg})(1\text{m/s}) + (1\text{kg})v = 0$$
$$5\text{m/s} + v = 0$$
$$v = \textbf{-5 m/s.}$$

So if the little fish approaches the big fish at 5 m/s, the momentum after lunch will be zero.

6 | Energy

1. It is easier to stop a lightly loaded truck than a heavier one moving at the same speed because it has less KE and will therefore require less work to stop.

2. For the same momentum, the lighter truck must have a greater speed, and therefore, a greater KE and thus require more work to stop. Whenever two bodies of different masses have the same momentum, the lighter one not only is the faster of the two, it also has the greater KE. That's because speed is squared for KE. (This idea is treated on pages 108 and 109, and in the footnote on page 109.)

3. The metal-to-metal contact of the body of an automobile side-swiping along the older-type metal rails produces considerably less friction to slow the vehicle than the contemporary design, which juts out at the bottom so that the rubber tires of the automobile make contact with the divider. The greater friction of concrete-to-rubber contact does more work in reducing the KE of the vehicles that sideswipe the divider.

4. The PE of the drawn bow as calculated would be an overestimate, (in fact, twice its actual value) because the force applied in drawing the bow begins at zero and increases to its maximum value when fully drawn. It's easy to see that less force and therefore less work is required to first draw the bow halfway, than to draw it the second half of the way to its fully-drawn position. So the work done is not *maximum force x distance drawn*, but *average force x distance drawn*. In this case where force varies directly with distance (and not as the square or some other complicated factor) the average force is simply equal to the initial force + final force, divided by 2. So the PE is equal to the average force applied (which would be half the force at its full-drawn position) multiplied by the distance through which the arrow is drawn.

5. When a rifle with a long barrel is fired, more work is done as the bullet is pushed through the longer distance. A greater KE is the result of the greater work, so of course, the bullet emerges with a greater velocity. (It might be mentioned that the force acting on the bullet is not constant, but decreases with increasing distance inside the barrel.)

6. The KE of the tossed ball relative to occupants in the airplane does not depend on the speed of the airplane. The KE of the ball relative to observers on the ground below, however, is a different matter. KE, like velocity, is relative. So is PE. See the answer to question 2 on page 102.

7. If an object has KE, then it must have momentum — for it is moving. But it can have potential energy without being in motion, and therefore without having momentum. And every object has "energy of being," — as is stated in the celebrated equation $E = mc^2$. So whether an object moves or not, it has some form of energy. If it has KE, then with respect to the frame of reference in which its KE is measured, it also has momentum.

8. The KE of a pendulum bob is maximum where it moves fastest, at the lowermost point; PE is maximum at the uppermost points; When the pendulum bob swings by the point that marks half its maximum height, half its energy is PE and the other half KE (in accordance with energy conservation: total energy = KE + PE).

9. If the ball is given an initial KE, it will return to its starting position with that KE and hit the instructor. (The usual classroom procedure is to release the ball from the nose at rest. Then when it returns it will have no motional energy to bump the nose.)

10. The design is impractical. Note that the summit of each hill on the roller coaster is the same height, so the PE of the car at the top of each hill would be the same. If no energy were spent in overcoming friction, the car would get to the second summit with as much energy as it starts with. But in practice there is considerable friction, and the car would not roll to its initial height and have the same energy. So the maximum height of succeeding summit should be lower to compensate for the work done by the roller coaster car in overcoming friction.

11. You agree with your second classmate. The coaster could just as well encounter a low summit before or after a higher one, so long as the higher one is enough lower than the initial summit to compensate for energy dissipation by friction.

12. Except for the very center of the plane, the force of gravity acts at an angle to the plane, with a component of gravitational force along the plane, and along the direction of motion. This means that the block goes somewhat against gravity when moving away from the central position, and moves somewhat with gravity when coming back. As the object slides farther out on the plane, it seems to be traveling "upward" against earth's gravity and slows down. It finally comes to rest and then slides back and the process repeats itself. It slides back and forth along the plane. From a flat-earth point of view the situation is equivalent to that shown in the sketch.

13. Yes, a car burns more gasoline when its lights are on. The overall consumption of gasoline does not depend on whether or not the engine is running. Lights and other devices run off the battery, which "run down" the battery. The energy used to recharge the battery ultimately comes from the gasoline.

14. Energy cannot be recycled, for energy degrades with each transformation. Although energy in total is not diminished, energy that is concentrated enough to be useful is dissipated. The graveyard of all forms of energy is heat (or more properly, internal energy).

15. Energy is dissipated into non-useful forms in an inefficient machine, and is "lost" only in the loose sense of the word. In the strict sense, it can be accounted for and is therefore not lost.

16. Your friend may not realize that matter itself is congealed energy, so you tell your friend that much more energy in its congealed form is put into the reactor than is put out by the reactor. Less than one percent of the fission fuel is converted to energy.

17. The work that the rock does on the ground is equal to its PE before being dropped, $mgh = 100$ joules. The force of impact, however, depends on the distance that the rock penetrates into the ground. If we do not know this distance we cannot calculate the force. (If we knew the time during which the impulse occurs we could calculate the force from the impulse-momentum relationship — but not knowing the distance or time of the rock's penetrating into the ground, we cannot calculate the force.)

18. When we speak of work done, we must understand work done *on what, by what*. Work is done on the car by an applied force that originates in the engine. The work done by the engine in moving the car is equal to the product of the applied force and the distance moved, not the net force that involves air resistance and other friction forces. When doing work, we think of applied force; when considering acceleration, we think of net force.

19. When air resistance is a factor, the ball will return with less speed (discussed in Exercise 46 in Chapter 4). It therefore will have less KE. The ball gives up energy to the air molecules it encounters. This does not contradict energy conservation, for energy is dissipated, not destroyed.

20. The ball strikes the ground with the *same* speed, whether thrown upward or downward. With respect to the ground below, each ball starts with the same KE and PE, and will strike with the same energy (all in the form of KE at ground level). So they will strike with the same speed. This is assuming negligible air resistance, for if air resistance is a factor, then the ball thrown upward will dissipate more energy in its longer path and strike with some-what less speed. Another way to look at this is to consider Figure 2.9 on page 30; in the absence of air resistance, the ball thrown upward will return to its starting level with the same speed as the ball thrown downward. Both hit the ground at the same speed.

21. Scissors and shears are levers. The applied force is normally exerted over a short distance for scissors so that the output force is exerted over a relatively long distance (except when you want a large cutting force like cutting a piece of tough rope, and you place the rope close to the "fulcrum" so you can multiply force). With metal-cutting shears, the handles are long so that a relatively small input force is exert-ed over a long distance to produce a large output force over a short distance.

22. Exaggeration makes the fate of teacher Paul Robinson easier to assess: Paul would not be so calm if the cement block were replaced with the inertia of a small stone, for inertia plays a role in this demonstration. If the block were unbreakable, the energy that busts it up would instead be transferred to the beds of nails. So it is desirable to use a block that will break upon impact. If the bed consisted of a single nail, finding a successor to Paul would be very difficult, so it is important that the bed have plenty of nails!

23. There is more to the "swinging balls" problem than momentum conservation, which is why the problem wasn't posed in the last chapter. Momentum is certainly conserved if two balls strike with momentum $2mv$ and one ball pops out with momentum $m(2v)$. $2mv = m2v$. We must consider kinetic energy. Two balls would strike with $2(1/2 \ mv^2)$. The single ball to pop out would have twice the energy input:

$$1/2 \ m(2v)^2 = 1/2 \ m(4v^2) = 2mv^2.$$

This is clearly a conservation of energy no-no!

24. An engine that is 100% efficient would not be warm to the touch, nor would its exhaust heat the air, nor would it make any noise, nor would it vibrate, nor would any of its fuel go unused. This is because all these are transfers of energy, which cannot happen if all the energy given to the engine is transformed to useful work.

Chapter 6 Problem Solutions

1. At three times the speed, it has nine times (3^2) the KE and will skid nine times as far; **135 m**.

2. 1 kilowatt-hour = 1000 joule/second for 1 hour. There are 60 x 60 = 3600 seconds in 1 hour, so the total number of joules is 1000 J/s x 3600 s = 3600000 J = **3.6 MJ**.

3. $(Fd)_{input} = (Fd)_{output}$

   $(100 \text{ N x } 10 \text{ cm})_{input} = (? \text{ x } 1 \text{ cm})_{output}$

So we see that the output force is **1000 N**.

4. The freight cars have only **half** the KE possessed by the single car before collision. Check:

   $KE_{before} = 1/2 \ mv^2$.

   $KE_{after} = 1/2 \ (2m)(v/2)^2 = 1/2 \ (2m) \ v^2/4 = 1/4 \ mv^2$.

What becomes of this energy? Most of it goes into heat, the graveyard of kinetic energy.

5. The bowling ball will have a greater momentum after the collision than the golf ball has before collision. This is because of the negative momentum of the golf ball as it rebounds after collision. Before collision, the momentum of the system of two balls is all in the moving golf ball. Call this 1 unit. Then after collision, the momentum of the rebounding golf ball is nearly -1 unit. The momentum (not the speed!) of the bowling ball will have to be nearly +2 units. Why? Because of momentum conservation: Only then will the total momentum before collision (+1) = the total momentum after collision (+2 -1 = +1). The golf ball, however, has the greater KE, very nearly as much as it had before impact. The KE of the bowling ball is very small, because its speed is very small. So although the bowling ball may have nearly twice the momentum of the golf ball, it has only a small fraction of its KE.

6. At 25% efficiency, we'll get only 1/4 of the 40 megajoules in one liter, or 10 MJ. This is the energy to do work, $F \times d$, where

   $F \times d = 1000 \text{ N} \times d = 10 \text{ MJ}$.

   So solve for d and convert MJ to J, and we get

   $$d = \frac{10 \text{ MJ}}{1000 \text{ N}} = \frac{10 \ 000000 \text{ J}}{1000 \text{ N}} = 10 \ 000 \text{ m} = \textbf{10 km}.$$

So under these conditions, the car gets 10 kilometers per liter. (A compact streamlined car encounters about half the 1000 N drag force cited in this problem, and will get twice the fuel economy.)

7. Since 3000 J of effort produce 1000 J of work, the efficiency of the pulley system is (work output)/(work input) = 1/3, or **33.3%**.

8. We can express efficiency as a ratio of (power output)/(power input), since the times for each are equal [where power = energy/time].

So, Efficiency = (power output)/(power input) = 100 W/1000 W = 1/10, or **10%**.

7 | Rotational Motion

Answers

1. Rotational inertia is most predominantly illustrated here, although the conservation of angular momentum also plays a role. The long distance to the front wheels increases the *rotational inertia* of the vehicle without appreciably adding to its weight. As the back wheels are driven clockwise, the chassis tends to rotate counterclockwise (*conservation of angular momentum*) and thereby lift the front wheels off the ground. The long leverage and greater rotational inertia counters this effect.

2. A solid sphere of any mass and size beats both a solid cylinder and a hollow ball of any mass and size. That's because a solid sphere has less rotational inertia *per mass* than the other shapes. A solid sphere has the bulk of its mass nearer the rotational axis that extends through its center of mass, whereas a cylinder or hollow ball has more of its mass farther from the axis. The object with the least rotational inertia per mass is the "least lazy" and will win the races. (See Figure 3 for relative rotational inertias.)

3. The larger radial distance of large steering wheels enables the driver to exert more torque for a given force. The large steering wheel behaves like a long wrench.

4. Yes, an object can rotate without an applied torque just as an object can move without an applied force. Getting an object to rotate, is another matter. Torques and forces are required to *change* the motion of things. If they initially move without friction, no torques or forces are required to maintain their motion (the laws of inertia). The earth, for example, perpetually rotates without the application of a torque.

5. The lever arm is the same whether a person stands, sits, or hangs from the end of the see saw, and certainly their weight is the same. So the net torque is the same also.

6. In prying open a stuck cover from a can of paint, a screwdriver with a long handle is more effective, because the longer lever arm provides more torque for a given force. But for turning a stubborn screw, the lever arm is the radius of the handle. The thicker handle will be more effective. (And if this doesn't work, wrap some cloth around the handle to make it even thicker and increase the lever arm.)

7. In the horizontal position the lever arm equals the length of the sprocket arm, but in the vertical position, the lever arm is zero because the line of action of forces passes right through the axis of rotation.

8. A rocking bus rocks about its center of mass at about its middle, which is the most comfortable seating. The farther one sits from the center of mass, the greater is the up and down motion — as on a see-saw.

9. The long drooping pole lowers the center of gravity of the balanced system, the tightrope walker and the pole. The rotational inertia of the pole contributes to the stability of the system also.

10. The center of mass of the solar system is not at the geometrical center of the sun because the constantly changing center of mass of all the planets is not located there. When all the planets are lined up to one side, the center of mass of the solar system is outside the sun altogether, about 2 solar radii from the sun's center.

11. The wobbly motion of a star is an indication that its center of mass is not at its geometric center, and is likely affected by a planet or system of planets.

12. You bend forward when carrying a heavy load on your back to shift the center of gravity of you and your load above the area bounded by your feet — otherwise you topple backward.

13. One may stand upright while carrying a bucket in each hand because the center of gravity will be in the center of the support base provided by your feet, without the need of leaning. (The same can be accomplished by carrying a single bucket on one's head.)

14. It is not necessary that the weights be centered on the equal-arm balance because the center of gravity of each hanging weight lies directly below the pivot point, whether or not the weights are in the middle of the pans.

15. The weight of the boy is counterbalanced by the weight of the board which is effectively at its CG on the opposite side of the fulcrum. He is in perfect balance when his weight multiplied by his distance from the fulcrum is equal to the weight of the entire board multiplied by the distance between the fulcrum and the midpoint (CG) of the board. (How do the relative weight of boy and board relate to the relative lever arms?)

16. The CG of a ball is not above a point of support when the ball is on an incline. The weight of the ball therefore acts at some distance from the point of support which behaves like a fulcrum. A torque is produced and the ball rotates. This is why a ball rolls down a hill.

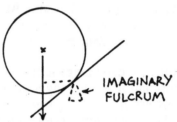

17. When a ball is kicked in the middle so the line of action of the force extends through the CG of the ball, it sails through the air without rotating. When it is kicked below or above the middle so the line of action does not extend through the CG, a torque is produced and the ball rotates as it sails through the air.

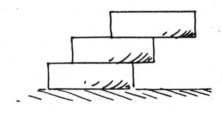

18. The top brick would overhang 3/4 of a brick length as shown. This is best explained by considering the top brick and moving downward; i.e., the CG of the top brick is at its midpoint; the CG of the top two bricks is midway between their combined length. Inspection will show that this is 1/4 of a brick length, the overhang of the middle brick.

19. It is dangerous to pull open the upper drawers of a fully-loaded file cabinet that is not secured to the floor because the CG of the cabinet can easily be shifted beyond the support base of the cabinet. When this happens, a torque is produced and the cabinet topples over.

20. An object is stable when its potential energy must be raised in order to tip it over, or equivalently, when its potential energy must be increased before it can topple. By inspection, the first cylinder undergoes the least change in potential energy compared to its weight in tipping. This is because of its narrow base.

21. The CG of Truck 1 is not above a point of support; the CG of Trucks 2 and 3 are above a point of support. Therefore, only Truck 1 will tip.

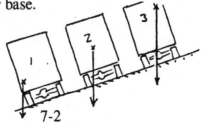

22. When you alter your body configuration while doing situps, you change two things that relate to the effort you expend; the torque due to gravity you must overcome, and the rotational inertia of your body about your hips. With your arms extended in front of you, they are closer to your hips and provide less torque to work against and less rotational inertia. But when your arms are behind your head, their greater distance from your hips means a greater torque to work against and a greater rotational inertia.

23. The track will remain in equilibrium as the balls roll outward. This is because the CG of the system remains over the fulcrum. For sake of explanation, suppose the billiard ball has twice the mass of the golf ball. By conservation of momentum, the twice-as-massive ball will roll outward at half the speed of the lighter ball, and at any time be half as far from the starting point as the lighter ball. So there is no CG change in the system of the two balls. We can see also that the torques produced by the weights of the balls multiplied by their relative distances from the fulcrum are equal at all points. This is because at any time the less massive ball has a correspondingly larger lever arm.

24. The acceleration of a freely-falling object at the surface of the earth decreases as the spin of the earth increases, in effect, decreasing g. This can be seen by the principle of exaggeration: if the earth spins fast enough, like at 12.5 times its present rate, g at the equator would effectively be zero and things wouldn't fall at all. At a still greater rate, things would fly off instead of falling. (At the poles of the earth, however, there would be no tangential speed and the value of g would not be affected as long as the vertical diameter of the earth doesn't change.)

25. The equator has a greater tangential speed than latitudes north or south. When a projectile is launched from any latitude, the tangential speed of the earth is imparted to the projectile, and unless corrections are made, the projectile will miss a target that travels with the earth at a different tangential speed. For example, if the rocket is fired south from the Canadian border toward the Mexican border, its Canadian component of speed due to the earth's turning is smaller than earth's tangential speed further south. The Mexican border is moving faster and the rocket falls behind. Since the earth turns toward the east, the rocket lands west of its intended longitude. (On a merry-go-round, try tossing a ball back and forth with your friends. The name for this is the *Coriolis effect*.)

26. The gold would weigh more in Alaska, for two reasons. The effective value of g depends on the spin of the earth (see the answer to Exercise 24), and the distance to the center of the earth. With respect to the spinning earth, the tangential speed is less in Alaska than in Mexico. So weight would be more in Alaska because of the lesser tangential speed. Because of the earth's spin, the equator bulges. This results in the earth's diameter being about 43 km greater at the equator than along the polar axis. So sea level in Alaska is a bit nearer the center of the earth than sea level in Mexico. This slight change of distance makes the weight a slight bit heavier.

27. The force acting against the motorcycle is an inward force, centripetal force. The reaction to this force is the outward force of the motorcycle acting against the wall (which only in a loose sense is a centrifugal force).

28. Tell your first friend that the satellite in circular orbit has a constant speed but not a constant velocity (because the direction changes from moment to moment). So your first friend is wrong, for the satellite does accelerate. Agree with your second friend, for the acceleration of the satellite is toward the center of its circular path, and is the result of gravitation.

29. Work is done on an object when a force or a component of a force acts along the direction of motion. The centripetal force acts perpendicular to the direction of motion when an object moves in a circular path. It therefore does no work on the object. Evidence to support this is the regularity of the moon's motion about the earth in its very nearly circular orbit. It moves with-

out appreciable change in its KE or PE because the force of earth gravity is perpendicular to its direction of motion and does no work on it.

30. The basketball will more easily balance when spinning, just as a spinning top is easier to balance. Once spinning about an axis, it tends to remain spinning about that axis (the principle of rotational inertia). This can also be explained in terms of torque and angular momentum: The torque that acts on the ball, spinning or not, is its weight multiplied by the lever arm (the distance its center of gravity is horizontally displaced from the supporting finger). The greater the rate of spin, the greater the angular momentum and the less effective will be the torque in changing the axis about which angular momentum is taking place.

31. The rotational inertia of you and the rotating turntable is least when you are at the rotational axis. As you crawl outward, the rotational inertia of the system increases (like the weights held outward in Figure 7-41). In accord with the conservation of angular momentum, as you crawl toward the outer rim, you increase the rotational inertia of the spinning system and decrease the angular speed.

32. Earth that washes down the river is being deposited at a larger distance from the earth's rotational axis. Just as the man on the turntable slows down when one of the weights is extended, the earth slows down in its rotational motion, extending the length of the day. The amount of slowing, of course, is exceedingly small.

33. Like the preceding exercises, the melted ice would take the form of water which would spread itself out over the earth, increasing r, decreasing v, thereby extending the length of the day. Again, the effect is exceedingly small.

34. In accord with the conservation of angular momentum, as the radial distance of mass increases, the angular speed decreases. The mass of material used to construct skyscrapers is lifted, slightly increasing the radial distance from the earth's rotational axis. This would tend to slightly decrease the earth's rate of rotation which in turn tends to make the days a bit longer. As a practical matter, the effect is quite negligible. The earth's mountain ranges are insignificant protrusions on a world that if scaled to the size of a billiard ball would be about as smooth.

35. All the earth's inhabitants walking eastward would result in an imparted westerly motion of the easterly-spinning earth, slowing it and extending the length of the day. When everyone stops walking, however, the earth would regain its prior speed, conserving angular momentum.

36. The angular momentum of the wheel-train system will not change in the absence of an external torque. So when the train moves clockwise, the wheel moves counterclockwise with an equal and opposite angular momentum. When the train stops, the wheel stops. When the train backs up, the wheel moves forward. If masses of the train and wheel are equal, they will move with equal speeds (since the mass of the wheel is as far from the axis as the mass of the train — for equal masses they will each have the same rotational inertias). If the train is more massive than the wheel, the wheel will "recoil" with more speed than the train, and vice versa. (This is a favorite demonstration of Paul Robinson, whose children David and Kristen are shown in the photo.)

37. Without the small propeller on its tail, both the helicopter and the rotor would rotate in opposite directions. The small propeller offsets the rotational motion that the helicopter would otherwise have.

38. Gravitational force acting on every particle by every other particle causes the cloud to condense. The decreased radius of the cloud is then accompanied by an increased angular speed because of angular momentum conservation. The increased speed results in many stars being thrown out into a dish-like shape.

Chapter 7 Problem Solutions

1. The mass of the stick is **1 kg** (this is a "freebie"; see the Check Question and answer on page 125).

2. Centrifugal force is directly proportional to the square of the speed ($F = mv^2/r$); therefore twice the speed, v, means **four times** the centrifugal force or "weight." (Twice the angular speed will be twice the tangential speed v at any point.)

3. Centripetal force (and "weight" and "g" in the rotating habitat) is directly proportional to radial distance from the hub. At half the radial distance, the g force will be **half** that at his feet. The man will literally be "light-headed."

4. This follows the preceding answer. If one's feet at full radius R undergo a centripetal acceleration of g, then the fractions of g closer to the hub will be in direct proportion to the fractions of R. At a distance from the hub of $R/2$, we get $g/2$, at $3R/4$ from the hub, we get $3g/4$, and so forth. Some thought will show that the fraction by which we decrease R is matched by an equal decrease of g. So for a decrease of 1/100 for g, we must move 1/100 closer to the hub. This means the hub would have to be 100 times farther from the feet than the head. The radius of the habitat would have to be **100 times greater than a person's height**. (This can be looked at in terms of the "gravity gradient" Δg, where $\Delta g = h/R$, where h is the height of the person and R the radius of the structure. For $\Delta g = 1/100$, the radius of the structure should be at least 100 times the height of the person.)

8 | Gravity

1. The reason that a heavy body doesn't fall faster than a light body is because the greater gravitational force on the heavier body (its weight), acts on a correspondingly greater mass (inertia). The ratio of force to mass for a freely falling body is the same — hence all bodies in free fall accelerate equally. (This is illustrated in Figures 4.13 and 4.14 back on page 64.)

2. Both the plane sheet and the crumpled sheet have the same mass, so they weigh the same. (Although the crumpled sheet will exert a more concentrated force [greater pressure] on your hand and seem heavier.)

3. The moon orbits not only the earth, but the sun as well. It is the earth-moon system as a whole that orbits the sun.

4. From Kepler's third law, $T^2 \sim R^3$, the period is greatest when the distance is greatest. So the periods of planets farther from the sun are longer than our year.

5. The magnitude of gravitational force on a 700-newton man is 700 N, and the force acts downward, toward the center of the earth. He calls this force his weight.

6. In accord with Newton's 3rd law, the weight of the earth in the gravitational field of the apple is 1 N; the same as the weight of the apple in the earth's gravitational field.

7. The earth and moon equally pull on each other in a single interaction. In accord with Newton's 3rd law, the pull of the earth on the moon is equal and opposite to the pull of the moon on the earth.

8. Your weight would increase if the mass of the earth increased, because gravitational force is proportional to the product of both your mass and the earth's mass. If either increases, the force increases also. (Note from the equation $F = Gm_1m_2/d^2$, there are three ways to increase F: Increase m_1, increase m_2, or decrease d.)

9. By the geometry of Figure 8.4 on page 145, tripling the distance from the small source spreads the light over 9 times the area, or 9 m². Five times the distance spreads the light over 25 times the area, or 25 m², and for 10 times as far, 100 m².

10. Objects weigh less at higher altitudes because they are farther from the center of mass of the earth. To get the most mass for a given weight, buy at a high altitude where mass weighs less, and sell at a lower altitude where its weight is more.

11. The gravitational force on a body, its weight, depends not only on mass but distance. On Jupiter, this is the distance between the body being weighed and Jupiter's center — the radius of Jupiter. If the radius of Jupiter were the same as that of the earth, then a body would weigh 300 times as much because Jupiter is 300 times more massive than earth. But Jupiter is also much bigger than the earth, so the greater distance between its center and the CG of the body reduces the gravitational force. The radius is great enough to make the weight of a body only 3 times its earth weight. How much greater is the radius of Jupiter? Onward to Exercise 12!

12. Jupiter's diameter is about 10 times that of the earth's. Our clue to this is our data that bodies on Jupiter weigh 3 times as much as on earth. If mass were the only factor, weight on

Jupiter would be 300 times earth weight. But Jupiter is bigger than earth. The greater radius of Jupiter diminishes weight by 100 (because 300/100 = 3). According to the inverse-square law, a 100-fold decrease means that the distance is 10 times as great. Jupiter must have a radius 10 times greater than the earth's. This means its diameter is 10 earth diameters also. (More accurately, the mean radius of Jupiter is about 11 times that of the earth, so your weight is closer to 2.5 times earth weight.)

13. Normally your insides are supported by parts of your body such as your pelvis. This occurs when you ride in a high-altitude jet plane. You are pulled down by gravity against the seat of the plane that supports you. But in an orbiting space vehicle, both you and the vehicle are in a state of free fall. The vehicle has no lift to support you, and you feel weightless.

14. Any body that moves in a circular path requires a centripetal force. Objects on the surface of the earth circle the earth with a force provided by gravity. The force of gravity is more than enough to hold them to the earth at its present rotational speed. Beyond certain speeds it is not. For example, if the earth revolved each 90 minutes instead of each 24 hours, objects at the equator would be traveling at 8 km/s, orbital speed. The earth's gravity is barely able to provide the centripetal force necessary for them to continue in circular motion. At this speed they would be on the verge of being thrown off the earth and would not press against its surface. At the poles, weight would be as usual, because there is no tangential velocity there (like being in the center of a rotating turntable). In the middle of the United States, tangential speed would be greater than zero and less than 8 km/s, so objects would still press against the earth's surface, but much less than at the poles.

15. In a car that drives off a cliff you feel weightless because the car no longer offers a support force. Both you and the car are in the same state of free fall. But gravity is still acting on you, as evidenced by your acceleration toward the ground.

16. The pencil has the same state of motion that you have. Relative to the earth, you are both falling. Relative to yourself, the pencil does not fall from you.

17. First of all, it is incorrect to say that the gravitational force of the distant sun is too small to be measured. Its small, but not immeasurably small. If, for example, the earth were supported so that the sun's pull showed on a scale, an 85-kg person would see a gain of 1/2 newton on the scale at midnight and a loss of 1/2 newton at noon. The key idea is *support*. There is no "sun support" because the earth and all objects on the earth — people, bathroom scales, and all — are continually falling around the sun. Just as a person is not pulled against the seat of a car that drives off a cliff, and just as a pencil is not pressed against the floor of an elevator in free fall, we are not pressed against or pulled from the earth by our gravitational interaction with the sun. That interaction keeps us and the earth circling the sun, but does not press us to the earth's surface. Our interaction with the earth does that.

18. As stated in the preceding answer, our "earthweight" is due to the gravitational interaction between our mass and that of the earth. The earth and its inhabitants are freely falling around the sun, the rate of which does not affect our local weights. (If a car drives off a cliff, the earth's gravity, however strong, plays no role in pressing the occupant against the car while both are falling. Similarly, as the earth and its inhabitants fall around the sun, the sun plays no role in pressing us to the earth.)

19. The gravitational pull of the sun on the earth is greater than the gravitational pull of the moon (page 150). The tides, however, are caused by the *differences* in gravitational forces by the moon on opposite sides of the earth. The difference in gravitational forces by the moon on opposite sides of the earth is greater than the corresponding difference in forces by the stronger pulling sun.

20. Just as differences in tugs on your shirt will distort the shirt, differences in tugs on the oceans distort the ocean and produce tides.

21. No. Tides are caused by differences in gravitational pulls. If there are no differences in pulls, there are no tides.

22. Ocean tides are not exactly 12 hours apart because while the earth spins, the moon moves in its orbit and appears at its same position overhead every 25 hours, instead of every 24 hours. So the two-high-tide cycle occurs at about 25-hour intervals, making high tides about 12.5 hours apart.

23. Lowest tides occur during the same cycle of highest tides — spring tides. So the spring tide cycle consists of higher-than-average high tides followed by lower-than-average low tides (best for digging clams!).

24. Whenever the ocean tide is unusually high, it will be followed by an unusually low tide. This makes sense, for when one part of the world is having an extra high tide, another part must be donating water and experiencing an extra low tide. Or as the hint in the exercise suggests, if you are in a bathtub and slosh the water so it is extra deep in front of you, that's when it is extra low in back of you — "conservation of water!"

25. Because of its relatively small size, different parts of the Mediterranean Sea are essentially equidistant from the moon (or from the sun). As a result, one part is not pulled with any appreciably different force than any other part. This results in extremely tiny tides. This is especially true for smaller bodies of water, such as lakes, ponds, and puddles. In a glass of water under a full moon you'll detect no tides because no part of the water surface is closer to the moon than any other part of the surface. Tides are caused by appreciable differences in pulls.

26. If a person were 12,800 kilometers tall, so his head was appreciably nearer the moon than his feet, then he could expect tidal effects comparable to that in the oceans. But for a 1-1/2 meter person, the difference between pulls by the moon on different parts of the body are negligible. One who gives credence to biological tides influenced by the moon's gravitational pull would logically have to give more credit for such tides to less massive but closer objects such as mountains.

27. The tidal bulges of the earth do sweep around the earth at supersonic speeds! The crest of the about 1-m high wave (of wavelength in the thousands of kilometers!) travels around the world faster than a jet plane, but the water doesn't. (It will be made clearer in Chapter 18 that only the disturbance rather than the medium travels in waves.) One would have to wait almost six hours for the trough of the wave to follow, so one doesn't notice the high bulge zooming towards the shore as the tide comes in.

28. Tides occur in the earth's crust and the earth's atmosphere for the same reason they occur in the earth's oceans. Both are large enough so there are appreciable differences in distances to the moon and sun, with corresponding gravitational differences as well.

29. In accord with the inverse-square law, twice as far from the earth's center diminishes the value of g to 1/4, or 2.45 m/s^2.

30. For a uniform-composition (uniform-density) planet, g inside at half the earth's radius would be 4.9 m/s^2. This can be understood via the spherical shell idea discussed on pages 151 and 152. Half way to the center of the earth, the mass of the earth in the outer shell can be neglected — the gravitational contribution of all parts of the shell cancel to zero. Only the mass

of the earth "beneath" contributes to g, the mass in the sphere of radius $r/2$. This sphere of half radius has only 1/8 the volume and only 1/8 the mass of the whole earth (volume varies as r^3). This effectively smaller mass alone would find the acceleration due to gravity 1/8 that of g at the surface. But consider the closer distance to the earth's center as well. This twice-as-close distance alone would make g four times as great (inverse-square law). Combining both factors, 1/8 of 4 = 1/2, so the acceleration due to gravity at $r/2$ is $g/2$.

31. Your weight would be less in the mineshaft. One way to explain this is to consider the mass of the earth above you which pulls upward on you. This effect reduces your weight, just as your weight is reduced if someone pulls upward on you while you're weighing yourself. Or more accurately, we see that you are effectively within a spherical shell in which the gravitational field contribution is zero; and that you are being pulled only by the spherical portion below you. You are lighter the deeper you go, and if the mine shaft were to theoretically continue to the earth's center, your weight moves closer to zero.

32. The increase in weight indicates that the earth is more compressed — more compact — more dense — toward the center. So referring to our analysis of Exercise 30, for example, the mass of the inner sphere of radius $r/2$ is considerably greater than 1/8 the total mass of the earth. So the weight that normally would be lost when in the deepest mine shafts due to cancellation of the surrounding "shell," is more than compensated by the added weight gained due to the closeness to the more dense center of the earth.

33. More fuel is required for a rocket that leaves the earth to go to the moon than the other way around. This is because a rocket must move against the greater gravitational field of the earth most of the way. (If launched from the moon to the earth, then it would be traveling with the earth's field most of the way.)

34. On a shrinking star, all the mass of the star pulls in a non-cancelling direction (beneath your feet) — you get closer to the overall mass concentration and the force increases. If you tunnel into a star, however, there is a cancellation of gravitational pulls; the matter above you pulls counter to the matter below you, resulting in a decrease in the net gravitational force.

35. $F \sim m_1 m_2 / d^2$, where m_2 is the mass of the sun (which doesn't change when forming a black hole, although its volume does), m_1 is the mass of the orbiting earth, and d is the distance between the center of mass of the earth and sun. None of these terms change, so the force F that holds the earth in orbit does not change.

36. Letting the gravitational force equation be a guide to thinking, we see that gravitational force and hence one's weight does not change if the mass and radius of the earth do not change. (Although one's weight would be zero inside a hollow uniform shell, on the outside one's weight would be no different than if the same-mass earth were solid.)

37. No contradiction: Gravitational forces, like all forces, can cancel one another when they are equal and opposite. And this is the case for the gravitational force everywhere inside a uniform hollow shell between the mass of the shell and any object inside. Force due to gravitation is cancelled — but not shielded, as the next exercise shows.

38. Occupants inside a hollow planet could sense the presence of a massive object on the outer surface. Gravitation between the hollow planet and its inner occupants cancels, but gravitation between the occupants and other massive objects does not. The force between an occupant of the hollow planet and a massive body on the surface is the same with or without the planet. The planet does not shield gravitation. [Suppose an equally massive body were located exactly on the opposite side of the planet: would gravitational forces from this pair of masses cancel for occupants everywhere inside? (Answer: Only at the center of the planet — why?)]

39. You weigh a tiny bit less in the lower part of a massive building because the mass of the building above pulls upward on you.

40. Tidal forces occur when there is a difference in gravitational field strength across a body. Nearing the singularity of a black hole feet first, the feet of the unfortunate astronaut would be pulled with so much more force than his midsection that separation would likely occur.

Chapter 8 Problem Solutions

1. In accord with the inverse-square law, four times as far from the earth's center diminishes the value of g to $1/4^2$, or $g/16$, or 0.6 m/s^2.

2. $F = G\dfrac{mM}{d^2} = 6.67 \times 10^{-11}\dfrac{(1\text{kg})(7.4 \times 10^{22})}{(3.8 \times 10^8)^2} = \textbf{3.42} \times \textbf{10}^{\textbf{-5}}$ **N.**

3. $F = G\dfrac{mM}{d^2} = 6.67 \times 10^{-11}\dfrac{(6 \times 10^{24}\text{kg})(2 \times 10^{30})}{(1.5 \times 10^{11})^2} = \textbf{3.56} \times \textbf{10}^{\textbf{22}}$ **N.**

4. Strength of steel $\dfrac{F}{A} = \dfrac{3.56 \times 10^{22} \text{ N}}{A} = 2 \times 10^{11}$ N/m^2;

   Solve for A:

$$A = \frac{3.56 \times 10^{22} \text{ N}}{2 \times 10^{11} \text{ N/m}^2} = 1.78 \times 10^{11} \text{ m}^2$$

Thickness of cable, its diameter, is found from $A = \pi\dfrac{D^2}{4}$, (area of circular cross-section) where

$$D = \frac{4A}{\pi} = \frac{4(17.8 \times 10^{10})}{3.14} = \textbf{4.76} \times \textbf{10}^{\textbf{5}} \text{ m};$$

or in miles, $476 \text{ km} \times \dfrac{1 \text{ mile}}{1.6 \text{ km}} \approx 300$ miles thick!

5. From $\dfrac{1 \text{ R}^2}{T_e^3} = \dfrac{10^2 R^2}{T_S^3}$, $T_e = 1$, so $T_S^3 = 100$. The cube root of 100 is about 4.6, so Saturn's year is about **4.6 earth years**.

9 | Satellite Motion

Answers

1. Gravity changes the speed of a cannonball when the cannonball moves in the direction of earth gravity. At low speeds, the cannonball curves downward and gains speed because there is a component of the force of gravity along its direction of motion. Fired fast enough, however, the curvature matches the curvature of the earth so the cannonball moves at right angles to the force of gravity. With no component of force along its direction of motion, its speed remains constant.

2. The astronaut is in a state of free fall. A skydiver similarly appears to float while freefalling, but with two important differences. The skydiver experiences air resistance, and floats for a relatively short time before parachute time and a sudden decrease in speed. The astronaut, however, is freely falling above the atmosphere and experiences no air resistance. Furthermore, the tangential speed of the astronaut is sufficient that he falls around and around the earth with no change in speed.

3. The moon doesn't crash into the earth simply because its tangential speed is sufficient to fall around and around the earth. If it stopped in its tracks for any reason, then it would crash into the earth.

4. Neither the speed of free fall nor the speed of a satellite in orbit depends on its mass. In both cases, a greater mass is balanced by a correspondingly greater gravitational force, so the acceleration remains the same (Newton's 2nd law).

5. The rocket departs form a vertical course until it is moving tangentially to the surface of the earth with a speed of at least 8 km/s. If it traveled only vertically at less than escape velocity, it would fall back to the surface.

6. Rockets for launching satellites into orbit are fired easterly to take advantage of the spin of the earth. Any point on the equator of the earth moves at nearly 0.5 km/s with respect to the center of the earth or the earth's polar axis. This extra speed does not have to be provided by the rocket engines. At higher latitudes, this "extra free ride" is less.

7. The component along the direction of motion does work on the satellite to change its speed. The component perpendicular to the direction of motion changes its direction.

8. In circular orbit there is no component of force along the direction of the satellite's motion so no work is done. In elliptical orbit, there is always a component of force along the direction of the satellite's motion (except at the apogee and perigee) so work is done of the satellite.

9. When the velocity of a satellite is everywhere perpendicular to the force of gravity, the orbital path is a circle (see Figure 9.11).

10. Gravity pulls harder on the satellite closest to the earth, which moves faster and therefore would appear to overtake the slower and higher satellite. (The value 8 km/s refers to speeds in low earth orbit — at higher altitudes orbital speed is less.)

11. If a wrench or anything else is "dropped" from an orbiting space vehicle, it has the same tangential speed as the vehicle and remains in orbit. If a wrench is dropped from a high-flying jumbo jet, it too has the tangential speed of the jet. But this speed is insufficient for the wrench to fall around and around the earth. Instead it soon falls into the earth.

12. When a capsule is projected rearward at 8 km/s with respect to the shuttle, which is itself moving forward at 8 km/s with respect to the earth, the speed of the capsule with respect to the earth will be zero. It will have no tangential speed for orbit. What will happen? It will simply drop to earth and crash.

13. Consider "Newton's cannon" fired from a tall mountain on Jupiter. To match the wider curvature of much larger Jupiter, and to contend with Jupiter's greater gravitational pull, the cannonball would have to be fired significantly faster. (Orbital speed about Jupiter is about 5 times that for earth.)

14. In accord with the work-energy relationship, $Fd = \Delta KE$, for a constant thrust F, the maximum change in KE will occur when d is maximum. The rocket will travel the greatest distance d during the brief firing time where it is traveling fastest — at the perigee. This can be seen also by considering the relative KEs given to the exhaust gases at the perigee and apogee. At the apogee, where the rocket coasts slower, much more KE of the system goes to the gases, whereas at the perigee most of the KE is with the rocket. (If orbital speed = rocket exhaust speed, the gases are motionless with respect to the earth and the rocket gets 100% of the KE.)

15. This is similar to Exercise 12. The tangential velocity of the earth about the sun is 30 km/s. If a rocket carrying the radioactive wastes were fired at 30 km/s from the earth in the direction opposite to the earths orbital motion about the sun, the wastes would have no tangential velocity with respect to the sun. They would simply fall into the sun.

16. The escape speeds from various planets refer to "ballistic speeds" — to the speeds attained *after* the application of an applied force. If the force is sustained, then a space vehicle could escape the earth at any speed, so long as the force is applied sufficiently long.

17. Maximum falling speed by virtue only of the earth's gravity is 11.2 km/s (see the footnote on page 173).

18. This is similar to Exercise 17. In this case, Pluto's maximum speed of impact on the sun, by virtue of only the sun's gravity, would be the same as the escape speed from the surface of the sun, which according to Table 9.1 on page 173 is 620 km/s.

19. The gravitational field at the surface of the earth would increase if the earth shrank (see Figure 8.22 back on page 156 in the previous chapter). Escape velocity would correspondingly be greater. (The value of escape velocity from any body is $v = \sqrt{2Gm/r}$, where G is the gravitational constant, m is the mass of the body, and r the distance from its center.)

20. The satellite experiences the greatest gravitational force at A, where it is closest to the earth; and the greatest speed and the greatest velocity at A, and by the same token the greatest momentum and greatest kinetic energy at A, and the greatest gravitational potential energy at the farthest point C. It would have the same total energy (KE + PE) at all parts of its orbit, likewise with angular momentum because it's conserved (*mvr* is the same everywhere in orbit). It would have the greatest acceleration at A, where F/m is greatest.

21. This is speculation, and it's plausible that no significant school or hospital construction was sacrificed to the funding of the space missions. Similarly, the level of assistance for citizens of Spain was not appreciably affected by the funding of the voyages of Columbus.

Chapter 9 Problem Solutions

1. Since all factors are equal except for distance, we see the only variable is distance, which follows the inverse-square law. The acceleration g will decrease by the ratio of the squares of the distances.

So g at high altitude $= \left(\dfrac{6370 \text{ km}}{(6370 + 200 \text{ km})}\right)^2 9.8 \text{ m/s}^2 = \left(\dfrac{6370}{6570}\right)^2 9.8 \text{ m/s}^2 = \mathbf{9.4 \text{ m/s}^2}.$

This is 96% of g at the earth's surface.

2. Force of gravity = centripetal force

That is, $G\,\dfrac{mM}{d^2} = \dfrac{mv^2}{d}$

Solve by cancelling m and d and we see $v = \sqrt{\dfrac{GM}{d}} = \sqrt{\dfrac{(6.67 \times 10^{-11})(2 \times 10^{30})}{1.5 \times 10^{11}}} = \mathbf{3 \times 10^4 \text{ m/s}}.$

3. $\sqrt{\dfrac{GM}{d}} = \sqrt{\dfrac{(6.67 \times 10^{-11})(6 \times 10^{24})}{3.8 \times 10^8}} = \mathbf{1026 \text{ m/s}}.$

4. $\sqrt{\dfrac{2GM}{d}} = \sqrt{\dfrac{2(6.67 \times 10^{-11})(6.4 \times 10^{23})}{3.4 \times 10^6}} = \mathbf{5.0 \times 10^3 \text{ m/s}}.$

1. The cat leaves a trail of molecules and atoms on the grass. These in turn leave the grass and mix with the air, where they enter the dog's nose, activating its sense of smell.

2. A body would have no odor if all its molecules remained intact. A body has odor only if some of its molecules enter a nose.

3. The speed at which the scent of a fragrance travels is much less than the speed of the individual molecules that make it up because of the many collisions among molecules. Although the molecular speed between collisions is very great, the rate of migration in a preferred direction through obstructing molecules is very much less.

4. The age of the atoms in either a newborn baby or in an elderly person are the same; appreciably older than the solar system.

5. The atoms that make up a newborn baby or anything else in this world originated in the explosions of ancient stars. (See Figure 10.1, my daughter Leslie.)

6. Brownian motion is apparent only for microscopic particles because of their low mass and small size. Their low mass makes them more responsive to being bumped about by the random motion of surrounding atoms and molecules. This random motion produces a jittery bumping against the particles. Against a large particle, the bumps average to steady forces on each side that average to zero, but for a small particle there are moments where appreciably more hits occur on one side than the other, producing a visible effect.

7. Atoms are smaller than the wavelengths of visible light, and therefore cannot be discerned by such relatively long waves (just as reeds of grass in water cannot be discerned by the long water waves that pass by). So atoms can't be seen even by the most powerful optical microscopes. The wavelengths of electron beams, however, are different. These wavelengths are more than 1000 times shorter than the wavelengths of visible light, and are short enough to discern atoms.

8. With a few exceptions (cobalt - nickel, tellurium - iodine, thorium - protactinium, uranium - neptunium, 106 - 107) the sequence of atoms would be the same if arranged by atomic mass rather than by atomic number.

9. The number of protons in the atomic nucleus determines the number of electrons that will surround the nucleus. It is the number and configuration of the electrons that determine the chemical properties of an element — how and with which other elements it will interact.

10. Of the atoms and molecules listed, only H_2, He, Na, and U are pure elements. H_2O and NaCl are a combination of two elements, and in H_2SO_4 there are three different elements.

11. If two protons are taken from the nucleus of an oxygen atom, the element is then carbon. (Taking only two protons leaves the isotope carbon with mass 14. Taking two neutrons as well leaves the isotope carbon with mass 12.)

12. Adding a single proton to a germanium nucleus makes arsenic.

13. Nitrogen plus one proton becomes Oxygen. (It will be the isotope oxygen with the mass of nitrogen, 14.)

14. Germanium has properties most like silicon, as it is in the same column, Group IV, as silicon in the periodic table (inside front cover).

15. Check the periodic table on the inside front cover and see that gold is atomic number 79. Taking a proton from the nucleus finds the atomic number 78, platinum — much more valuable than adding a proton to get mercury, atomic number 80.

16. There are 16 grams of oxygen in 18 grams of water. We can see from the formula for water, H_2O, there are twice as many hydrogen atoms (each of atomic mass 1) as oxygen atoms (each of atomic mass 16). So the molecular mass of H_2O is 18, with 16 parts oxygen by mass.

17. A carbon atom is 12 times as massive as a hydrogen atom, or 3 times as massive as four hydrogen atoms. A bit of reasoning will show that for every 4 grams of hydrogen there will be 3 x 4 = 12 grams of carbon, which when totaled gives 16 grams. So there are 4 grams of hydrogen in 16 grams of methane.

18. The mass of element A is 3/2 the mass of element B. Why? Gas A have three times the mass as Gas B. If the equal number of molecules in A and B had equal numbers of atoms, then the atoms in Gas A would simply be three times as massive. But there are twice as many atoms in A, so the mass of each atom must be half of three times as much — 3/2.

19. The water and alcohol molecules actually fit into one another and take up less space when combined than they do individually. Hence, when water and alcohol are mixed, their combined volume is less than the sum of their volumes separately.

20. The principal variable that determines whether atoms form a solid, liquid, or gas is temperature.

21. The volume of the oil is like the volume of a very large but very thin pancake, and equals its area multiplied by its thickness. $V = Ah$, where V is the volume (known) and A is the area (known from measurement) and h is the thickness, or diameter of the oil molecule. Solving for the thickness we get $h = V/A$, which produces a microscopic value from the ratio of two macroscopic values. Quite nice! (This makes a good lab exercise with diluted oleic acid.)

22. When a body is cremated, the atoms are immediately recycled into the environment where they are integrated into other forms, living and nonliving. The atoms in a body encased in an air-tight casket, however, are confined to the casket and are not recycled to the environment — at least not right away. At a later time the casket and its contents dissipate to the overall environment.

23. You really are a part of every person around you in the sense that you are composed of atoms not only from every person around you, but from every person who ever lived on earth! Little Manuel Hewitt's statement on page 177 is indisputable.

24. With every breath of air you take, it is highly likely that you inhale one of the atoms exhaled during your very first breath. This is because the number of atoms of air in your lungs is about the same as the number of breaths of air in the atmosphere of the world.

25. The amount of matter that a given amount of antimatter would annihilate is the same as the amount of antimatter. Annihilation is atom for anti-atom. The whole world could not be annihilated by antimatter unless the mass of antimatter were at least equal to the mass of the world.

Chapter 10 Problem Solutions

1. From the hint:

$$\frac{\text{number of molecules in thimble}}{\text{number of molecules in ocean}} = \frac{\text{number of molecules in question}}{\text{number of molecules in thimble}}$$

$$\frac{10^{23}}{10^{46}} = \frac{x}{10^{23}}; \quad x = \frac{10^{46}}{10^{46}} = 1$$

2. There are 10^{22} breaths of air in the world's atmosphere, which is the same number of atoms in a single breath. So for any one breath evenly mixed in the atmosphere, we sample one atom at any place or any time in the atmosphere.

3. The total number of people who ever lived is $4 \times 10^9 \times 30 = 120 \times 10^9$ which is roughly 10^{11} people altogether. So incredibly, there are about 10^{11} more molecules of air in your lungs than the total number of people who ever lived! How much greater is 10^{22} molecules than 10^{11} people? The ratio $10^{11}/10^{11}$ is equal to the ratio $10^{11}/1$: that is,

$$\frac{10^{22} \text{ molecules}}{10^{11} \text{ people}} = \frac{10^{11} \text{ people}}{1 \text{ person}}$$

11 Solids

1. Physical properties have to do with the order, bonding, and structure of atoms that make up a material, and with the presence of other atoms and their interaction in the material. The silicon in glass is amorphous, whereas in semiconductors it is crystalline. The presence of other elements is different in glass and in semiconductors also; hence the physical properties of each differ.

2. Evidence for crystalline structure include the symmetric diffraction patterns given off by various materials, micrographs such as the one on page 192, and even brass doorknobs that have been etched by the perspiration of hands.

3. Iron is denser than cork, but not necessarily heavier. A common cork from a wine bottle, for example, is heavier than an iron thumbtack — but it wouldn't be heavier if the volumes of each were the same.

4. When you squeeze a loaf of bread its mass remains unchanged. Its volume decreases, so its density increases.

5. Density has not only to do with the mass of the atoms that make up a material, but with the spacing between the atoms as well. The atoms of the metal osmium, for example, are not as massive as uranium atoms, but due to thier close spacing they make up the densest of the metals. Uranium atoms are not as close spaced in uranium metal

6. The top part of the spring supports the entire weight of the spring and stretches more than, say the middle, which only supports half the weight and stretches half as far. Parts of the spring toward the bottom support very little of the spring's weight and hardly stretch at all.

7. A twice-as-thick rope has four times the cross-section and is therefore four times as strong. The length of the rope does not contribute to its strength. (Remember the old adage, a chain is only as strong as its weakest link — the strength of the chain has to do with the thickness of the links, not the length of the chain.)

8. Case 1: Tension at the top   Case 2: Compression at the top
   and compression at the bottom.   and tension at the bottom.

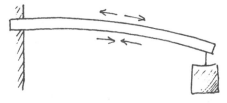 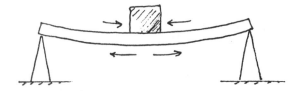

9. A horizontal I-beam is stiffer when the web is vertical because most of the material is in where it is needed for the most strength, in the top and bottom flanges. When supporting a load, one flange will be under tension and the other flange under compression. But when the web is horizontal, the only the edges of the flanges, much smaller than the flanges themselves, play these important roles.

10. The design to the left if better because the weight of water against the dam puts compression on the dam. Compression tends to jam the parts of the dam together, with added strength like the compression on an arch. The weight of water puts tension on the dam at the right, which tends to separate the parts of the dam.

11. Like the dams in the preceding exercise, the ends should be concave as on the left. Then the pressure due to the wine inside produces compression on the ends that strengthens rather than weakens the barrel. If the ends are convex as on the right, the pressure due to the wine inside produces tension, which tends to separate the boards that make up the ends.

12. A triangle is the most rigid of geometrical structures. Consider nailing four sticks together to form a rectangle, for example. It doesn't take much effort to distort the rectangle so that it collapses to form a parallelogram. But a triangle made by nailing three sticks together cannot collapse to form a tighter shape. When strength is important, triangles are used. That's why you see them in the construction of so many things.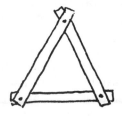

13. Scale a beam up to twice its linear dimensions, I-beam or otherwise, and it will be four times as thick. Along its cross-section then, it will be four times as strong. But it will be eight times as heavy. Twice the strength supporting eight times the weight results in a beam only half as strong as the original beam. The same holds true for a bridge that is scaled up by two. In comparison, the larger bridge will be only half as strong compared to its weight. (Larger bridges have different designs than smaller bridges. How they differ is what architects and engineers get paid for!)

14. The candymaker needs less taffy for the larger apples because the surface area is less per kilogram. (This is easily noticed by comparing the peelings of the same number of kilograms of small and large apples.)

15. The person twice as heavy has twice the volume, but not twice the surface area. She has more area than the smaller person, but less than twice as much (actually 1.587 times as much).

16. Kindling will heat to a higher temperature in a shorter time than large sticks and logs. Its greater surface area per mass results in most of its mass being very near the surface, which quickly heats from all sides to its ignition temperature. The heat given to a log, on the other hand, is not so concentrated as it conducts into the greater mass. Sticks and logs are slower to reach the ignition temperature.

17. The answer to this question is the same as the answer to the previous exercise. The greater surface area of the coal in the form of dust insures an enormously greater proportion of carbon atoms in the coal having exposure to the oxygen in the air. The result is very rapid combustion.

18. A chain reaction dies out when particles leak through the surface of uranium. Small pieces have more area for leaking, whereas the same pieces assembled into a larger piece has less surface. When pieces are combined, the overall surface area decreases. A chain reaction is therefore favored in large pieces of uranium.

19. Absorption occurs through the surface area. Long thin rods have more surface area than short fat rods of the same volume. The greater area of the long thin rods then favor absorption.

20. A sphere has the least surface area for a given volume than any geometrical shape. A dome-shaped structure similarly has less surface area per volume than conventional block designs. Less surface exposed to the climate = less heat loss.

21. Apartment buildings have less area per unit exposed to the weather than single family units. The smaller proportion of area means less heat loss per unit. (It is interesting to see the nearly cubical shapes of apartment buildings in northern climates — a cube has the least surface area for a rectangular shaped solid.)

22. More potato is exposed to the cooking oil when sliced thinly than in larger pieces. Thin fries will therefore cook faster than larger fries.

23. A sphere has less surface area per volume of material than any other shape. When a spherical meatball is flattened, its surface area increases. The greater the surface area, the greater will be the heat transfer from the stove to the meat.

24. Cupcakes have more surface area per amount of material than a cake, which means there is more area exposed to the heat that the oven will provide, which means cooking will be facilitated. This also means the cupcakes will be overcooked if they are cooked for the time specified for a cake. (Now you see why recipes call for a "shallow pan" or a "deep dish" when baking times are given.)

25. Mittens have less surface than gloves. Anyone who has made mittens and gloves will tell you that much more material is required to make gloves. Hands in gloves will cool faster than hands in mittens.

26. Fingers, toes, and ears have a disproportionately large surface area than other parts of the body and are therefore more prone to frostbite.

27. Small animals radiate more energy per bodyweight, so the flow of blood is correspondingly greater, and the heartbeat faster.

28. As an organism increases in size, surface area decreases in proportion to the increasing size. Therefore, a large organism such as a human being must have a many-folded intestinal tract so that the area will be large enough to digest food.

29. The inner surface of the lungs is not smooth, but is spongelike. As a result, there is an enormously greater surface exposed to the air that is breathed. This is nature's way of compensating for the proportional decrease in surface area for large bodies. In this way, the adequate amount of oxygen vital to life is taken in.

30. Cells of all creatures have essentially the same upper limit in size dictated by the surface area per volume relationship. The nourishment of all cells takes place through the surface by the process called osmosis. As cells grow they require more nourishment, but the proportional increase in surface area falls behind the increase in mass. The cell overcomes this liability by dividing into two cells. The process is repeated and there is life that takes the form of whales, mice, and us.

31. Large raindrops fall faster than smaller raindrops for the same reason that heavier parachutists fall faster than lighter parachutists. Both larger things have less surface area and therefore less air resistance compared to their weights,.

32. To understand why large fish swim faster than small fish, consider dropping a large and small fish through the air. The larger fish will more easily "plow through" the air like the heavier parachutist in the previous answer. The situation is the same in water. The larger fish has more mass, and therefore more strength, compared to its smaller surface area and therefore smaller resistance. So large fish feed by simply swimming with their mouths open after smaller fish.

33. The effects of scaling hinder small swimmers. Larger swimmers have more mass per surface area, and therefore more strength compared to the water resistance they encounter. Now you know why champion swimmers are usually larger than average people.

34. Scaling plays a significant role in the design of the hummingbird and the eagle. The wings of a hummingbird are proportionally small because the small surface area of the wings is large compared to the even smaller weight. Swift maneuvers are possible because the small rotational inertia of the short wings permits rapid flapping that would be impossible for wings as large as those of an eagle. If a hummingbird were scaled up to the size of an eagle, its wings would be much shorter than those of an eagle, so it couldn't soar. Its customary rate of flapping would be insufficient to provide lift for its disproportionately greater weight. Such a giant hummingbird couldn't fly, and unless its legs were disproportionately thicker, it would have great difficulty walking. The great difference in the design of hummingbirds and eagles is a natural consequence of the area to weight ratio of scaling. Isn't that neat?

35. The idea of scaling, that changes in one part of a system often result in disproportionately different changes in other parts of the system, goes beyond geometry. Rules that work well for a system of one size may be disastrous when applied to a system of a different size. The rules for running a small town well may not work at all for a large city. Other examples are left to you. This is an open-ended question that may provoke thought — or better, discussion.

Chapter 11 Problem Solutions

1. Density $= \dfrac{\text{mass}}{\text{volume}} = \dfrac{5 \text{ kg}}{V}$. Now the volume of a cylinder is its round area x it height $(\pi r^2 h)$.

So density $= \dfrac{5 \text{ kg}}{\pi r^2 h} = \dfrac{5000 \text{ g}}{(3.14)(3^2)(10)\text{cm}^3} = $ **17.7 g/cm³**.

2. 45 N is three times 15 N, so the spring will stretch three times as far, **9 cm**. Or from Hooke's law; $F = kx$, $x = F/k = 45$ N/(15 N/3 cm) = 9 cm. (The spring constant $k = 15$ N/3 cm.)

3. When the springs are arranged as in (a), each spring supports half the weight, stretches half as far (**2 cm**), and reads 5 N. In position (b) each spring supports the full weight, each stretches **4 cm**, and each reads 10 N. Both springs stretch 4 cm so the weight pulls the combination down a total distance of 8 cm.

4. If the spring is cut in half, there is only half as much spring to stretch so it will only stretch half as much for the same load. So the 10 N load will stretch it **2 cm**. (Cutting the spring in half doubles the spring constant k. Initially $k = 10$ N/4 cm = 2.5 N/cm; when cut in half, $k = 10$ N/2 cm = 5 N/cm.)

5. If the linear dimensions of a storage tank are reduced to half, then the area is reduced to **one quarter** and the volume is reduced to **one eighth**. (Compare the cubes in Figure 11.15.)

6. The big sphere will have twice the diameter of the 1-mm spheres, and will have only one half as much surface area as the total surface area of the eight little spheres. The scaling principles here are not restricted to spheres, and apply to any shapes that are similar to each other. The simplest shapes to consider are cubes, and with the help of Figure 11.15 on page 202 we can better understand this exercise by considering the mercury to be in the form of little cubes. In the figure we can see that the combination of eight little cubes form a single cube of twice the linear dimensions. To simplify, suppose each little cube has a unit area for each face — then the total surface area for each cube is 6 units (because it has 6 sides). So all eight cubes have a total surface area of 8 x 6 = 48 units. But when they combine, note the big cube formed has 24 units total surface area. So their total surface area after combination is only half what it was before. Likewise if they were spheres. (Now do you see why mice and other creatures ball up in little clusters to reduce their total surface area in cold weather?)

12 | Liquids

1. A person lying on a waterbed experiences less bodyweight pressure because more of the body is in contact with the supporting surface. The greater area reduces the support pressure.

2. A sharp knife cuts better than a dull knife because it has a thinner cutting area which results in more cutting pressure for a given force.

3. More water will flow from a downstairs open faucet because of the greater pressure. Since pressure depends on depth, the downstairs faucet is effectively "deeper" than the upstairs faucet. The pressure downstairs is greater by an amount = density x depth, where the depth is the vertical distance between faucets.

4. A woman with spike heels exerts considerably more pressure on the ground than an elephant! Example: A 500-N woman with 1-cm^2 spike heels puts half her weight on each foot and exerts a presssure of (250N/1 cm^2) = 250N/cm^2. A 20,000-N elephant with 1000 cm^2 feet exerting 1/4 its weight on each foot produces (5000N/1000 cm^2) = 5N/cm^2; about 1/50 as much pressure. (So a woman with spike heels will make greater dents in a new linoleum floor than an elephant.)

5. Joe Pizzo got the idea for this neat classroom demonstration when he inadvertently ran across some broken glass without cutting his bare feet while jogging one day. Luckily, there was enough broken glass for a relatively large area of contact so that the pressure was not great enough to cut his feet. Joe has been demonstrating pressure with broken glass before his students ever since. He is careful that the pieces are small and numerous enough to make the area of contact as large as possible. A large enough area of contact with the sharp glass results in insufficient pressure to cut his feet.

6. Your body gets more rest when lying than when sitting or standing because when lying, the heart does not have to pump blood to the heights that correspond to standing or sitting. Blood pressure is normally greater in the lower parts of your body simply because the blood is "deeper" there. Since your upper arms are at the same level as your heart, the blood pressure in your upper arms will be the same as the blood pressure in your heart.

7. The water can be no deeper than the spouts, which are at the same height, so both teapots hold the same amount of liquid.

8. (a) The reservoir is elevated so as to produce suitable water pressure in the faucets that it serves. (b) The hoops are closer together at the bottom because the water pressure is greater at the bottom. Closer to the top, the water pressure is not as great, so less reinforcement is needed there.

9. Both blocks have the same volume and therefore displace the same amount of water.

10. A one-kilogram block of aluminum is larger than a one-kilogram block of lead. The aluminum therefore displaces more water.

11. A 10-N block of aluminum is larger than a 10-N block of lead. The aluminum therefore displaces more water. Only for the case of Exercise 9 were the volumes of the block equal. In this and the preceding exercise, the aluminum block was larger. (These exercises serve only to emphasize the distinction between volume, mass, and weight.)

12. From a physics point of view, the event was quite reasonable, for the force of the ocean on his finger would have been quite small. This is because the pressure on his finger has only to do with the depth of the water, specifically the distance of the leak below the sea level — not the weight of the ocean. A numerical example should make this point: Suppose the leak were 1 meter below sea level. Then the water pressure would have been = density x depth = 1000 kg-weight/m^3 x 1 m = 1000 kg-wt/m^2 (slightly more because of the slightly greater density of salt water). That's pressure. Force is pressure x area: the area of the boy's finger was about 1 square centimeter, which is 1/10,000 square meter. So force = 1000 kg-wt/m^2 x 1/10,000 m^2 = 1/10 kg-weight; about 1 newton. If the leak were 5 meters below the water line the force would only have been about 5 newtons.

13. A typical plumbing design involves short sections of pipe bent at 45-degree angles between vertical sections two-stories long. The sewerage therefore undergoes a succession of two-story falls which results in a moderate momentum upon reaching the basement level.

14. Water seeking its own level is a consequence of pressure depending on depth. In a bent U-tube full of water, for example, the water in one side of the tube tends to push water up the other side until the pressures in each tube are equal. The corresponding depths of water contributing to these pressures must also be equal.

15. The use of a water-filled garden hose as an elevation indicator is a practical example of water seeking its own level. The water surface at one end of the hose will be at the same elevation above sea level as the water surface at the other end of the hose.

16. In deep water, one is buoyed up by the water displaced and as a result, one does not exert as much pressure against the stones on the bottom. When you are up to your neck in water, you hardly feel the bottom at all.

17. Buoyant force is the result of differences in pressure; if there are no pressure differences, there is no buoyant force. This can be illustrated by the following example: A Ping-Pong ball pushed beneath the surface of water will normally float back to the surface when released. If the container of water is in free fall, however, a submerged Ping-Pong ball will fall with the container and make no attempt to reach the surface. In this case there is no buoyant force acting on the ball because there are no pressure differences — the local effects of gravity are absent.

18. The submerged carton displaces 1 liter of water, or 9.8 N of water. If the weight of the carton is negligible, then 9.8 N of force is required to push it beneath the surface. Otherwise the force required to push it beneath the surface is 9.8 N minus its weight. (Of course if its weight exceeds 9.8 N you will have to exert a force to hold it up!)

19. The same. If 3/4 of a body floats beneath the surface of water, for example, then the density of the body is 3/4 that of water. Or if it just barely floats, so all of it is submerged, then its density is equal to the density of water.

20. Mountain ranges are very similar to icebergs: both float in a denser medium, and extend farther down into that medium than they extend above it. Mountains, like icebergs, are bigger than they appear to be.

21. No buoyant force acts on the plug unless water is beneath it pushing it up. So when a plug is nestled in the drain, no water pressure is beneath it and there is no buoyant force on it. When lying submerged on the tub bottom, however, there is water pressure on all sides and there is a buoyant force on the plug. (In the special case where the bottom of the plug is dry against the tub bottom, and water does not push up against sloping sides, then no buoyant force acts on the plug. There must be a pressure difference to produce a buoyant force.)

22. Heavy objects may or may not sink, depending on their densities (a heavy log floats while a small rock sinks, or a corkstopper floats while a paper clip sinks, for example). The statement likely implies that dense objects, not necessarily heavy objects, sink in the fluid in which they are immersed. Be careful to distinguish between how heavy an object is and how dense it is.

23. The block of wood would float higher if the piece of iron is suspended below it rather than on top of it. This is because when the iron is below — submerged — buoyancy on it reduces its effective weight and less of the wood is pulled beneath the water line. Or by the law of flotation: The iron-and-wood unit displaces its combined weight and the same volume of water whether the iron is on top or the bottom. When the iron is on the top, more wood is in the water; when the iron is on the bottom, less wood is in the water.

24. When a ship is empty its weight is least and it displaces the least water and floats highest. Carrying a load of anything increases its weight and it floats lower. It will float as low carrying a few tons of styrofoam as it will carrying the same number of tons of iron ore. So the ship floats lower in the water when loaded with styrofoam than when empty. If the styrofoam were outside the ship, below water line, then the ship would float higher as a person would with a life preserver.

25. A sinking submarine will continue to sink to the bottom so long as the density of the submarine is greater than the density of the surrounding water. In practice, water is blown out of its tanks to adjust its density so that the density of the submarine matches the density of the surrounding water.

26. The water level will fall. This is because the iron will displace a greater amount of water while floating than submerged. A floating object displaces its weight of water while a submerged object displaces only its volume. (This may be done in the kitchen sink by supposing the boat to be a dish in a dishpan full of water. Silverware in the dish takes the place of the scrap iron. Note the level of water at the side of the dishpan, and then throw the silverware overboard. The floating pan will float higher and the water level at the side of the dishpan will fall. Will the volume of the silverware displace enough water to bring the level to its starting point? No, not as long as it is more compact for its mass than water.)

27. For the same reason as in the previous exercise, the water level will fall. (Try this one in your kitchen sink also. Note the water level at the side of the dishpan when a bowl floats in it. Tip the bowl so it fills and submerges, and you'll see the water level at the side of the dishpan fall.)

28. The balloon will sink to the bottom because its density increases with depth. The balloon is compressible, so the increase in water pressure beneath the surface compresses it and reduces its volume, thereby increasing its density. Density is further increased as it sinks to regions of greater pressure and compression. This sinking is understood also from a buoyant force point of view. As its volume is reduced by increasing pressure as it descends, the amount of water it displaces becomes less. The result is a decrease in the buoyant force that initially was sufficient to barely keep it afloat.

29. You are compressible, whereas a rock is not, so when you are submerged, the water pressure tends to squeeze in on you and reduce your volume. This increases your density. (Be careful when swimming — at shallow depths you may still be less dense than water and be buoyed to the surface without effort, but at greater depths you may be pressed to a density greater than water and you'll have to swim to the surface.).

30. When you exhale, your rib-cage volume is reduced, and the volume of water you displace decreases — so you sink lower until a volume of water equal to your weight is displaced.

31. A body floats higher in a more dense fluid because it does not have to sink as far to displace a weight of fluid equal to its own weight. A smaller volume of the displaced denser fluid is able to match the weight of the floating body.

32. Since both preservers are the same size, they will displace the same amount of water when submerged and be buoyed up with equal forces. Effectiveness is another story. The amount of buoyant force exerted on the heavy lead-filled preserver is insignificant, and sinking occurs. The same amount of buoyant force exerted on the lighter styrofoam preserver is greater than its weight and floating occurs. The amount of the force and the effectiveness of the force are two different things. Think critically.

33. No, there does not have to actually be 14.5 N of fluid in the skull to supply a buoyant force of 14.5 N on the brain. To say that the buoyant force is 14.5 N is to say that the brain is taking up the space that 14.5 N of fluid would occupy if fluid instead of the brain were there. The amount of fluid in excess of the fluid that immediately surrounds the brain does not contribute to the buoyancy on the brain. (A ship floats the same in the middle of the ocean as it would if it were floating in a small lock just barely larger than the ship itself. As long as there is enough water to press against the hull of the ship, it will float. It is not important that the amount of water in this tight-fitting lock weigh as much as the ship — think about that, and don't let a literal word explanation "a floating object displaces a weight of fluid equal to its own weight" and the idea it represents confuse you.)

34. Ice cubes will float lower in a mixed drink because the mixture of alcohol and water is less dense than water. In a less dense liquid a greater volume of liquid must be displaced to equal the weight of the floating ice. In pure alcohol, the volume of alcohol equal to that of the ice cubes weighs less than the ice cubes, and buoyancy is less than weight and ice cubes will sink. Submerged ice cubes in a cocktail indicate that it is predominantly alcohol.

35. When the ice cube melts the water level at the side of the glass is unchanged (neglecting temperature effects). To see this, suppose the ice cube to be a 5 gram cube; then while floating it will displace 5 grams of water. But when melted it becomes the same 5 grams of water. Hence the water level is unchanged.

36. The water level will be unchanged when the ice cube with the air bubbles melts. Whether the ice cube is hollow or solid, in both cases and for the same reason stated in the answer to the previous exercise, it will displace as much water floating as it will melted. If the ice cube contains grains of heavy sand, however, upon melting, the water level at the edge of the glass will drop. This is similar to the case of the scrap iron of Exercise 26.

37. If water doesn't overflow, the reading on the scale will increase by the ordinary weight of the fish; the water level after all, will be higher, an amount of which equals the ordinary weight of the fish. However, if the bucket is brim filled so a volume of water equal to the volume of the fish overflows, then the reading will not change.

38. The additional weight that must be put on the right side to restore balance will equal twice the weight of water displaced by the submerged ball. Why twice? Because what the left side gains because of submersion and increased level of water, the right side loses. (If each side initially weighs 10 N and the left side gains 2 N to become 12 N, the right side loses 2 N to become 8 N. So an additional weight of 4 N, not 2 N, is required on the right side to restore balance.) Because the density of water is less than half the density of the iron ball, the restoring weight will be less than the weight of the ball.

39. If the gravitational field of the earth increased, both water and fish would increase in weight with equal increases in density, so the fish would stay at its prior level in water.

40. Both we and the water would have half the weight density as on earth, and we would float with the same proportion of our body above and beneath the water line as on earth. The vertical components of splashing water, however, would move at half earth speed, since the same mass would be subjected to half the "gravity force". Waves on the water surface would move slower as well (at less than half speed since $v_{wave} \sim \sqrt{g}$).

41. A Ping-Pong ball in water in a zero-g environment would experience no buoyant force. This is because buoyancy depends on a pressure difference on different sides of a submerged body. In this weightless state, no pressure difference would exist because no water pressure exists. (See the answer to Exercise 17, and Home Project 2.)

42. Part of whatever pressure you exert on the water is transmitted to the hungry crocodiles, via Pascal's principle. If the water were confined, that is, not open to the atmosphere and maybe in a closed pipe, the crocs would receive every bit of pressure you exert. But even if you were able to slip into the pool to quietly float without exerting pressure via swimming strokes, your displacement of water raises the water level in the pool. This ever-so-slight rise, and accompanying ever-so-slight increase in pressure at the bottom of the pool, is an ever-so-welcome signal to the hungry crocodiles.

43. The strong man will be unsuccessful. He will have to push with 50 times the weight of the 10 kilograms. The hydraulic arrangement is arranged at his disadvantage. Ordinarily, the input force is applied against the smaller piston and the output force is exerted by the large piston — this arrangement is just the opposite.

44. In Figure 12.19, the increased pressure in the reservoir is a result of the applied force distributed over the input piston area. This increase in pressure is transmitted to the output piston. In Figure 12.20, however, the pressure increase is supplied by the mechanical pump, which has nothing to do with the area of fluid interface between the compressed air and the liquid.

47. Because of surface tension, which tends to minimize the surface of a blob of water, its shape without gravity and other distorting forces will be a sphere.

48. When water is hot, the molecules are moving more rapidly and do not cling to one another as well as when they are slower moving, so the surface tension is less. The lesser surface tension of hot water allows it to pass more readily through small openings.

49. We call the phenomenon of water climbing in thin spaces *capillarity*. To name the phenomenon is not to give its reason. Hence, to say the reason is because of capillarity begs the question. The reason has to do with the greater forces of adhesion between the tube material and water compared to the cohesive forces between the water molecules themselves.

50. Surface tension accounts for the walking of water striders, needles that appear to float, and even razor blades that also appear to float. In these cases the weights of the objects are less than the restoring forces in the water surface that tends to resist stretching.

Chapter 12 Problem Solutions

1. The pressure applied to the fluid in the reservoir must equal the pressure the piston exerts against the fluid in the cylinder. This is the weight of 2000 kg divided by 400 cm². That's (2000 kg-wt)/400 cm² = 5 kg-wt/cm², or **49 N/cm²**.
   [Converted to standard units this is 490 000 N/m², or 490 kPa.]

2. Pressure is **5 kg-wt/cm²**, or 490 kPa. Note that this amount of pressure lifts the car in the previous problem!

3. The volume of the extra water displaced will weigh as much as the 400-kg horse. And the volume of extra water displaced will also equal the area of the barge times the extra depth. That is,

   $V = Ah$, where A is the horizontal area of the barge; Then $h = \dfrac{V}{A}$.

   Now A = 5m x 2m = 10 m²; to find the volume V of barge pushed into the water by the horse's weight, which equals the volume of water displaced, we know that

   $$density = \frac{m}{V}. \text{ Or from this, } V = \frac{m}{density} = \frac{400kg}{1000kg/m^3} = 0.4 \text{ m}^3.$$

   So $h = \dfrac{V}{A} = \dfrac{0.4 \text{ m}^3}{10 \text{ m}^2} = \textbf{0.04 m},$ which is 4 cm deeper.

4. Each horse will push the barge 4 cm deeper. How many 4-cm increments will make 15 cm? 15/4 = 3.75, so **3 horses** can be carried without sinking. 4 horses will sink the barge.

13 | Gases and Plasmas

Answers

1. Some of the molecules in the earth's atmosphere *do* go off into outer space — those like helium with speeds greater than escape speed. But the average speeds of most molecules in the atmosphere are well below escape speed, so the atmosphere is held to earth by earth gravity.

2. There is no atmosphere on the moon because the speed of a sizable fraction of air molecules at ordinary temperatures exceeds lunar escape velocity (because of the moon's smaller gravity). Any appreciable amounts of gas have long leaked away, leaving the moon airless.

3. The weight of a truck is distributed over the part of the tires that make contact with the road. Weight/surface area = pressure, so the greater the surface area, or equivalently, the greater the number of tires, the greater the weight of the truck can be for a given pressure. What pressure? The air pressure in its tires. Can you see how this relates to Home Project 1?

4. The ridges near the base of the funnel allow air to escape from a container it is inserted into. Without the ridges, air in the container would be compressed and would tend to prevent filling as the level of liquid rises.

5. The density of air in a deep mine is greater than at the surface. This is because air simply fills up the mine and by its own weight is more squashed at the bottom.

6. Gas pressure in the bubble is equal to the pressure of the surrounding liquid at any depth. As bubbles rise closer to the surface, liquid pressure is less, pressure on the bubble is less, and volume is greater in accord with Boyle's Law.

7. We are acclimated so that our bodies push out as hard as the atmospheric pressure pushes in. At higher altitudes where atmospheric pressure is less, our bodies push out a little harder than the atmosphere is pushing in; hence, our ears pop.

8. To begin with, the two teams of horses used in the Magdeburg hemispheres demonstration were for showmanship and effect, for a single team and a strong tree would have provided the same force on the hemispheres. So if two teams of nine horses each could pull the hemispheres apart, a single team of nine horses could also, if a tree or some other strong object were used to hold the other end of the rope.

9. If the item is sealed in an air-tight package at sea level, then the pressure in the package is about 1 atmosphere. Cabin pressure is reduced for high altitude flying, so the pressure in the package is greater than the surrounding pressure and therefore puffs outwards.

10. Airplane windows are small because the pressure difference between the inside and outside surfaces result in large net forces that are directly proportional to the window's surface area. (Larger windows would have to be proportionally thicker to withstand the greater net force — windows on bathyspheres are similarly small.)

11. The can collapses under the weight of the atmosphere. When water was initially boiling in the can, much of the air inside was driven out by the steam. Pressure inside the can was a result of fewer molecules moving at greater speeds. Then, the cap was fastened so that molecules could not return when the can was cooled. When the vapor inside cooled and condensed back to the liquid state, a partial vacuum was effectively produced in the can which could not withstand the crushing force of the atmosphere outside.

12. Because of the partial vacuum inside a TV tube, it implodes when it is broken. The pressure of the atmosphere simply pushes the parts of the broken tube inward.

13. Unlike water, the density of the atmosphere depends on the depth. Air is compressible, like the foam bricks, and is more dense at the earth's surface and less dense with increasing altitude.

14. A vacuum cleaner wouldn't work on the moon. A vacuum cleaner operates on earth because the atmospheric pressure pushes dust into the machine's region of reduced pressure. On the moon there is no atmospheric pressure to push the dust anywhere.

15. A perfect vacuum pump could pump water no higher than 10.3 m. This is because the atmospheric pressure that pushes the water up the tube weighs as much as 10.3 vertical meters of water of the same cross-sectional area.

16. If barometer liquid were half as dense as mercury, then to weigh as much, a column twice as high would be required. A barometer using such liquid would therefore have to be twice the height of a standard mercury barometer.

17. The height of a barometer has to do with relative fluid pressures; that of the liquid mercury and that of the gaseous atmosphere. Fluid pressures depend on density and depth — pressure at the bottom of a wide column of mercury is no different than the pressure at the bottom of a narrow column of mercury of the same depth. The weight of fluid per area of contact is the same for each. Likewise with the surrounding air. Therefore barometers made with wide barometer tubes are the same height as barometers with narrow tubes of mercury.

18. Mercury can be drawn a maximum of 76 cm with a siphon. This is because 76 vertical cm of mercury exert the same pressure in a column of air that extends to the top of the atmosphere. Or looked at another way; water can be lifted 10.3 m by atmospheric pressure. Mercury is 13.6 times denser than water, so it can only be lifted only 1/13.6 times as high as water.

19. Drinking through a straw is slightly more difficult atop a mountain. This is because the reduced atmospheric pressure is less effective in pushing soda up into the straw.

20. If an elephant steps on you, the pressure that the elephant exerts is over and above the atmospheric pressure that is all the time exerted on you. It is the *extra* pressure the elephant's foot produces that crushes you. For example, if atmospheric pressure the size of an elephant's foot were somehow removed from a patch of your body, you would be in serious trouble. You would be soothed, however, if an elephant stepped onto this area!

21. You agree with your friend, for the elephant displaces far more air than a small helium-filled balloon, or small anything. The *effects* of the buoyant forces, however, is a different story. The large buoyant force on the elephant is insignificant compared to its enormous weight. The tiny buoyant force acting on the balloon of tiny weight, however, is significant.

22. One's lungs, like an inflated balloon, are compressed when submerged in water, and the air within is compressed. Air will not of itself flow from a region of low pressure into a region of higher pressure. The diaphragm in one's body reduces lung pressure to permit breathing, but this limit is strained when nearly 1 m below the water surface. It is exceeded at more than 1 m.

23. The wood has the greater mass. Why? Because the scale reading is weight, mg, minus the buoyant force. The wood has a greater volume and therefore a greater buoyant force (displaces more air). To yield the same scale reading it must therefore have a greater mass than the iron. (How much greater? An amount equal to the difference in buoyant force on the wood and iron blocks.)

24. Any object that displaces air is buoyed upwards by a force equal to the weight of air displaced (unless somehow air is prevented from interacting with its bottom surface). Objects therefore weigh less in air than in a vacuum. For objects of low densities, like bags of compressed gases, this can be important. For high-density objects like rocks and boulders the difference is usually negligible.

25. The air tends to pitch toward the rear (law of inertia), moreso than the less-dense balloon, so the air in the rear of the car interior behind the balloon becomes more dense than the air in front of the balloon. The denser air exerts more pressure on the balloon, and there is a net forward force on the balloon. In this case the balloon is buoyed both forward and upward, so the string of the balloon makes an angle. The pitch of the balloon will always be in the direction of the acceleration. Step on the brakes and the balloon pitches backwards. Round a corner and the balloon noticeably leans radially towards the center of the curve. Neat! (Another way to look at this involves the effect of two accelerations, g and the acceleration of the car. The string of the balloon will be parallel to the resultant of these two accelerations. Neat again!)

26. Helium is less dense than air, and will weigh less than an equal volume of air. A helium-filled bottle would weigh less than the air bottle (assuming they are filled to the same pressure). However, the helium-filled bottle will weigh more than the empty bottle.

27. An object floats only when buoyant force equals or exceeds weight. A steel tank of anything weighs more than the air it displaces, so won't float. A helium-filled balloon weighs less than the air it displaces and rises.

28. The air-filled balloon weighs more than the buoyant force that is exerted on it, so it falls. The helium-filled balloon weighs less than the buoyant force, so it rises.

29. The rubber of an inflated balloon is stretched, requiring force. This force is provided by the greater pressure of the compressed air within the balloon. (The fact that air pressure is greater in an inflated balloon is evident when it is punctured — the air "explodes" outward.)

30. The end supporting the punctured balloon tips upwards as it is lightened by the amount of air that escapes. The weight of air in the inflated balloon (which exceeds the buoyant force acting on it) makes that end move down.

31. The balloon which is free to expand will displace more air as it rises than the balloon which is restrained. Hence, the balloon, which is free to expand will have more buoyant force exerted on it than the balloon that does not expand, and will rise higher.

32. The rotating habitat is a centrifuge, and denser air is "thrown to" the inner rim. Like on earth, the maximum air density is at "ground level," and becomes less with increasing altitude. Air density in the rotating habitat is least at the zero-g region, the hub.

33. The helium-filled balloon will be buoyed from regions of greater pressure to regions of lesser pressure, and will "rise" in a rotating air-filled habitat. In the habitat, the maximum "height" is the hub. The balloon will be buoyed to this region where it will tend to remain.

34. The principal difference between ballooning and hang gliding in the atmosphere of a rotating space habitat and in the atmosphere of the earth has to do with the decreasing "gravity" experienced as one ascends. On earth, the decrease of gravity with altitude is negligible, and for practical purposes is constant. A balloonist or hang glider is always in danger of falling. In the rotating habitat, the decrease in "gravity" is significant, and reaches zero at the hub. So the "higher" one goes in the habitat, the less dangerous "gravity" becomes. At the hub, maximum

altitude, one doesn't fall at all. There are other differences in "gravity" that have to do with whether or not one is moving in the direction of rotation or against the direction of rotation. Centrifugal force increases with increasing angular speed so one would feel more "gravity" when sailing in the direction of rotation, and less when sailing in the opposite direction. These and other not-so-subtle differences will likely add new interest to these sports in the future.

35. The force of the atmosphere is on both sides of the window; the net force is zero, so windows don't normally break under the weight of the atmosphere. In a strong wind, however, pressure will be reduced on the windward side (Bernoulli's Principle) and the forces no longer cancel to zero. Many windows are blown *outward* in strong winds.

36. A taller chimney produces a better "draw." Atmospheric pressure at the top of a chimney is less than that below — the taller the chimney, the greater the difference in air pressures across its ends, and the greater the rate of flow of exhaust and hence, rate of flow of oxygen into the fire. (This can be likened to any fluid flow in a pipe where the rate of flow is proportional to the differences in pressures across its ends.)

37. Air blows over the top of the beach ball and reduces the air pressure there (Bernoulli's Principle). The greater pressure in the non-moving air below pushes the ball upward.

38. Air moves faster over the spinning top of the frisbee and pressure against the top is reduced. The bowl shape of the bottom contains a relatively dead air space underneath, that exerts near-normal pressure against the bottom. So like the beach ball in the previous exercise, there is a difference in pressures against the frisbee that produces an upward lift.

39. According to Bernoulli's Principle, the pressure will be less on the side of the car where the air is moving fastest. This is the side of the car nearest the truck, resulting in the car's being pushed by the atmosphere towards the truck.

40. With respect to the car, the interior air is at rest and the air above and outside the roof is in motion. So atmospheric pressure is greater inside the car than it is outside. The canvas roof top is therefore pushed upwards towards the region of lesser pressure.

41. Like the reason for the bulging canvas roof in the preceding exercise, with respect to the train windows, the interior air is at rest and the air outside is in motion. The atmospheric pressure against the inner surface of the window is therefore greater than the atmospheric pressure against the outside. When the difference in pressures is significant enough, the window is blown out.

42. Like an airplane wing, the air moves fastest over the crest. Pressure is therefore lowest at the top of the crests than down below in the troughs. The greater pressure in the troughs pushes the water into even higher crests.

43. Air moves faster past the convex portions of the flag and slower past the concave portions of the flag's surfaces, producing pressure differences as in the last exercise. Increased pressure on the concave side of the flag is met with decreased pressure on the convex side of the flag, with the result that the "waves" increase in amplitude, extending into the wind, which blows them along the length of the flag with the result that the free end flaps to and fro. (We should give some credit to your friend who stated a flag flaps because of Bernoulli's principle. To one who understands Bernoulli's principle, the answer is sufficient. To one who isn't, more explanation should be given.)

44. A solid-walled wharf is disadvantageous to ships pulling alongside because water currents are constrained and speed up between the ship and the wharf. This results in a reduced water

pressure, and the normal pressure on the other side of the ship then forces the ship against the wharf. The pilings avoid this mishap by allowing the freer passage of water between the wharf and the ship.

45. According to Bernoulli's principle, when a fluid gains speed in flowing through a narrow region, the pressure of the fluid is reduced. The gain in speed, the cause, produces reduced pressure, the effect. But one can argue that a reduced pressure in a fluid, the cause, will produce a flow in the direction of the reduced pressure, the effect. For example, if you decrease the air pressure in a pipe by a pump or by any means, neighboring air will rush into the region of reduced pressure. In this case the increase in air speed is the result, not the cause of, reduced pressure. Cause and effect are open to interpretation. Bernoulli's principle is a controversial topic with many physics types!

46. The atoms in the gas in a fluorescent lamp are in a gaseous state when current is not flowing in the tube. When current flows and electrons are knocked from the atoms, they are ionized and form a plasma.

47. At nighttime when the energizing sun no longer shines on the upper atmosphere, ionic layers settle closer together and better reflect the long radio waves of AM signals. The far-away stations you pick up at night are reflected off the ionosphere.

Chapter 13 Problem Solutions

1. To find the buoyant force that the air exerts on you, find your volume and multiply by the weight density of air (From Table 13.1 on page 231 we see that the mass of 1 m^3 of air is about 1.25 kg. Multiply this by 9.8 N/kg and you get 12.25 N/m^3). You can estimate your volume by your weight and by assuming your density is approximately equal to that of water (a little less if you can float). The density of water is $10^4 N/m^3$, which we'll assume is your density. By ratio and proportion:

$$\frac{10^4 N}{m^3} = \frac{\text{(your weight in newtons)}}{\text{(your volume in meters}^3)}$$

If your weight is a heavy 1000 N, for example, your volume is 0.1 m^3. So buoyant force = 12.25 N/m^3 x 0.1 m^3 = about **1.2 N**, the weight of a big apple). (A useful conversion factor is 4.45 N = 1 pound.)

2. If the atmosphere were composed of pure water vapor, the atmosphere would condense to a depth of 10.3 m. Since the atmosphere is composed of gases that have less density in the liquid state, their liquid depths would be more than 10.3 m, **about 12 m**.

3. If you're of average size, your total surface area is about two square meters, so the force of the atmosphere on you is about 2 x 10^5 N (which is about 22 tons, the weight of a freight car!). This is the force of air pressing against your body, to which your body pushes back in kind. So the total force of the atmosphere against you is enormous, as enormous as the force with which your body pushes back on the atmosphere. Be glad of atmospheric pressure, for without it, you'd bloat to death. The force of the atmosphere is "required" to keep you from bloating outward. In contrast, the buoyant force of the atmosphere on you is very small, only because the atmospheric force on you is not quite equal in all directions, and is slightly greater from below than from above, the difference being the buoyant force estimated in Problem 1.

14 | Temperature, Heat, and Expansion

Answers

1. Inanimate things such as tables, chairs, furniture, and so on, have the same temperature as the surrounding air (assuming they are in thermal equilibrium with the air — i.e., no sudden gush of differen-temperature air or such). People and mammals, however, generate their own heat and have body temperatures that are normally higher than air temperature.

2. Since Celcius degrees are larger than Fahrenheit degrees, an increase of 1 C° is larger. It's 9/5 as large.

3. Gas molecules move haphazardly and move at random speeds. They continually bound into one another, sometimes giving kinetic energy to neighbors, sometimes receiving kinetic energy. In this continual interaction, it would be statistically impossible for any large number of molecules to have the same speed. Temperature has to do with average speeds.

4. You cannot establish by your own touch whether or not you are running a fever because there would be no temperature difference between your hand and forehead. If your forehead is a couple of degrees higher in temperature than normal, your hand is also a couple of degrees higher.

5. The hot coffee has a higher temperature, but not a greater internal energy. Although the iceberg has less internal energy per mass, its enormously greater mass gives it a greater total energy than that in the small cup of coffee. (For a smaller volume of ice, the fewer number of more energetic molecules in the hot cup of coffee may constitute a greater total amount of internal energy — but not compared to an iceberg.)

6. If glass and mercury expanded at the same rate with increasing temperature, a mercury thermometer would not be feasible. This is because an increase in volume of the mercury would be met with an equal increase in the volume of the glass reservoir, so the level in the tube would not change.

7. A vacuum itself has no temperature. Something placed in a vacuum does. So when we talk of the temperature of a vacuum, we mean the temperature that an object would have there.

8. Temperature is a measurement of the degree of hotness or coldness of a substance, measured in degrees (or kelvins). More precisely it is a measure of the average kinetic energy per molecule in a substance.

9. The hot rock will cool and the cool water will warm, regardless of the relative amounts of each. The amount of temperature change, however, does depend in great part on the relative masses of the materials. For a hot rock dropped into the Atlantic Ocean, the change in temperature would be too small to measure. Keep increasing the mass of the rock or keep decreasing the mass of the ocean and the change will be evident.

10. Other affects aside, the temperature should be slightly higher, because the PE of the water above has been transformed to KE below. This increased KE is measured as an increased temperature. (On his honeymoon, James Prescott Joule could not be long diverted from his preoccupation with heat, and he attempted to measure the temperature of the water above and below a waterfall in Chamonix. The temperature increase he expected, however, was offset by cooling due to evaporation as the water fell.)

11. Increasing temperature means increasing KE which means increasing momentum of molecules, which means greater impact and greater pressure against the walls of the container. Simply put, as the temperature of a confined gas is increased, the molecules move faster and exert a greater pressure on the walls of the container.

12. The climate of Bermuda, like that of all islands, is moderated by the high specific heat of water. The climate is moderated by the large amounts of energy given off and absorbed by water for small changes in temperature. When the air is cooler than the water, the water warms the air; when the air is warmer than the water, the water cools the air.

13. As the ocean off the coast of San Francisco cools in the winter, the heat it loses warms the atmosphere it comes in contact with. This warmed air blows over the California coastline to produce a relatively warm climate. If the winds were easterly instead of westerly, the climate of San Francisco would be chilled by winter winds from dry and cold Nevada. The climate would be reversed also in Washington D.C., because air warmed by the cooling of the Atlantic Ocean would blow over Washington D.C. and produce a warmer climate in winter there.

14. In winter months when the water is warmer than the air, the air is warmed by the water to produce a seacoast climate warmer than inland. In summer months when the air is warmer than the water, the air is cooled by the water to produce a seacoast climate cooler than inland. This is why seacoast communities and especially islands do not experience the high and low temperature extremes that characterize inland locations.

15. The more internal energy states that a molecule has, the more energy it can absorb in those states. This greater capacity for absorbing potential energy is a higher specific heat.

16. Sand has a low specific heat, as evidenced by its relatively large temperature changes for small changes in internal energy. A substance with a high specific heat, on the other hand, must absorb or give off large amounts of internal energy for comparable temperature changes.

17. Water has a high specific heat capacity, which is to say, it normally takes a long time to heat up, or cool down. So the water in the watermellon resists changes in temperature, so once cooled it will stay cooler than other substances under the same conditions. Be glad water has a high specific heat capacity the next time you're enjoying cool watermellon on a hot day!

18. Gas is sold by volume. The gas meter that tallies your gas bill operates by measuring the number of cubic units that pass through it. Warm gas is expanded gas and occupies more space, and if it passes through your meter, it will be registered as more gas than if it were cooled and more compact. The gas company gains if gas is warm when it goes through your meter because the same amount of warmer gas has a greater volume.

19. Every part of a metal ring expands when it is heated — not only the thickness, but the outer and inner circumference as well. Hence the ball that normally passes through the hole when the temperatures are equal will more easily pass through the expanded hole when the ring is heated. (Interestingly enough, the hole will expand as much as a disk of the same metal undergoing the same increase in temperature. Blacksmiths mounted metal rims in wooden wagon wheels by first heating the rims. Upon cooling, the contraction resulted in a snug fit.)

20. Brass expands and contracts more than iron for the same changes in temperature. Since they are both good conductors and are in contact with each other, one cannot be heated or cooled without also heating or cooling the other. If the iron ring is heated, it expands — but the brass expands even more. Cooling the two will not result in separation either, for even at the lowest temperatures the shrinkage of brass over iron would not produce separation.

21. The gap in the ring will become wider when the ring is heated. Try this: draw a couple of lines on a ring where you pretend a gap to be. When you heat the ring, the lines will be farther apart — the same amount as if a real gap were there. Every part of the ring expands proportionally when heated uniformly — thickness, length, gap and all.

22. When a mercury thermometer is warmed, the outside glass is heated before heat gets to the mercury inside. So the glass is the first to expand, momentarily opening (like the ring in Exercise 15) which allows the mercury to drop from the glass tube into the slightly enlarged reservoir. When the mercury warms to the same temperature of the glass, it is then forced up the glass tube because of its greater expansion rate.

23. In the construction of a light bulb, it is important that the metal leads and the glass have the same rate of heat expansion. If the metal leads expand more than glass, the glass may crack. If the metal expands less than glass upon being heated, air will leak in through the resulting gaps.

24. On a hot day a steel tape will expand more than the ground. You will be measuring land with a "stretched" tape. So you'll get more land. (If you're measuring land *already* staked, then your measurements will be less than the actual land. In this case the land will be measured smaller than it actually is.)

25. Water is the most dense at 4°C; therefore, either cooling or heating at this temperature will result in an expansion of the water. A small rise in water level would be ambiguous and make a water thermometer impractical in this temperature region.

26. The combined volume of all the billions of "open rooms" in the hexagonal ice crystals of a piece of ice is equal to the volume of the part of the ice that extends above water when ice floats. When the ice melts, the open spaces are exactly filled in by the amount of ice that extends above the water level. This is why the water level doesn't rise when ice in a glass of ice water melts — the melting ice "caves in" and exactly fills the open spaces.

27. The curve for density versus temperature is:

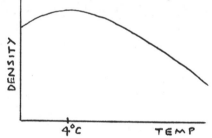

28. It is important to keep water in pipes from freezing because water expands more than the pipe material, which will fracture the pipes if water in them freezes.

29. If cooling occurred at the bottom of a pond instead of at the surface, ice would still form at the surface, but it would take much longer for ponds to freeze. This is because all the water in the pond would have to be reduced to a temperature of $0°C$ rather than $4°C$ before the first ice would form. Ice that forms at the bottom where the cooling process is occuring would be less dense and would float to the surface (except for ice that may form about material anchored to the bottom of the pond).

30. Ponds would be more likely to freeze if water had a lower specific heat. This is because the temperature would undergo more decrease when water gives up energy; water would more readily be cooled to the freezing point.

Chapter 14 Problem Solutions

1. a. $32°F = 0°C$ b. $0°C = 32°F$ c. $180°C$ between each
       $50°F = 10°C$ $10°C = 50°F$
       $68°F = 20°C$ $20°C = 68°F$
       $212°F = 100°C$ $100°C = 212°F$
       $-40°F = -40°C$ $-40°C = -40°F$

2. If a 1-m long bar expands 1/2 cm when heated, a bar of the same material that is 100 times as long will expand 100 times as much, 0.5 cm for each meter, or **50 cm**. (The heated bar will be 100.5 m.)

3. For a $10°C$ increase, the steel bridge will expand 10 parts in 10^5, or one part in 10,000 (10^4). The bridge will expand by one-tenthousandth of 1.3 kilometers, or one-ten-thousandths of 1300 meters, which is **13 centimeters**. So the main span of the Golden Gate bridge expands 13 centimeters when the temperature increases by $10°C$.

   By formula: $\Delta L = L_o\alpha\Delta T = (1300m)(10^{-5}/°C)(10°C) = 0.13$ m

4. If a snugly fitting steel pipe that girdled the world were heated by 1 Celsius degree, it would stand nearly 64 meters off the ground! The most straight-forward way to see this is to consider the radius of the 40 000 kilometer pipe, which is the radius of the earth, 6370 kilometers. Steel will expand one part in a hundred thousand for each $C°$ increase in temperature; the radius as well as the circumference will expand by this amount. So one hundred thousandths of 6370 kilometers = **63.7 meters**.

   Or by formula for the earth's radius, $\Delta L = L_o\alpha\Delta T = (6370 \times 10^3m)(10^{-5}/°C)(1°C) = $ **63.7 m**.

5. $mgh = mc\Delta T$
    $$\Delta T = \frac{gh}{c} = \frac{(9.8m/s^2)(170m)}{4187 \text{ J/kgC}°} = \mathbf{0.4°C}$$

15 | Heat Transfer

Answers

1. It is difficult to estimate the temperature of things by touching because in addition to the uncertainties of subjective judgements, the thermal conductivities of the things beings touched, such as shown in Figure 15.1, gives rise to different sensations of hotness or coldness.

2. Air at 70°F feels comfortable principally because it is a poor conductor. Our warmer skin is slow to transfer heat to the air. Water, however, is a better conductor of heat than air, so our warmer bodies in water more readily transfer heat to the water.

3. When the temperatures of the blocks are the same as the temperature of your hand, then no heat transfer occurs. Heat will flow between your hand and something being touched only if there is a temperature difference between them.

4. Energy "flows" from higher to lower temperature, from your hand to the ice. It is the energy, heat, flowing from your hand that produces the sensation of coolness. There is no flow from cold to hot; only from hot to cold.

5. Silver is a very good conductor and will quickly come to the temperature of the food with which it is in contact. This quality is often unfavorable when very hot food is being eaten.

6. The main reason for serving potatoes wrapped in aluminum foil is to increase the time that the potatoes remain hot after being removed from the oven. This is because heat transfer by radiation is minimized as radiation from the potatoes is internally reflected, and heat transfer by convection is minimized as circulating air cannot make contact with the shielded potatoes.

7. In touching the tongue to very cold metal, enough heat can be quickly conducted away from the tongue to bring the saliva to sub-zero temperature where it freezes, locking the tongue to the metal. In the case of relatively non-conducting wood, much less heat is conducted from the tongue and freezing does not take place fast enough for sudden sticking to occur.

8. Air is an excellent insulator. The reason that fiberglass is a good insulator is principally because of the vast amount of air spaces trapped in it.

9. Heat from the relatively warm ground is conducted by the gravestone to melt the snow in contact with the gravestone. Likewise for trees or any materials that are better conductors of heat than snow, and that extend into the ground.

10. The snow and ice of the igloo is a better insulator than wood. You would be warmer in the igloo than the wooden shack.

11. The earth is insulated by its atmospheric blanket. This blanket keeps us from getting cold at night and too hot in the day. Isn't that nice?

12. To more effectively cool something with ice, put the ice on top of the object to cool. Warm air around the object tends to rise and carry energy away from it. Ice on top facilitates this.

13. Much of the energy of the flame is readily conducted through the paper to the water. The relatively large amount of water, compared to the paper, absorbs the energy that would otherwise raise the temperature of the paper. The upper limit of 212°F for the water is well below the ignition temperature of the paper, 451°F (hence the title "451" of Ray Bradbury's science fiction novel about book burning).

14. You can hold your fingers quite close to the side of a candle flame without harm because the air between is a good insulator. But you will burn your fingers if you hold them above the flame because of the convection of hot gases in the flame. (Interestingly enough, candle flames will quickly snuff out in orbiting space facilities or any gravity free region. This is because convection depends on gravity, and without convection new oxygen cannot get to the flame.)

15. Air is a poor conductor, whatever the temperature. So holding your hand in hot air for a short time is not harmful because very little heat is conducted by the air to your hand. But if you touch the hot conducting surface of the oven, heat readily conducts to you — ouch!

16. Wood is a poor conductor (as little Joshua states on page 265) whatever the temperature, so you can safely grab a pan by its wooden handle for a short time. Like the hot air in the previous exercise, this is because very little heat will be conducted to your hand. Touching the iron part of the hand is another story, for then heat is readily conducted to your hand. Ouch again!

17. The conductivity of wood is relatively low whatever the temperature — even in the stage of red hot coals. You can safely walk barefoot across red hot wooden coals if you step quickly (like removing the wooden-handled frying pan with bare hands quickly from the hot oven in the previous exercise) because very little heat is conducted to your feet. Because of the poor conductivity of the coals, energy from within the coals does not readily replace the energy that transfers to your feet. This is evident in the diminished redness of the coal after your foot has left it. Stepping on red-hot iron coals, however, is a different story. Because of the excellent conductivity of iron, very damaging amounts of heat would transfer to your feet. More than simply ouch!

18. In terms of buoyancy, the smoke, like hot air, is less dense than the surroundings and is buoyed upward. It cools with contact with the surrounding air and becomes more dense. When its density matches that of the surrounding air, its buoyancy and weight balance and rising ceases. Another explanation is that the smoke particles initially have a high temperature and move faster than air molecules, which allows them to readily migrate through the air. Net migration is in the direction of least obstruction, upward, since air density becomes less with increasing height. Rising is short lived, for they give up kinetic energy via collisions with molecules in the air. When the kinetic energy of the smoke particles is equal to the kinetic energy of the surrounding air, they no longer have a speed advantage and further upward migration ceases.

19. To say that helium, nitrogen, and oxygen have the same temperature is to say they have the same kinetic energy. The smaller mass of helium, however, is compensated by an increased speed to produce the same kinetic energy. Hence, helium travels faster than nitrogen and oxygen molecules even though all have the same temperature. Unlike the smoke particles that give up excess energy in the preceding problem, the helium will not lose energy in interacting with the surrounding air because all molecules have the same average kinetic energy.

20. Hydrogen molecules will be the faster moving when mixed with oxygen molecules. They will have the same temperature, which means they will have the same average kinetic energy. Recall that $KE = 1/2\ mv^2$. Since the mass of hydrogen is considerably less than oxygen, the velocity must correspondingly be greater. [This reasoning is spelled out in more detail for the similar case of helium in the footnote on page 269.]

21. Like the explanation of the previous exercise, the molecules of gas with the lesser mass will have the higher average speeds. A look at the periodic table will show that argon (A = 18) is less massive than krypton (A = 36). The faster molecules are those of argon. This is the case whether or not the gases are in separate containers.

22. When we increase the temperature of the air (the cause), it expands (the effect). Cause produces effect. It does not logically follow that the effect will produce the cause; that is, the process of expanding a volume of air does not cause an increase in its temperature. It is in fact the other way around; expanding a volume of air will lower its temperature.

23.

24. The mixture expands when it is ejected from the nozzle, and therefore cools. At the freezing temperature of 0°C, ice forms.

25. Because of the high specific heat of water, sunshine warms water very little compared to land. As a result, air is warmed over the land and rises. Cooler air from above the cool water takes its place and convection currents are formed. If land and water were heated equally by the sun, such convection currents (and the winds they produce) wouldn't be.

26. Black is the most efficient color for steam radiators. Much of the heat a steam radiator produces, however, is a result of the convection it produces, which has to do with its temperature rather than its radiating ability.

27. A good emitter, by virtue of molecular-or-whatever design, is also a good absorber. A good absorber appears black because radiation that impinges upon it is absorbed; just the opposite of reflection. The blackness of materials is evidence for their absorption. By the same token the blackness is also evidence for their emission. The radiation that an object emits at normal temperatures is too low in frequency to be seen by the eye. (A hot black pot will emit more energy in a shorter time than a hot silver pot of the same mass and material.)

28. If good absorbers were not also good emitters, then thermal equilibrium would not be possible. If a good absorber only absorbed, then its temperature would climb above that of poorer absorbers in the vicinity. And if poor absorbers were good emitters, their temperatures would fall below that of better absorbers.

29. A good reflector is a poor radiator of heat, and a poor reflector is a good radiator of heat.

30. Put the cream in right away for at least three reasons. Since black coffee radiates more heat than white coffee, make it whiter right away so it won't radiate and cool so quickly while you are waiting. Also, by Newton's law of cooling, the higher the temperature of the coffee above the surroundings, the greater will be the rate of cooling — so again add cream right away and lower the temperature to that of a reduced cooling rate, rather allowing it to cool fast and then bring the temperature down still further by adding the cream later. Also — by adding the cream, you increases the total amount of liquid, which for the same surface area, cools slower.

31. Heat radiates into the clear night air and the temperature of the car goes down. Normally, heat is conducted to the car by the relatively warmer ground, but the rubber tires prevent the conduction of heat from the ground. So heat radiated away is not easily replaced and the car cools to temperatures below that of the surroundings. In this way frost can form on a below-freezing car in the above-freezing environment.

32. When it is desirable to reduce the radiation that comes into a greenhouse, whitewash is applied to the glass to simply reflect much of the incoming radiation. Energy reflected is energy not absorbed.

33. For maximum warmth, wear the plastic coat on the outside and utilize the greenhouse effect.

34. If the upper atmosphere permitted the escape of more terrestrial radiation than it does presently, more energy would escape and the earth's climate would cool. If less radiation were to escape than presently, the earth's climate would become warmer.

35. Kelvins and Celsius degrees are the same size, and although ratios of these two scales will produce very different results, differences in Kelvins and differences in Celsius degrees will be no different from each other. Since Newton's law of cooling involves temperature differences, either scale may be used (this applies also to the Fahrenheit scale).

36. Turn your heater off altogether and save fuel. When it is cold outside, your house is constantly losing heat. How much is lost depends on the insulation and the difference in inside and outside temperature (Newton's law of cooling). Keeping ΔT high consumes more fuel. To consume less fuel, keep ΔT low and turn your heater off altogether. Will more fuel be required to reheat the house when you return? Not at all. This is confusing to many people because they don't understand that the amount of internal energy in a warm house is very small compared to the amount of heat that is constantly escaping. Filling up a house with internal energy consumes much less fuel than to keep it filled up when it is cold outside. While it is "filling" ΔT is lower and the amount of heat lost per minute is less than the amount that will be lost per minute at higher house temperatures. Your fuel bill is primarily for heat that leaks from your house — not the lesser amount required to fill it in the first place. (Compare this to the greater amount of water required to keep a leaky bucket filled, to the lesser amount of water that leaks at lower water levels while it is being filled. In this case, the rate of water that leaks is proportional to ΔP (difference in pressure). The amount that leaks while refilling is less per minute because the pressure is less than that of the filled can.)

37. Turn the air conditioner off altogether to keep ΔT small, as in the preceding answer. Heat leaks at a greater rate into a cold house than into a not-so-cold house. The greater the rate at which heat leaks into the house, the greater the amount of fuel consumed by the air conditioner.

38. In accordance with Newton's law of cooling, if the earth's temperature increases, its rate of radiating will increase. And if much of this extra terrestrial radiation is blocked, and the temperature of the earth increases more, then its rate of radiating simply increases further. A new and higher equilibrium temperature is established.

16 | Change of State

Answers

1. When a wet finger is held to the wind, evaporation is greatest on the windy side, which feels cool. The cool side of your finger is windward.

2. When you blow over the top of a bowl of hot soup, you increase net evaporation and its cooling effect by removing the warm vapor which tends to condense and reduce net evaporation. Also, the moving air reduces pressure atop the soup (Bernoulli's Principle) and increases the rate of evaporation.

3. Hot coffee poured into a saucer cools (1) because the greater surface area of the coffee permits more evaporation to take place, and (2) by the conservation of energy, the internal energy that heats up the saucer comes from the coffee, which subsequently is cooled.

4. From our macroscopic point of view, it appears that nothing is happening in a covered glass of water, but at the atomic level there is chaotic motion as molecules are continually bumbling about. Molecules are leaving the water surface to the air above while vapor molecules in the air are leaving the air and plunging into the liquid. Evaporation and condensation are taking place continually, even though the net evaporation or net condensation is zero. Here we distinguish between the processes and the net effect of the processes.

5. Evaporation would not be a cooling process if all the molecules in a liquid had the same speed. This is because the energy of molecules to exit via evaporation would be no different than the energy of molecules left behind. Although internal energy of the liquid would decrease with evaporation, energy per molecule would not change. No temperature change would occur.

6. The energy that keeps the dunking duck in operation comes from the sun, lamps, or whatever is heating the lower chamber where evaporation is taking place. To see this, simply direct heat energy to the lower chamber of the duck and you'll see an increase in the number of times per minute the duck dunks.

7. If the perfume doesn't evaporate it will produce no odor. The odor of a substance is evidence for its evaporation.

8. In a porous canvas bag, the faster-moving molecules are most prone to seep through the canvas material and evaporate into the air, leaving the slower-moving molecules behind. The motion of the car increases the rate of evaporation and cools the water inside, just as blowing over a hot bowl of soup tends to cool the soup (Exercise 2).

9. A bottle wrapped in wet cloth will cool by the evaporation of liquid from the cloth. As evaporation progresses, the average temperature of the liquid left behind in the cloth can easily drop below the temperature of the cool water that wet it in the first place. So to cool a bottle of beer, soda, or whatever at a picnic, wet a piece of cloth in a bucket of cool water. Wrap the wet cloth around the bottle to be cooled. As evaporation progresses, the temperature of the water in the cloth drops, and cools the bottle to a temperature below that of the bucket of water.

10. The body keeps its temperature a normal $37°C$ by the process of evaporation. When the body tends to overheat, perspiration occurs, which cools the body if the perspiration is allowed to evaporate. (Interestingly enough, if you're immersed in hot water, perspiration occurs profusely, but evaporation and cooling do not follow — that's why it is inadvisable to stay too long in a hot bath.)

11. Air above the freezing temperature is chilled in the vicinity of an iceberg and condensation of the water vapor in the air results in fog.

12. Aside from the connotation of kissing molecules and parking on a cool night, the warm air generated in the car's interior meets the cold glass and a lessening of molecular speed results in condensation of water on the inside of the windows.

13. On a day where the outside of the windows are warmer than the inside, condensation will occur on the outside of the windows.

14. Air swept upward expands in regions of less atmospheric pressure. The expansion is accompanied by cooling, which means molecules are moving at speeds low enough for coalescing upon collisions; hence the moisture that is the cloud.

15. Clouds tend to form over islands because land has a lower specific heat than water, so the land is warmed faster than the surrounding water. This causes updrafts above the warmed land; the rising air laden with H_2O expands, cools, and coalesces (Figure 16-7).

16. When water is boiling, it is being cooled by the boiling process as fast as it is being heated by the stove. Hence its temperature remains the same — 100°C.

17. You could not cook food in low-temperature water that is boiling by virtue of reduced pressure. Food is cooked by the high temperature it is subjected to, not by the bubbling of the surrounding water. For example, put room-temperature water in a vacuum and it will boil. But this doesn't mean the water will transfer more internal energy to an egg than before boiling — an egg in this boiling water won't cook at all!

18. As in the answer to the previous exercise, high temperature and the resulting internal energy given to the food is responsible for cooking — if the water boils at a low temperature (presumably under reduced pressure) insufficient energy is given to cook the food.

19. The air in the flask is very low in pressure, so that the heat from your hand will produce boiling at this reduced pressure. (Your instructor will want to be sure that the flask is strong enough to resist implosion before handing it to you!)

20. Cooking time will be no different for vigorously boiling water and gently boiling water, for both have the same temperature. The reason spaghetti is cooked in vigorously boiling water is simply to ensure the spaghetti doesn't stick to itself and the pan. For fuel economy, simply stir your spaghetti in gently boiling water .

21. The lid on the pot traps heat which quickens boiling; the lid also increases pressure on the boiling water which raises its boiling temperature. The hotter water correspondingly cooks food in a shorter time.

22. The boiling point is higher in a nuclear reactor because of increased pressure. It behaves like a pressure cooker.

23. After a geyser has erupted, it must refill and then undergo the same heating cycle. If the rate of filling and heating doesn't change, then the time to boil to the eruption stage will be the same.

24. Regelation would not occur if ice crystals weren't open structured. The pressure of the wire on the open network of crystals caves them in and the wire follows. With the pressure immediately above the wire relieved, the molecules again settle to their low energy crystalline state. Interestingly enough, the energy score balances for these changes of state: The energy

given up by the water that refreezes above the wire is conducted through the wire thickness to melt the ice being crushed beneath. The more conductive the wire, the faster regelation occurs. For an insulator like string, regelation won't occur at all. Try it and see!

25. Pressure of your feet is greater on the bumps on ice, as the area of contact is less. The greater pressure lowers the melting point of the ice as ice crystals are "crushed" to the liquid state. It is the water on ice that makes ice slippery. Hard frozen ice that is not pressurized to liquid at the surface is not slippery.

26. Snowfall certainly is possible on very cold days. But once snowing, the temperature of the air increases because of the change of state of the H_2O from gas to solid. So one's observation is warmness when snowing, and one's misinterpretation is therefore that snowfall can't happen if it is cold. (Similarly, it is a fact that our ears continue to grow all through life. So old people usually have big ears. Some people who see children with big ears mistakenly say they are destined to have a long life.)

27. The H_2O absorbs energy in the change of state from ice to water. If this energy is supplied by the surrounding air, then the temperature of the surrounding air is decreased.

28. This is an example illustrating Figure 16.7. Water vapor in the warm air condenses on the low-temperature metal surface of the unit.

29. The practice of wrapping newspaper around ice in an icebox is inadvisable, unless one only wants to make the ice last longer at the expense of reducing the cooling effect. The insulating newspaper slows the melting process, which diminishes the extraction of heat from the surroundings. The surroundings are cooled principally because the ice melts. To inhibit this melting is to reduce the desired cooling process.

30. Figure 16.7 again. Water vapor in the warm air condenses on the relatively low-temperature surface of the can.

31. Every gram of water that undergoes freezing releases 80 calories of energy to the cellar. This continual release of energy by the freezing water keeps the temperature of the cellar from going below $0^{\circ}C$. Sugar and salts in the canned goods prevents them from freezing at $0^{\circ}C$. Only when all the water in the tub freezes, will the temperature of the cellar go below $0^{\circ}C$ and then freeze the canned goods. The farmer must, therefore, replace the tub before or just as soon as all the water in it has frozen.

32. The answer to this is similar to the previous answer, and also the fact that the coating of ice acts as an insulating blanket. Every gram of water that freezes releases 80 calories, much of it to the fruit; the thin layer of ice then acts as an insulating blanket against further coldness.

33. As more freezing takes places and the polar icecaps grow, less water surface is exposed for evaporation. This results in less clouds and consequently, less precipitation. Without the pile-up of new snow, melting can more readily occur. The ice age withdraws.

34. On the very hot skillet, a layer of vapor is formed and maintained at the bottom of drops of water. This vapor actually provides an insulating layer between the drop and the very hot skillet, which impedes the transfer of energy from the skillet to the water drops.

35. Your friend has been bilked — better had he donated that sum of money to a worthy charity and walked across his own hot coals. Although a mind-over-matter manner of thinking may have its beneficial points in some cases, it is not demonstrated in firewalking. One can walk on hot coals of wood or charcoal without harm for two reasons that are straight physics. First,

wood is a poor conductor, even when it is hot (which accounts for the wooden handles in cooking ware). Very little heat energy is transferred if contact is brief, so quick steps on red hot coals will transfer safe amounts of heat to the feet. Secondly, just as you can touch a hot clothes iron with a wetted finger, vaporization of the moisture on your feet absorbs heat energy that would otherwise burn you. Nevertheless, this *is* a dangerous activity and many people have been harmed by stepping on unseen hot nails or coals that tend to stick to the feet. So the practice is not advised. (As for the charlatan types who collect the money: If they really want to demonstrate mind over matter, let them walk barefoot on red hot coals of metal!)

Chapter 16 Problem Solutions

1. a. 1 kg 0°C ice to 0°C water requires 80 kilocalories.
   b. 1 kg 0°C water to 100°C water requires 100 kilocalories.
   c. 1 kg 100°C water to 100°C steam requires 540 kilocalories.
   d. 1 kg 0°C ice to 100°C steam requires (80 + 100 + 540) = **720 kilocalories**, or 720000 calories.

2. From -273°C "ice" to 0°C ice requires (273)(0.5) = 136.5 calories.
   From 0°C ice to 0°C water requires 80 calories.
   From 0°C water to 100°C water requires 100 calories.
                 The total is **316.5 calories**.
   Compared to 540 calories for a change of state of 1 gram of 100°C water, this is about **1.7 times the energy!**

3. First, find the number of calories that 10 g of 100°C steam will give in changing to 10 g of 0°C ice.
   10 g of steam changing to 10 g of boiling water at 100°C releases 5400 calories.
   10 g of 100°C water cooling to 0°C releases 1000 calories.
   So 6400 calories are available for melting ice.

$$\frac{6400 \text{ cal}}{80 \text{ cal/g}} = \textbf{80 grams of ice.}$$

4. $mgh = 334000$ J
$$h = \frac{334000 \text{ J}}{9.8 \text{ m/s}^2} = 34000 \text{ m} = \textbf{34 km.}$$

Note that the mass cancels. So in the ideal case of no energy losses along the way, any piece of ice that freely falls 34 km will completely melt upon impact.

5. $mgh = mc\Delta T$

$$\Delta T = \frac{mgh}{mc} = \frac{(99.8)(100)}{460} = 2.1°C$$

And 60% of 2.1°C = **1.3°C**.

17 | Thermodynamics

Answers

1. You do work on the liquid when you shake it back and forth, which increases its internal energy. This is noted by an increase in temperature.

2. The work done in compressing the air increases its internal energy, which is evidenced by an increase in temperature.

3. The tire becomes hot for two reasons: First, the work done in compressing the air increases its internal energy which is conducted to and shared with the pump. The second reason for the increase in temperature involves friction, for the piston rubs against the inner wall of the pump cylinder.

4. A given amount of mechanical energy can be easily and commonly converted to heat; any body moving with kinetic energy that is brought to rest by friction transforms all its kinetic energy into heat (like a car skidding to rest on a horizontal road). The converse is not true, however. In accord with the 2nd law of thermodynamics, only a fraction of a given amount of internal energy can be converted to mechanical energy. For example, when steam in a steam engine expands against a piston, only some of the internal energy is converted to work — the rest goes into overcoming friction.

5. The high compression of fuel mixture in the cylinders of a diesel engine heats the mixture to the ignition point, so spark plugs are not needed.

6. When a blob of air rises in the atmosphere it does work on the surrounding lower-pressure air as it expands. This work output is at the expense of its internal energy, which is diminished, which in turn is evidenced by a lower temperature. Hence the temperature of air at the elevation of mountain tops is less than down below.

7. When we say energy "deteriorates", we simply mean it is dissipated into less concentrated and therefore less useful forms. It still exists, however, and this transfer of energy is in accord with the 1st law.

8. This transfer would not violate the 1st law because energy has been transferred without loss or gain. It would violate the 2nd law, because internal energy will not freely transfer from a cooler to a warmer object.

9. The term pollution refers to an undesirable by-product of some process. The desirability or undesirability of a particular by-product is relative, and depends on the circumstances. For example, ejecting hot water into cooler water can be quite desirable from one point of view and undesirable from another point of view.

10. According to the 2nd law, it is not possible to construct a heat engine that is without exhaust. If the exhausted heat is undesirable then the engine is a polluter. If the exhausted heat is desirable, heating a swimming pool for example, then in this sense the heat engine produces no thermal pollution.

11. It is advantageous to use steam as hot as possible in a steam-driven turbine because the efficiency is higher if there is a greater difference in temperature between the source and the sink (see Sadi Carnot's equation on page 313).

12. As in the preceding exercise, efficiency is higher with greater difference in temperature between the heat source (combustion chamber in the engine) and sink (air surrounding the exhaust). All other things equal, and strictly speaking, a car is more efficient on a cold day.

13. When the temperature is lowered in the reservoir into which heat is rejected, efficiency increases; substitution of a smaller value of T_{hot} into $(T_{hot} - T_{cold})/T_{hot}$ will confirm this. (Reexpress the equation as $1 - T_{cold}/T_{hot}$ to better see this.)

14. As in the preceding exercise, inspection will show that decreasing T_{cold} will contribute to a greater increase in efficiency than by increasing T_{hot} by the same amount. For example, let T_{hot} be 600K and T_{cold} be 300K. Then efficiency = (600 - 300)/600 = 1/2. Now let T_{hot} be increased by 200K. Now efficiency = (800 - 300)/800 = 5/8. Compare this with T_{cold} decreased by 200K, in which case efficiency = (600 - 100)/600 = 5/6, which is clearly greater.

15. Only when the sink is absolute zero (0 K) will an engine have an ideal efficiency of 100%.

16. Even if the refrigerator were 100% efficient, the room wouldn't be cooled because the heat sink is also in the room. That's why the condensation coils are in a region outside the region to be cooled. What actually happens in the case of the refrigerator being operated with its door open in a closed room is that the room temperature increases. This is because the refrigerator motor warms the surrounding air.

17. Work must be done to establish a temperature difference between the inside of the refrigerator and the surrounding air. The greater the temperature difference to be established, the more work and hence more energy is consumed. This temperature difference is greater when the room is warm rather than cold.

18. Most people know that electric lights are inefficient when it comes to converting electrical energy into light energy, so they are surprised to learn there is a 100% conversion of electrical energy to thermal energy. If the building is being heated electrically, the lights do a fine job of heating, and it is not at all wasteful to keep them on while heating is desirable. It is a wasteful practice if the air conditioners are on and cooling is desired, for the energy input to the air conditioners must be increased to remove the extra thermal energy given off by the lights.

19. Most of the electric energy that goes into lighting a lamp turns immediately into internal energy. In the case of an incandescent lamp, only about 5% goes into light, and in a fluorescent lamp, about 20% goes to light. But all of the energy that takes the form of light is converted to internal energy when the light is absorbed by materials upon which it is incident. So by the lst law, all the electrical energy is ultimately converted to internal energy. By the second law, organized electrical energy degenerates to the more disorganized form, internal energy.

20. Heat energy in the universe is tending toward unavailability with time. Hotter things are cooling as cooler things are warming. The universe is tending toward a common temperature. With no temperature differences, the "heat death" of the universe, heat energy can do no work.

21. No, the entropy principle has not been violated because the order of the salt crystals is at the expense of a greater disorder of the water in the vapor state after evaporation. Even if we confine the system to the crystals themselves, there would be no violation of entropy because there is work input to the system by sunlight or other means.

22. No, the freezing of water is not an exception to the entropy principle because work has been put into the refrigeration system to prompt this change of state. There is actually a greater net disorder when the environment surrounding the freezer is considered.

Chapter 17 Problem Solutions

1. Metal heated until twice as hot means it has twice the internal energy, or twice the *absolute* temperature. It begins at 10 + 273 = 283K and is doubled to 566K. We convert to Celsius by subtracting 273, and find the twice-as-hot metal **293°C**.

2. If by "twice as cold" is meant one half the internal energy, then the weather will be one half its absolute temperature, or (1/2)(273 +10) = 141.5K. To find how many Celsius degrees below 0°C this is, we first subtract 141.5K from 273K; this is 273 - 141.5 = 131.5K below the freezing point of ice, or **-131.5°C**. (Or simply, 141.5 - 273 = -131.5°C.) Quite nippy!

3. Adiabatic compression would heat the confined air by about 10°C for each kilometer decrease in elevation. The -35°C air would be heated 100C° and have a ground temperature of about (-35 + 100) = **65°C**. (This is 149°F, roasting hot!)

4. a. Ideal efficiency $= \dfrac{T_h - T_c}{T_h} = \dfrac{900 - 400}{900} =$ **0.55**

   b. Actual efficiency $= \dfrac{\text{Work out}}{\text{work in}} = \dfrac{18 \text{ kJ}}{68 \text{ kJ}} =$ **0.26**

5. a. Ideal efficiency $= \dfrac{T_h - T_c}{T_h} = \dfrac{800 - 300}{800} =$ **0.63**

   b. Actual efficiency $= \dfrac{\text{Work out}}{\text{work in}} = \dfrac{50 \text{ kJ}}{100 \text{ kJ}} =$ **0.5**

18 Vibrations and Waves

Answers

1. The period of a pendulum depends on the acceleration due to gravity. Just as a ball will fall faster, a pendulum will swing to and fro faster in a stronger gravitational field. (The exact relationship, $T = 2 \sqrt{l/g}$, is shown in the footnote on page 323). So high in the mountains where the gravitational field of the earth is slightly less, a pendulum will oscillate with a slightly longer period, and a clock will run just a bit slower and will "lose" time.

2. A shorter pendulum has less rotational inertia and will consequently swing to and fro with a higher frequency and shorter period.

3. Assuming the center of gravity of the suitcase doesn't change when loaded with books, the pendulum rate of the empty case and loaded case will be the same. This is because the period of a pendulum is independent of mass. Since the length of the pendulum doesn't change, the frequency and hence the period is unchanged.

4. The period is actually less when you stand on a playground swing, for the pen-dulum is effectively shorter. That's because the center of mass of the pendulum "bob" (you) is raised and is closer to the pivot. Or put another way, the rotational inertial is decreased as the pendulum tends to change from a "bob" configuration ($I = mr^2$) to that of a "stick" ($I = 1/3 \ mL^2$). (See Figure 7.3 back on page 117).

5. A short pendulum swings with a smaller period and higher frequency than a long pendulum. People walk with a pendulum-like motion of the legs; people with short legs therefore walk with quicker strides than people with long legs. (Recall the earlier discussion of this idea in Chapter 7 when we treated rotational inertia).

6. You bend your arms when you run for the same reason you bend your legs — to shorten their length to increase their pendulum frequency (or to reduce their rotational inertia and thereby increase the frequency with which they tend to oscillate).

7. Shake the garden hose to and fro in a direction perpendicular to the hose to produce a sine-like curve.

8. To produce a transverse wave with a slinky, shake it to and fro in a direction that is per-pendicular to the length of the slinky itself (as with the garden hose in the previous exercise). To produce a longitudinal wave, shake it to and fro along the direction of its length, so that a series of compressions and rarefactions is produced.

9. The fact that gas can be heard escaping from a gas tap before it is smelled indicates that the pulses of molecular collisions (the sound) travel more quickly than the molecules migrate. [There are three speeds to consider: (1) the average speed of the molecules themselves, as evidenced by temperature—quite fast, (2) the speed of the pulse produced as they collide—about 3/4 the speed of the molecules themselves, and (3) the very much slower speed of molecular migration.]

10. Frequency and period are reciprocals of one another; $f = 1/T$, and $T = 1/f$. Double one and the other is half as much. So doubling the frequency of a vibrating object halves the period.

11. The frequency of the second hand of a clock is one cycle per minute; the frequency of the minute hand is one cycle per hour; for the hour hand the frequency is one cycle per 12 hours.

To express these values in hertz, we need to convert the times to seconds. Then we find for the second hand the frequency = 1/60 hertz: for the minute hand the frequency = 1/3600 hertz; for the hour hand the frequency = 1/(12 x 3600) = 1/(43,200) hertz.

12. As you dip your fingers more frequently into still water, the waves you produce will be of a higher frequency (we see the relationship between "how frequently" and "frequency"). The higher-frequency waves will be closer together — their wavelengths will be shorter.

13. The frequency of vibration and the number of waves passing by each second are the same.

14. Think of a period as one cycle in time, and a wavelength as one cycle in space, and a little thought will show that in a time of one period, a wave travels a full wavelength. Formally, we can see this as follows:

distance = speed x time

where speed = frequency x wavelength, which when substituted for speed,

distance = frequency x wavelength x time

distance = 1/period x wavelength x period = wavelength.

(Rather than formally proving this as above, it is best to visualize it — to "see" that one wave form is generated in each cycle, the time of which is the period — and that the wave form moves outward a distance equal to its own wavelength during this time. Conceptualize physics!)

15. The energy of a water wave spreads along the increasing circumference of the wave until its magnitude diminishes to a value that cannot be distinguished from thermal motions in the water. The energy of the waves adds to the internal energy of the water.

16. The circular patterns made by expanding waves is evidence that the wave speeds are the same in all radial directions. This is because all parts of the circle have gone equal distances from the center in equal times.

17. The speed of light is 300 000 km/s, about a million times faster than sound. Because of this difference in speeds, lightning is seen a million times sooner than it is heard.

18. The Doppler effect is a change in frequency as a result of the motion of source, receiver, or both. So if you moved toward a stationary sound source, yes, you would encounter waves more frequently and the frequency of the received sound would be higher. Or if you moved away from the source, the waves would encounter you less frequently, and you would hear sound of a lower frequency.

19. There is no Doppler effect when motion of the sound source is at right angles to the listener. In this case, the source is neither approaching and crowding waves, nor receding and spreading waves.

20. Police use radar waves which are reflected from moving cars. From the shift in the returned frequencies, the speed of the reflectors (car bodies) is determined.

21. The bow or shock wave is actually the superposition of many lesser amplitude waves that interfere constructively. When the crest of one wave overlaps the crest of another, and then another, a wave of greater amplitude is produced.

22. The conical angle of a shock wave becomes narrower with greater speeds. We see this in the sketches:

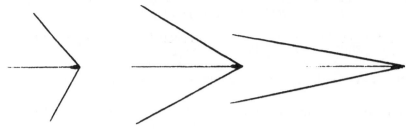

23. The fact that you hear an airplane in a direction that differs from where you see it simply means the airplane is moving, and not necessarily faster than sound (a sonic boom would be evidence of supersonic flight). If the speed of sound and the speed of light were the same, then you'd hear a plane where it appears in the sky. But because the two speeds are so different, the plane you see appears ahead of the plane you hear.

24. A shock wave and the resulting sonic boom are produced whenever an aircraft is supersonic, whether or not the aircraft has just become supersonic or has been supersonic for hours. It is a popular misconception that sonic booms are principally produced at the moment an aircraft becomes supersonic. This is akin to saying that a boat produces a bow wave at the moment it exceeds the wave-speed of water. It begins to produce a bow wave at this crucial moment, but if it moved no faster, the overlapping pattern of waves would not extend very far from the bow. Likewise with an aircraft. Both the boat and the aircraft must appreciably exceed wave speed to produce an ample bow and shock wave.

25. The speed of the sound source rather than the loudness of the sound is crucial to the production of a shock wave. At subsonic speeds, no overlapping of the waves will occur to produce a shock wave. Hence no sonic boom is produced.

26. Yes, a supersonic fish in water would produce a shock wave and hence a sonic boom for the same reason it would if traveling faster than sound in air.

Chapter 18 Problem Solutions

1. The skipper notes that 15 meters of wave pass each 5 seconds, or equivalently, that 3 meters pass each 1 second, so the speed of the wave must be

$$\text{Speed} = \frac{\text{distance}}{\text{time}} = \frac{15 \text{ m}}{5 \text{ s}} = \textbf{3 m/s.}$$

Or in wave terminology:

Speed = frequency x wavelength = (1/5 Hz)(15 m) = **3 m/s.**

2. a. Frequency = 2 bobs/second = **2 hertz;**
   b. Period = 1/f = **1/2 second;**
   c. and the amplitude is the distance from the equilibrium position to maximum displacement, one-half the 20-cm peak-to-peak distance, which is **10 cm.**

3. To say that the frequency of radio waves is 100 Mz and that they travel at 300 000 km/s, is to say that there are 100 million wavelengths packed into 300 000 kilometers of space. Or expressed in meters, 300 million m of space. Now 300 million m divided by 100 million waves gives a wavelength of 3 meters per wave. Or

$$\text{Wavelength} = \frac{\text{speed}}{\text{frequency}} = \frac{(300 \text{ megameters/s})}{(100 \text{ megahertz})} = \textbf{3 m.}$$

4. d = vt = (340 m/s)(1/600 s) = **0.56 m.**

5. a. Frequency stays **the same** (see the Next-Time Question on this question).
   b. So the speed of sound is 340 + 34 = **374 m/s.**
   c. Wavelength doesn't change.

$$\text{From } v = f\lambda, \quad \lambda = \frac{v}{f} = \frac{374}{440} = \textbf{0.85 m.}$$

19 | Sound

CONCEPTUAL **Physics** 7th EDITION

1. Bees buzz when in flight because they flap their wings at audio frequencies.

2. The shorter wavelengths are heard by bats (higher frequencies have shorter wavelengths).

3. Light travels about a million times faster than sound, so you see a distant event a million times sooner than you hear it.

4. When sound passes a particular point in the air, the air is first compressed and then rarefied as the sound passes. So its density is increased and then decreased as the it passes.

5. At the instant that a high pressure region is created just outside the prongs of a tuning fork, a low pressure region is created between the prongs. This is because each prong acts as a Ping-Pong paddle in a region full of Ping-Pong balls. Just as a forward motion of the paddle would crowd Ping-Pong balls in front of it, and leave more space between balls in back of it, each prong of the tuning fork that moves into the air molecules creates similar high and low-pressure regions. While a high-pressure region is produced on one side, a low-pressure (rarefied) region is produced on the other side. A half-cycle later when the prongs swing in toward the center, a high pressure region is produced between the prongs and a low-pressure region is produced just outside the prongs.

6. Because snow absorbs well, it reflects little sound, which is responsible for the quietness.

7. The fact that we can see a ringing bell but can't hear it indicates that light is a distinctly different phenomenon than sound. When we see the bell "ringing" in a vacuum, we know that light can pass through a vacuum. The fact that we can't hear the bell indicates that sound does not pass through a vacuum. Sound needs a material medium for its transmission; light does not.

8. The moon is described as a silent planet because it has no atmosphere to transmit sounds.

9. The pitch of the tapped glass decreases as the glass if filled. This is because the size of the water column increases and vibrates at a lower frequency, just as larger xylophone keys vibrate at lower frequencies. (If you've attempted an answer to this exercise without actually trying it, shame on you!)

10. If the speed of sound was different for different frequencies, say, faster for higher frequencies, then distant music would be distorted, for the higher frequency notes would reach the ear of the listener first. (Be glad this is so, particularly if you like outdoor concerts.)

11. If the frequency of sound is doubled, its speed will not change at all, but its wavelength will be crowded to half its original size. The speed of sound depends only on the medium through which it travels, rather than on the properties of sound itself.

12. Sound travels faster in warm air because the air molecules that compose warm air themselves travel faster and therefore don't take as long before they bump into each other. This lesser time for the molecules to bump against one another results in a faster speed of sound.

13. Sound travels faster in moist air because the less massive water vapor molecules, H_2O, travel faster than the more massive N_2 and O_2 molecules at the same temperature. This faster speed results in sound traveling faster as discussed in Exercise 12.

14. Refraction is the result of changing wave speeds, where part of a wave travels at a different speed than other parts. This occurs in nonuniform winds and nonuniform temperatures. But if winds, temperatures, or other factors cannot change the speed of sound, then refraction would not occur. (The fact that refraction does indeed occur is evidence for the changing speeds of sound.)

15. The tremor in the ground can be felt before a distant explosion is heard because sound travels faster in the solid ground than in air.

16. Sound is more easily heard when the wind traveling toward the listener at elevations above ground level travels faster than wind near the ground. Then the waves are bent downward as is the case of the refraction of sound shown in Figure 19.7.

17. The short wavelengths of ultrasound allow the imaging of smaller objects. This is similar to the smaller detail seen by short-wavelength blue light in microscopes, and the still smaller detail seen with ultra-short-wavelength electron microscopes, briefly discussed in Chapter 10. (We will see later in Chapter 28 that shorter wavelengths produce clearer images by decreasing a wave effect called *diffraction* .)

18. An echo is weaker than the original sound because sound spreads and is therefore less intense with distance. If you are at the source, the echo will sound as if it originated on the other side of the wall from which it reflects (just as your image in a mirror appears to come from behind the glass). It is weaker still because the wall is likely not perfectly reflecting.

19. You can estimate your distance from a distant thunderstorm if you count the number of seconds between the lightning flash and the thunder that follows. Then multiply the number of seconds by the speed of sound (340 m/s), and the distance in meters is closely approximated.

20. The rule is correct: this is because the speed of sound in air (340 m/s) can be rounded off to 1/3 km/s. Then, from distance = speed x time = (1/3)km/s x (number of seconds). Note that the time in seconds divided by 3 yields the same value.

21. If a single disturbance at some unknown distance away sends longitudinal waves at one known speed, and transverse waves at a lesser known speed, and you measure the difference in time of the waves as they arrive, you can calculate the distance. The wider the gap in time, the greater the distance — which could be in any direction. If you use this distance as the radius of a circle on a map, you know the disturbance occurred somewhere on that circle. If you telephone two friends who have made similar measurements of the same event from different locations, you can transfer their circles to your map, and the point where the three circles intersect is the location of the disturbance.

22. Marchers at the end of a long parade will be out of step with marchers nearer the band because time is required for the sound of the band to reach the marchers at the end of a parade. They will step to the delayed beat they hear.

23. Soldiers break step when crossing a bridge so they will not set the bridge into forced vibration or resonance.

24. A harp produces relatively softer sounds than other stringed instruments because it does not have the sounding boards that typify other stringed instruments.

25. There are two principal reasons why bass notes are more distinctly heard through walls than higher-frequency notes. One is that waves that vibrate more often per second transfer sound

energy into heat more rapidly than waves of lower frequency. The higher-frequency waves are thermally "eaten up" by the material in the walls, while the lower-frequency vibrations pass with less effort through the material. Another reason is that the natural frequency of large walls, floors, and ceilings, is lower than the natural frequency of smaller surfaces. The large surfaces are more easily set into forced vibrations and resonance.

26. The sound is louder when a struck tuning fork is held against a table because a greater surface is set into vibration. In keeping with the conservation of energy, this reduces the length of time the fork keeps vibrating. Loud sound over a short time spends the same energy as weak sound for a long time.

27. A tuning fork eventually stops vibrating because of its interaction with the surrounding air (air resistance) and because of internal friction.

28. The interference that depends on the location of the listener with respect to the speakers depends also on the wavelength of the sound. A location that cancels one wavelength and its multiples will not cancel other wavelengths. Considering the many wavelengths of sound in music, the average listener does not discern this — mainly because of the multiple reflections of sound from walls, ceiling, floor or such that "fill in" dead spots. In an accoustical chamber, on the other hand, interference is discernable. When speakers are out of phase with one another, interference is quite discernable, in or out of an acoustical chamber, for all wavelengths are affected (not just those for whom differences in distance is the main factor).

29. These devices use interference to cancel the sound of the jackhammer in the ears of its operator. Because of the resulting low jackhammer noise in the ears of the operator, he can hear your voice clearly. But you, however, without the earphones experience no such cancellation of sound, so the voice of the operator is drowned out by the loud jackhammer noise.

30. Think of pushing a child on a swing: If you pushed twice as often as the child's period, you would push against the child's motion with every other push, and similarly with increased multiples of frequency. Such matches of pushes and period disrupt motion. On the other hand, if you pushed the child every other swing, your pushes would match the child's motion and amplitude would increase. So submultiple pushes will not disrupt motion. Similarly with sound.

31. The piano tuner should loosen the piano string. When she first heard 3 beats per second, she knew she was 3 hertz off the correct frequency. But this could be either 3 hertz above or 3 hertz below. When she tightened the string and increased its frequency, a lower beat frequency would have told her she was on the right track. But the greater beat frequency told her she should have been loosening the string. When there is no beat frequency, the frequencies match.

Chapter 19 Problem Solutions

1. Wavelength = speed/frequency $= \dfrac{340 \text{ m/s}}{340 \text{ Hz}} = $ **1 m**.

Similarly for a 34 000 hertz wave; wavelength $= \dfrac{340 \text{ m/s}}{34\ 000 \text{ Hz}} = 0.01 \text{ m} = $ **1 cm**.

2. The ocean floor is 4590 meters deep. The 6-second time delay means that the sound reached the bottom in 3 seconds. Distance = speed x time = 1530 m/s x 3 s = **4590 m**.

3. Assuming the speed of sound to be 340 m/s, the cave is 170 meters away. This is because the sound took 1/2 second to reach the wall (and 1/2 second to return).

Distance = speed x time = 340 m/s x 1/2 s = **170 m**.

4. The woman is about **340 meters** away. The clue is the single blow you hear after you see her stop hammering. That blow originated with the next-to-last blow you saw. The very first blow would have appeared as silent, and succeeding blows synchronous with successive strikes. In one second sound travels 340 meters.

5. There are 3 possible beat frequencies, 2 Hz, 3 Hz, and 5 Hz. These are of differences in fork frequencies: 261 - 259 = **2 Hz**; 261 - 256 = **5 Hz**; 259 - 256 = **3 Hz**.

20 | Musical Sounds

Answers

1. A low pitch will be produced when a guitar string is (a) lengthened, (b) loosened so that tension is reduced, and (c) made more massive, usually by windings of wire around the string. That's why bass strings are thick — more inertia.

2. The greater mass increases the inertia of the string which decreases the frequency at which it will vibrate.

3. A plucked guitar string will vibrate for a longer time, because less air is set into motion per unit of time, which means the energy of the vibrating string will persist for a longer time.

4. The fundamental for a string occurs when only two nodes exist; one at each end of the string, so that it vibrates in one segment. By touching the midpoint, a third node is imposed there and the string vibrates in two segments. The wavelengths are shortened by one half, so the frequency increases by two. (This is because the speed of the wave along the string doesn't change; speed = frequency x wavelength)

5. In addition to pieces of paper at the supporting ends of the string, when a string vibrates in two segments a piece may be placed at the node in its center. For three segments, two pieces can be supported, each one third the total distance from each end.

6. If the wavelength of a vibrating string is reduced, such as pressing it with your finger against the neck of a guitar, the frequency of the vibration increases. This is heard as an increased pitch.

7. The amplitude in a sound wave corresponds to the overpressure of the compression or equivalently the underpressure of the rarefaction.

8. The pattern shown to the left has the higher frequency and therefore the higher pitch. The pattern on the right has the greater amplitude and is therefore louder.

9. The range of human hearing is so wide that no single mechanical audio speaker can faithfully reproduce all the frequencies. So hi-fi speakers divide the range into two (and three) parts. A speaker with a relatively large surface has more inertia and is not as responsive to higher frequencies as a speaker with a smaller surface. So the larger speaker pushes the longer wavelengths, or lower frequencies, and the smaller speaker pushes the shorter wavelengths, or higher frequencies. (Ideally, the diameter of the speaker should be 1/2 the wavelength of a given sound — so a 12-inch speaker corresponds to about 550 hertz — still larger speakers are best for bass notes).

10. The person with the more acute hearing is the one who can hear the faintest sounds — the one who can hear 5 dB.

11. Normal human hearing spans at maximum from 10 to 20000 Hz. Starting from the very lowest frequency, one can double 10 eleven times to get 20480. Nine or ten octaves is the span of hearing for most young people. A common piano keyboard spans 7 octaves.

12. An organ produces the sounds of various musical instruments by duplicating the sine tones that make up the overall waves produced by these instruments.

13. Helium molecules and oxygen molecules at the same temperature have the same kinetic energies. Kinetic energy equals $1/2 mv^2$. The smaller mass of helium is compensated for by a greater speed (see the footnote on page 269). The higher speed results in a higher temper, like when blowing air faster through a bugle.

14. Your voice sounds fuller in a shower principally because of the small enclosure that causes your voice to reverberate as it reflects from wall to wall.

15. The small and low range of frequencies transmitted by a telephone is too low to carry the higher-frequency overtones of music that contribute to its quality.

16. The first harmonic is the fundamental, which is the same 440 Hz. The second harmonic is twice this, 880 Hz. The third harmonic is three times the first, 3 x 440 = 1320 Hz.

17. Although the speed of sound past a listener on a windy day will change, the wavelength will correspondingly change also, resulting in no change in frequency or pitch. Or look at it this way: suppose a friend is placing bottles on a conveyor belt, say at a "frequency" of one each second. Then you, at the other end of the belt, take off one bottle each second. Now suppose your friend increases the speed of the belt, but still puts on one bottle each second. Can you see that the bottles (farther apart now) will still arrive to you at the rate of one per second?

18. When water is poured into a glass, the pitch of the sound of the filling glass increases. This is because sound waves in the glass column form standing waves. As the length of the column shortens, the wavelength of the waves that reinforce one another to form standing waves will be shortened. This results in standing wave segments of higher frequency which are heard as a higher pitch. So when you pour liquid into a glass, the glug glug glug you hear increases in pitch as the glass fills.

19. The pitch of the tapped glass decreases as the glass is filled; just the opposite of the increasing pitch of the glug, glug, glug. This time it is not the vibration of the air column you are hearing, but the vibration of the water column. As its size increases, like a growing xylophone key, its frequency decreases and gives a lower pitch.

20. We each perceive what we have been taught or have learned to perceive. This applies to our appreciation of art, our taste for food, and drink, and to the value we give to that which we smell, and to the textures we touch. Our perception of what is real in terms of religious beliefs, political beliefs, and our notions about where we fit in the scheme of things, is a product of what we have learned (or have not learned).

Chapter 20 Problem Solutions

1. The decibel scale is based upon powers of 10. The ear responds to sound intensity in logarithmic fashion. Each time the intensity of sound is made 10 times larger, the intensity level in decibels increases by 10 units.
So a sound of
       a. 10 dB is **ten** times louder than the threshold of hearing
       b. 30 dB is **one thousand** times louder than the threshold of hearing
       c. 60 dB is **one million** times louder than the threshold of hearing.

2. A sound of 40 dB is **ten times** as loud as a sound of 30 dB.

3. One octave above 1000 Hz is **2000 Hz**, and two octaves above 1000 Hz is **4000 Hz**. One octave below 1000 Hz is **500 Hz**, and two octaves below 100 Hz is **250 Hz**.

4. To find the number of octaves in the range 20 to 14000 Hz, see how many times you can double 20 before surpassing 14000. This turns out to be 9, and almost 10. (Ten octaves above 20 Hz is 20480 Hz.) The author can hear **9 octaves**.

5. The wavelength of the fundamental is twice the length of the string, or 1.5 m.

$v = f\lambda = 220$ Hz x 1.5 m = **330 m/s**.

21 | Electrostatics

Answers

1. There are no positives and negatives in gravitation — the interactions between masses are only attractive, whereas electrical interactions may be attractive as well as repulsive. The mass of one particle cannot "cancel" the mass of another, whereas the charge of one particle can cancel the effect of the opposite charge of another particle.

2. Clothes become charged when electrons from a garment of one material are rubbed onto another material. If the materials were good conductors, discharge between materials would soon occur. But the clothes are nonconducting and the charge remains long enough for oppositely charged garments to be electrically attracted and stick to one another.

3. When the wool and plastic rub against each other, electrons are rubbed from the plastic onto the wool. The deficiency of electrons on the plastic bag results in its positive charge.

4. Excess electrons rubbed from your leave it with a positive charge; excess electrons on the comb give it a negative charge.

5. The wires at toll-collecting stations are used to discharge the cars so that the toll collector and passenger aren't shocked when the fare is collected.

6. Just a few years ago, before truck tires were made electrically conducting, chains or wires were commonly dragged along the road surface from the bodies of trucks. Their purpose was to discharge any charge that would otherwise build up because of friction with the air. Electrically-conducting tires are now commonly used to prevent the buildup of static charge that could produce a spark — especially dangerous for trucks carrying flammable cargoes.

7. The leaves, like the rest of the electroscope, acquire charge from the charged object and repel each other because they both have the same sign of charge. The weight of the conducting gold foil is so small that even tiny forces are clearly evident.

8. Cosmic rays produce ions in air, which offer a conducting path for the discharge of charged objects in the vicinity. Cosmic rays are (fortunately!) absorbed to a great degree in the atmosphere. But at higher altitudes where the atmosphere is thinner, there is a greater influx of cosmic rays and a resulting greater amount of ions in the air. Charged objects more quickly lose their charge at higher altitudes.

9. It would not be necessary for the charged body to touch the ball of an electroscope. If a negative charge is simply brought near, some electrons in the ball are driven to the gold leaves, and the ball is left positively charged. Or if a positive charge is brought near the ball, some electrons will move up to the ball to make it negative and leave the leaves positively charged. This is charge separation due to *induction*. (If by small chance you are attempting an answer to this question without having witnessed this, pity, pity, pity! Better that your time is spent studying the physics of familiar things.)

10. When an object acquires a positive charge, it loses electrons and its mass decreases. How much? By an amount equal to the mass of the electrons that have left. When an object acquires a negative charge, it gains electrons, and the mass of the electrons as well. (The masses involved are incredibly tiny compared to the masses of the objects. Like for a balloon rubbed against your hair, the extra electrons on the balloon comprise less than a billionth of a billionth of a billionth the mass of the balloon.)

11. By induction; bring the positively charged object near the object to be charged and the far side of the uncharged object will become positively charged. If you then touch the far side, you will in effect remove this charge because electrons will flow from your body to the positive charge. Remove your finger and the object then has a negative charge. (Interestingly enough, touching any side will produce the same result.)

12. The electrons to be stripped are in the fields of both the positive nucleus and the negative neighboring electrons. Plucking the outer ones is relatively easy, for the electric field set up by the positive nucleus (which attracts electrons) is diminished by the electric field set up by other electrons (which repel electrons) in the atom. As more electrons are stripped, the electric field is predominantly that of the attracting nucleus. When one or two electrons are all that remain, you can imagine the difficulty in pulling them away from the overwhelming field due primarily to 92 or so close-packed positive charges. Only in recent years have researchers at U.C. Berkeley succeeded in removing the innermost electrons of heavy elements like uranium.

13. When a pair of charged particles are brought to half their separation distance the force is quadrupled; to one quarter their separation, the force is increased 16 fold. But four times as far apart, the force is reduced by 1/16. This is in accord with the inverse-square law.

14. A neutral atom in an electric field is electrically distorted (see Figure 21.10 on page 381). If the field is strong enough, the distortion results in ionization, where the charges are torn from each other. The ions then provide a conducting path for an electric current.

15. The tree is likely to be hit because it shortens the path between the cloud overhead and the ground. The tree and the supporting ground is then raised to a high potential, which diminishes with distance. If you stand with your legs far apart, one leg on a higher-potential part of the ground than the other, or if you lie down and straddle a significant potential difference in the ground, you may find yourself a conducting path. That, you want to avoid!

16. In both the case of electrical and heat conductors, the conduction is via electrons, which in a metal are loosely bound, easy flowing, and easy to get moving. (Many fewer electrons in metals take part in heat conduction compared to electric conduction, however.)

17. The mechanism of sticking is charge induction. If it's a metal door, the charged balloon will induce an opposite charge on the wall. It will accomplish this by attracting opposite charges to it and repelling like charges to parts of the door farther away. The balloon and the oppositely-charged part of the door are attracted and the balloon sticks. If the door is an insulator, the balloon induces polarization of the molecules in the door material. Oppositely-charged sides of the molecules in the surface of the door face the balloon and attraction results. So whether you consider the door to be an insulator or a conductor, the balloon sticks by induction.

18. Electrically neutral atoms and molecules attract one another because they become to some degree electrically polarized in each other's fields. Although the atoms as a whole are electrically neutral, the closest parts of neighboring polarized atoms are oppositely charged and attract one another. Their attraction is greater than the repelling force of the farther-away like charges. Only when atoms are close together do the differences in distance between near and far sides of neighboring atoms become sufficient for net electrical attraction.

19. The forces on the electron and proton would be equal in magnitude, but opposite in direction. Because of the greater mass of the proton, its acceleration will be less than that of the electron, and be in the direction of the electric field. How much less? Since the mass of the proton is nearly 2000 times that of the electron, its acceleration will be about 1/2000 that of the

electron. The greater acceleration of the electron will be in the direction opposite to the electric field. The electron and proton accelerate in opposite directions.

20. By convention only, the direction of an electric field is the direction in which a positive test charge would move if placed at that point. A positive charge placed in the vicinity of a proton would move away from the proton, hence, the direction of the electric field vector is away from the proton.

21. The bits of thread become polarized in the electric field, one end positive and the other negative, and become the electric counterparts of the north and south poles of the magnetic compass. Opposite forces on the end of the fibers (or compass needle) produce torques that orient the fibers along the field direction (look ahead to Figure 23.3 on page 418).

22. 10 joules per coulomb is 10 volts. When released, its 10 joules of potential energy, will be becomes 10 joules of kinetic energy as it passes its starting point.

23. Voltage $= \dfrac{0.5 \text{ J}}{0.0001 \text{ C}} = 5000 \text{ V}$.

24. . Because charges of like sign mutually repel one another, when lightning hits a conductor such as an automobile, the charges will spread out over the outer conducting surface. To move into the interior would require they move toward each other, which mutual electric repulsion prohibits. The distribution of charges that flow along the surface of the conductor on their way to ground is such that any electrical effects inside are cancelled (see the answer to the next exercise).

25. You would feel no electrical effects inside any statically charged conducting body. The distribution of mutually-repelling charges is such that complete cancellation of the interior electric field occurs. The electric field inside any conductor is zero, whether the conductor is charged or not. (If the electric field were not zero, then conduction electrons would move in response to the field until electrical equilibrium was established — which is a zero electric field.)

Chapter 21 Problem Solutions

1. By the inverse-square law, twice as far is 1/4 the force; **5 N.**

2. Ratio: $\dfrac{F_{ele}}{F_{grav}} = \dfrac{k\,QQ/r^2}{GmM/r^2} = \dfrac{9 \times 10^9 (1.6 \times 10\text{-}19)^2/r^2}{6.67 \times 10^{-11}(9.1 \times 10\text{-}31)(1.67 \times 10^{-27})/r^2} =$ **2.2 x 10³⁹**.

   The electrical force between the electron and proton is more than
   1000000000000000000000000000000000000000 times greater!

3. $E = \dfrac{F}{q} = \dfrac{3.2 \times 10^{-4}\text{N}}{8 \times 10^{-13}\text{C}} =$ **4 x 10⁸ N/C**

4. a. From $E = \dfrac{F}{q}$ we see that $q = \dfrac{F}{E} = \dfrac{mg}{E} = \dfrac{(1.1 \times 10^{-14})(9.8)}{1.68 \times 10^5} =$ **6.4 x 10⁻¹⁹ C**

   b. Number of electrons $= \dfrac{6.4 \times 10^{-19}\text{C}}{1.6 \times 10^{-19}\text{C/electron}} =$ **4 electrons**

5. a. $\Delta V = \dfrac{\text{energy}}{\text{charge}} = \dfrac{12\text{ J}}{0.0001\text{ C}} =$ **120000 volts**

   b. ΔV for twice the charge is $\dfrac{24\text{ J}}{0.0002} =$ **same 120 kV**

22 | Electric Current

Answers

1. You cannot say which way the charge will flow if you only know the electric potential energy of each object. You must know the electric potential energy PER CHARGE, or the electric potential (voltage). This is analogous to the difference between heat and temperature. Just as heat does not flow from the object of greater internal energy to the object of less internal energy, but from the object of greater temperature to the object of lower temperature, charge flows from the object of higher electric potential to the object of lower electric potential. (If this is not clear, check to see that you know the difference between electric potential energy and electric potential.)

2. The flow of charge is an indication that the electrical potentials differ for the objects connected by the wire. The current will flow in a direction from the higher to the lower potential.

3. The cooling system of an automobile better illustrates the current in an electric circuit because like an electric system it is a closed system. The water hose does not recirculate the water as the auto cooling system does.

4. As the current in the filament of a light bulb increases, the bulb glows brighter.

5. Your tutor is wrong. An ampere measures current, and a volt measures electric potential (electric pressure). They are entirely different concepts; voltage produces amperes in a conductor.

6. Only circuit number 5 is complete and will light the bulb. (Circuits 1 and 2 are "shortcircuits" and will quickly drain the cell of its energy. In circuit 3 both ends of the lamp filament are connected to the same terminal and are therefore at the same potential. Only one end of the lamp filament is connected to the cell in circuit 4.)

7. Current flows *through* electrical devices, just as water flows through a plumbing circuit of pipes. If a water pump produces water pressure, water flows through both the pump and the circuit. Likewise with electric current in an electric circuit. For example, in a simple circuit consisting of a battery and a lamp, the electric current that flows in the lamp is the same electric current that flows through the wires that connect the lamp and the same electric current that flows through the battery. Current flows through these devices. As a side point, it is common to speak of electric current flowing in a circuit, but strictly speaking, it is electric *charge* that flows in an electric circuit; the flow of charge *is* current (grammar types cringe if you say something like "electric current flows from higher to lower potentials"; it is redundant to say "current flows." If you wish to use the conceptual or easy-to-visualize word "flow", you must introduce the word "charge," and say that charge flows. If you wish to use the word "current," then the word "flow" is a grammatical no-no.)

8. Energy is obtained from electricity by transformation to other forms. The energy put into a system (battery, generator, etc.) goes to electrical devices (toasters, electrical toothbrushes, radios, etc.) and is transformed into other forms (heat in a toaster, mechanical motion in a toothbrush, sound in a radio, etc.).

9. An electric device does not "use up" electricity, but rather *energy*. And strictly speaking, it doesn't "use up" energy, but transforms it from one form to another. It is common to say that energy is used up when it is transformed to less concentrated forms — when it is degraded. Electrical energy ultimately becomes heat energy. In this sense it is used up.

10. All other things being equal, a material with a short mean free path offers more resistance to electron flow and has a higher electrical resistance. For all materials, the application of heat imposes more molecular chaos and shortens the path even more, increasing resistance in most materials. So to lengthen the path, simply cool the material. Conductivities are greatly increased in most materials cooled to low temperatures.

11. A lie detector circuit relies on the resistivity of your body to change when a lie is told. Nervousness promotes perspiration, which lowers the body's electrical resistance, and increases whatever current flows. If a person is able to lie with no emotional change and no change in perspiration, then such a lie detector will not be effective. (Better lying indicators focus on the eyes.)

12. Most of the energy, typically 95%, of the electrical energy in an incandescent lamp goes directly to heat. Heat energy is the graveyard of all forms of energy.

13. Thick wires have less resistance and will more effectively carry currents without excessive heating.

14. The thick filament has less resistance and will draw (carry) more current than a thin wire connected across the same potential difference. (Important point: It is common to say that a certain resistor "draws" a certain current, but this may be misleading. A resistor doesn't "attract" or "draw" current, just as a pipe in a plumbing circuit doesn't "draw" water; it instead "allows" or "provides for" the passage of current when an electrical pressure is established across it.)

15. Current will be greater in the bulb connected to the 220-volt source. Twice the voltage would produce twice the current if the resistance of the filament remained the same. (In practice, the greater current produces a higher temperature and greater resistance in the lamp filament, so the current is greater than that produced by 110 volts, but appreciably less than twice as much for 220 volts. A bulb rated for 110 volts has a very short life when operated at 220 volts.)

16. Damage generally occurs by excess heating when too much current is driven through an appliance. For an appliance that converts electrical energy directly to thermal energy this happens when excess voltage is applied. So don't connect a 110-volt iron, toaster, or electric stove to a 220-volt circuit. Interestingly enough, if the appliance is an electric motor, then applying too *little* voltage can result in overheating and burn up the motor windings. (This is because the motor will spin at a low speed and the reverse "generator effect" will be small and allow too great a current to flow in the motor.) So don't hook up a 220-volt power saw or any 220-volt motor-driven appliance to 110 volts. To be safe use the recommended voltages with appliances of any kind.

17. More current flows in the 100-watt bulb. We see this from the relationship "power = current x voltage." More current for the same voltage means less resistance. So a 100-watt bulb has less resistance than a 60-watt bulb. Less resistance for the same length of the same material means a thicker filament. The filaments of high wattage bulbs are thicker than those of lower-wattage bulbs. (It is important to note that both Watts and Volts are printed on a light bulb. A bulb that is labeled 100W, 120V, is 100W *only* if there are 120 volts across it. If there are only 110 volts across it, and the resistance remains unchanged, then the power output would be only 84 watts!)

18. In the first case the current passes through your chest; in the second case current passes only through your arm. You can cut off your arm and survive, but you cannot survive without your heart.

19. (a) Electric power in your home is likely supplied at 60 hertz via 110-volt to 120-volt electrical outlets. This is ac (and delivered to your home via transformers between the power source and your home. We will see in Chapter 24 that transformers require ac power for operation.) (b) Electric power in your car must be able to be supplied by the battery. Since the + and - terminals of the battery do not alternate, the current they produce does not alternate either. It flows in one direction and is dc.

20. The amount of current any device puts through any conductor depends upon the voltage of the device and the resistance of the conductor. Also important is the amount of charge the device can deliver; a relatively large amount of charge at high voltage represents high energy (like that from a power line) while a small amount of charge at high voltage represents low energy (like discharging a balloon rubbed on your hair). The device being warned about is likely highly energized to a high voltage, and should be respected. It possesses no current to be warned about, but because of its high energy and high voltage, may produce a lethal current in anyone offering a conducting path from it to the ground.

21. The sign is a joke. High voltage may be dangerous, but high resistance is a property of all nonconductors.

22. If the parallel wires are closer than the wing span of birds, a bird could short circuit the wires by contact with its wings, be killed in the process, and interrupt the delivery of power.

23. Zero. Power companies do not sell electrons; they sell energy.

24. How quickly a lamp glows after an electrical switch is closed does not depend on the drift velocity of the conduction electrons, but depends on the speed at which the electric field is established in the circuit — about the speed of light.

25. Electrons in a circuit move not by collisions with one another, but by interacting with the electric field which is set up in the conductor at a speed nearly that of light. Sound travels by molecular collisions — a much slower process.

26. A light bulb burns out when a break occurs in the filament or when the filament disintegrates or falls apart.

27. Bulbs will glow brighter when connected in parallel, for the voltage of the battery is impressed across each bulb. When two identical bulbs are connected in series, half the voltage of the battery is impressed across each bulb. The battery will run down faster when the bulbs are in parallel.

28. Most of the electric energy in a lamp filament is transformed to heat. For low currents in the bulb, only a small amount of heat is produced, not enough to make the filament glow red or white hot.

29. Bulb C is the brightest because the voltage across it equals that of the battery. Bulbs A and B share the voltage of the parallel branch of the circuit and have half the current as bulb C (assuming resistances are independent of voltages). If bulb A is unscrewed, the top branch is no longer part of the circuit and current ceases in both A and B. They no longer give light, while bulb C glows as before. If bulb C is instead unscrewed, then it goes out and bulbs A and B glow as before.

30. As more bulbs are connected in series, more resistance is added to the single circuit path and the resulting current produced by the battery is diminished. This is evident in the dimmer light from the bulbs. On the other hand, when more bulbs are connected to the battery in parallel, the

brightness of the bulbs is practically unchanged. This is because each bulb in effect is connected directly to the battery with no other bulbs in its electrical path to add to its resistance. Each bulb has its own current path.

31. Line current decreases as more devices are connected in series. But line current increases as more devices are connected in parallel. This is because the circuit resistance is increased when devices are added in series, but decreased (more pathways) when devices are added in parallel.

32. Yes, there will be a decrease in brightness if too many lamps are connected in parallel because of the excess current that flows through the battery. Internal voltage drop increases with current in the battery, which means reduced voltage to the circuit it powers. If the parallel circuit is powered by a stronger source such as the power utility provides via common wall sockets, no dimming of bulbs will be seen as more and more parallel paths are added.

33. Household appliances are not connected in series for at least two reasons. First, the voltage, current, and power for each appliance would vary with the introduction of other appliances. Second, if one device burns out, the current in the whole circuit ceases. Only if each appliance is connected in parallel to the voltage source, can the voltage and current through each appliance be independent of the others.

34. The 100-watt bulb has the thicker filament and lower resistance (as we discussed in the answer to Exercise 17) so in series where the current is the same in each bulb, less energy is dissipated in going through the lower resistance. This corresponds to lower voltage across the resistance — a lower voltage drop. So the greater voltage drop is across the 60-watt bulb in series. So interestingly enough, in series the 60-watt bulb is brighter than the 100-watt bulb! When connected in parallel, the voltage across each bulb is the same, and the current is greater in the lower resistance 100-watt bulb, which glows brighter than the 60-watt bulb.

Chapter 22 Problem Solutions

1. From "Power = current x voltage," 60 watts = current x 120 volts, current = $\frac{60W}{120V}$ = **0.5 A**.

2. From current = $\frac{voltage}{resistance}$, resistance = $\frac{voltage}{current}$ = $\frac{120V}{20A}$ = **6 Ω**.

3. From power = current x voltage, current = $\frac{power}{voltage}$ = $\frac{1200W}{120V}$ = **10 A**.

   From the formula derived above, resistance = $\frac{voltage}{current}$ = $\frac{120V}{10A}$ = **12 Ω**.

4. Two headlights draw 6 amps, so the 60 ampere-hour battery will last for about **10 hours**.

5. a. From power = current x voltage, current = power/voltage = 4W/120V = **1/30 A**.
   b. From current = voltage/resistance (Ohm's law), resistance = voltage/current =
      120 V/(1/30 A) = **3600 Ω**.
   c. First, 4 watts = 0.004 kilowatt. Secondly, there are 8760 hours in a year
      (24 hours/day x 365 days = 8760 hours). So 8760 hours x 0.004 kilowatt = **35.04 kwhr**
   d. At the rate of 8 cents per kwhr, the annual cost is 35.04 kwhr x $0.08/kwhr = **$2.80**.

23 | Magnetism

Answers

1. All magnetism originates in moving electric charges. For an electron there is magnetism associated with its spin about its own axis, with its motion about the nucleus, and with its motion as part of an electric current.

2. All iron materials are not magnetized because the tiny magnetic domains are most often oriented in random directions and cancel one another's effects.

3. An electron always experiences a force in an electric field because that force depends on nothing more than the field strength and the charge. But the force an electron experiences in a magnetic field depends on an added factor: relative motion. If there is no relative motion between an electron and a magnetic field in which it is located, no magnetic force acts. Furthermore, if motion is along the magnetic field direction, and not at some angle to it, then no magnetic force acts also. Magnetic force, unlike electric force, depends on the relative velocity of the charge with respect to the magnetic field.

4. The iron and nickel that composes the earth's core is too hot for permanent alignment of magnetic domains, and therefore does not make up a permanent magnet. The earth's magnetism more likely originates in electric currents surrounding the earth's core.

5. A magnet will induce the magnetic domains of a nail or paper clip into alignment. Opposite poles in each material are then closest to each other and attraction results (this is similar to a charged comb attracting bits of electrically neutral paper (Figure 21.12). A wooden pencil, on the other hand, does not have magnetic domains that will interact with a magnet.

6. Domains in the paper clip are induced into alignment in a manner similar to the electrical charge polarization in an insulator when a charged object is brought nearby. Either pole of a magnet will induce alignment of domains in the paper clip: attraction results because the pole of the aligned domains closest to the magnet's pole is always the opposite pole, resulting in attraction.

7. The needle is not pulled toward the north side of the bucket because the south pole of the magnet is equally attracted southward. The net force on the needle is zero.

8. The net force on a compass needle is zero because its north and south poles are pulled in opposite directions with equal forces in the earth's magnetic field. When the needle is not aligned with the magnetic field of the earth, then a pair of torques is produced (Figure 23.3). This pair of equal torques, called a "couple," rotates the needle into alignment with the earth's magnetic field.

9. The mechanism of alignment involves two factors: The factor that makes the magnet is the inducement of domain alignment in the iron by the field set up by the bar magnet. These aligned domains interact with the magnetic field to produce opposite forces on each end of the filing. The other factor is the pair of equal torques that result whenever the filings are not parallel to the magnetic field lines. These torques rotate the filings into alignment with the field lines like little compass needles.

10. Suppose the magnetic poles of the earth were marked by wooden poles. If we had to paint either an N or an S on the magnetic pole near the north geographical pole, we should paint an S, which is the magnetic pole that attracts the N pole of a compass. So the N ("north-seeking")

pole of a compass is attracted geographically north, but to the earth's south magnetic pole. Similarly, we should paint an N on the magnetic pole that lies in the southern hemisphere, for that is the pole that attracts the S pole of a magnetic compass.

11. Tell your first friend that the magnetic field of the earth is continuous from pole to pole, and certainly doesn't make a turnaround at the earth's equator; so a compass needle that is aligned with the earth's field likewise does not turn around at the equator. Your other friend could correctly argue that compass needles point southward in the southern hemisphere (but the same pole points southward in the northern hemisphere). A compass does no turnaround when crossing the equator.

12. Moving electrons are deflected from their paths by a magnetic field. A magnet held in front of a TV picture deflects the electron beam from its correct path and distorts the picture.

13. Back to Newton's 3rd law! Both A and B are equally pulling on each other. If A pulls on B with 50 newtons, then B also pulls on A with 50 newtons. Period!

14. Newton's 3rd law again: Yes, the paper clip as part of the interaction, certainly does exert a force on the magnet — just as much as the magnet pulls on it. The magnet and paper clip pull equally on each other to comprise the single interaction between them.

15. Beating on the nail allows atoms in the domains to realign themselves with the earth's magnetic field. Thus, domains aligned with the earth's magnetic field grow and the others shrink.

16. Just as a nail is magnetized by beating on it, an iron ship is beat upon in its manufacture, making it a permanent magnet. Its initial magnetic field orientation, which is a factor in subsequent magnetic measurements, is in effect recorded on the brass plaque.

17. Relative motion is required for a magnetic force on an electron; that is, either the electron moves through a stationary magnetic field, or a magnetic field moves by an electron, or both. So an electron at rest in a stationary magnetic field will feel no force to set it in motion. In an electric field, however, an electron will be accelerated whether or not motion is involved. (The combination of magnetic and electric fields are used in particle accelerators such as cyclotrons. The electric field accelerates the charged particle, and the magnetic field deflects it in a circular path. [Exercise 19])

18. A necessary condition for magnetic force between a charged particle and a magnetic field is that motion must exist between the two. If the plasma is "at rest" (has no net motion because ions are moving randomly in all directions) then no net force will act on it.

19. The electric field in a cyclotron or any charged particle accelerator forces the particles to higher speeds, while the magnetic field forces the particles into curved paths. A magnetic force can only change the direction (not the speed) of a charged particle because the force is always perpendicular to the particle's instantaneous velocity. [Interestingly enough, in some accelerators (e.g., a betatron) the electric field is produced by a changing magnetic field.]

20. Recall that *work = force x distance*, where force and distance are along the same direction. Since the magnetic force that acts on a beam of electrons is everywhere perpendicular to the beam, there is no component of magnetic force along the instantaneous direction of motion. Therefore a magnetic field can do no work on a charged particle. [Indirectly, however, a *time-varying magnetic field* can induce an electric field that *can* do work on a charged particle.]

21. If the particles move in the same direction in the field and are deflected in opposite directions, the charges must be of opposite sign.

22. Associated with every moving charged particle, electrons, protons, or whatever, is a magnetic field. Since a magnetic field is not unique to moving electrons, there would be a magnetic field about moving protons as well. The only difference, compared to a beam made up of an equal number of electrons moving at the same speed, is the field direction. The field lines about the proton beam circle in the opposite direction to the field lines about an electron beam moving in the same direction.

23. If the field interacts with a bar magnet it is magnetic; with an electroscope it is electric. If a rotating loop of wire produces an electric current, the field is magnetic. If a stationary charged object such as a pith ball experiences a force then the field is electric. If a force acts only on a moving charge, the field is magnetic. So any of the classes of experiments that deal with electric charge at rest and electric charge in motion could be used to determine the nature of the field in the room.

24. The Van Allen radiation belts are occupied with swarms of dangerous high-energy charged particles. Astronauts, therefore, make an effort to keep below these belts.

25. Charged particles moving through a magnetic field are deflected most when they move at right angles to the field, and least when they move parallel to the magnetic field lines. If we consider cosmic rays that are directly incident upon the earth's surface; that is, perpendicular to the earth's surface, then in northern Canada they will be nearly parallel to the magnetic field lines of the earth. The rays are not deflected very much and hit the earth. In regions closer to the equator like Mexico, the incoming cosmic rays are more nearly at right angles with the earth's magnetic field, and are deflected back out into space.

26. Singly-charged ions traveling with the same speed through the same magnetic field will experience the same magnetic force. The extent of their deflections will then depend on their accelerations, which in turn depend on their respective masses. The least massive nuclei will be deflected the most and the very massive nuclei will be deflected least. (See Figure 32-13, page 622, for a diagram of a mass spectrograph.)

27. A habitat in space could be shielded from cosmic radiation if a magnetic field were set up about the habitat, just as the magnetic field of the earth shields us from much of the cosmic radiation that would otherwise strike the earth. Another way is positioning thick slag from outer space mining operations around the habitat.

28. To determine only by their interactions with each other which of two bars is a magnet, place the end of the bar #1 to the midpoint of bar #2 (like making a "T"). If there is an attraction, then bar #1 is the magnet. If there isn't, then bar #2 is the magnet.

Answers

1. The magnetic domains that become aligned in the iron core contribute to the overall magnetic field of the coil and therefore increase its magnetic induction.

2. The magnetic field of the iron core adds to the magnetic field of the coil, as stated in the answer to the previous exercise. Greater magnetic field means greater torque on the armature.

3. Work must be done to move a current-carrying conductor in a magnetic field. This is true whether or not the current is externally produced or produced as a result of the induction that accompanies the motion of the wire in the field. (This is fairly well stated by little Earl's explanation to his mother Jane on page 371.)

4. A cyclist will coast farther if the lamp is disconnected from the generator, as per Earl's explanation on page 371. The energy that goes into lighting the lamp is taken from the bike's kinetic energy, so the bike slows down. The work saved by not lighting the lamp will be the extra "force x distance" that the bike will lose to coast farther.

5. Part of the earth's magnetic field is enclosed in the wide loop of wire imbedded in the road. If this enclosed field is somehow changed, then in accord with the law of electromagnetic induction, a pulse of current will be produced in the loop. Such a change is produced when the iron parts of a car pass over it and effectively alter its inductance. A practical application in use for several years now is triggering automobile traffic lights. (You can usually tell if triggered lights make use of this idea by the square-shaped scars on the road surface where the wires have been embedded.)

6. Like the previous answer, inductance of the loop is changed with the presence of iron. When you walk through the loop with a piece of iron and change the inductance of the loop, a changing current activates an alarm.

7. When the ground shakes, inertia of the suspended massive magnet tends to resist such shaking. But the coils of wire are fixed to the earth and shake relative to the magnet. Motion of the magnet within conducting loops induces a current, which depends on the strength of the earthquake. So the law of inertia and the law of electromagnetic induction underlie the operation of this device.

8. There is no fundamental difference between an electric motor and electric generator. When mechanical energy is put into the device and electricity is induced, we call it a generator. When electrical energy is put in and it spins and will do mechanical work, we call it a motor. (While there are usually some practical differences in the designs of motors and generators, some devices are designed to be either motors or generators, depending only on whether the input is mechanical or electrical.)

9. When you mechanically turn the rotor of the generator, electric current is the output. If you reverse the roles, and put electric current into the turns about the rotor, it will spin and do mechanical work. Then the generator is a motor.

10. In accord with Faraday's law of induction, the greater the rate of change of magnetic field in a coil or armature, the greater the induced voltage. So voltage output increases when the generator spins faster.

11. Yes, like the armature of a galvanometer, when it has rotated as far as it can, it tends to rotate no more. Or if the loop is oriented so that no magnetic field lines are enclosed by the loop, say when the axis of the loop is parallel to the magnetic field lines, then there is also no tendency to rotate.

12. In accord with electromagnetic induction, if the magnetic field alternates in the hole of the ring, an alternating voltage will be induced in the ring. Because the ring is metal, its relatively low resistance will result in a correspondingly high alternating current. This current is evident in the heating of the ring.

13. Since all the electric resistance in this case is merely that of the wire itself (no other external load), twice the wire length means twice the resistance. So although twice the number of loops normally means twice the voltage, twice-as-much resistance results in the same current.

14. Induction occurs only for a *change* in the intercepted magnetic field. The galvanometer will show a current reading when the current in the first coil is either increasing or decreasing. If the current in the first coil is steady, no current is induced in the secondary and the galvanometer reads zero. The galvanometer needle will swing in opposite directions for increasing and decreasing currents in the primary coil.

15. The iron core increases the magnetic field of the primary coil, as stated in the answer to Exercise 1. The greater field means a greater magnetic field change in the primary, and a greater voltage induced in the secondary. The iron core in the secondary further increases the changing magnetic field through the secondary and further increases the secondary voltage. Furthermore, the core guides more magnetic field lines from the primary to the secondary. The effect of an iron core in the coils is the induction of appreciably more voltage in the secondary.

16. When the secondary voltage is twice the primary voltage, the secondary current is half the value of current in the primary. This is in accord with energy conservation, or since the time intervals for each are the same, "power conservation." Power input = power output; or (current x voltage)$_{primary}$ = (current x voltage)$_{secondary}$: with numerical values, (1 x V)$_{primary}$ = (1/2 x 2V)$_{secondary}$. [Note that twice the voltage in the secondary produces twice the current in the secondary (in accord with Ohm's law), which is half the current in the primary.]

16. When the secondary voltage is doubled, the current in the secondary is also doubled. But it is half the value of current in the primary. This is in accord with energy conservation, or since the time intervals for each are the same, "power conservation." Power input = power output; or (current x voltage)$_{primary}$ = (current x voltage)$_{secondary}$: with numerical values, (1 x V)$_{primary}$ = (1/2 x 2V)$_{secondary}$.

17. A transformer is like a lever in that it can multiply voltage at the expense of current and vice versa, just as a lever can multiply force at the expense of distance and vice versa. In both cases, energy and power is conserved.

18. The hum heard when a transformer is operating on a 60 hertz AC line is a 60 hertz forced vibration of the iron slabs in the transformer core as their magnetic polarities alternate. The hum is greater if any other mechanical parts are set into vibration.

19. By symmetry, the voltage across the bulb is 120 V. At the 10/1 turns ratio, the current in the bulb will be 1/10 that of the 1 A in the middle "primary," so the current in the bulb is 0.1 A.

20. Oops! This is a dc circuit. Unless there is a changing current in the primary, no induction takes place. No voltage and no current is induced in the meter.

21. The lamp will not be lit, simply because it is not part of a closed circuit. Note that although there is a potential difference of (240 - 120)V across the lamp, there is no pathway for a complete circuit. The iron core doesn't help because the wires of the primary and secondary coils must be insulated from each other and the iron core. (Without insulation, the current of the primary would short circuit and travel through no loops at all.)

22. Your friend is correct if he or she means high voltage across a particular load will produce high current in that same load. Where your friend may be confused is thinking the power line itself is the load. The power lines are simply extended terminals from the power source to the load, which is usually many kilometers away. A high voltage is impressed across the lines at the power source and is extended to the distant load. But in between the power lines and the load is a step-down transformer that delivers power to the load at a lower voltage. The current drawn by the load depends on this lower voltage and the resistance of the load. The power drawn by the load = the power delivered through the lines, which = current in the lines x voltage across the lines. Hence a high voltage in the lines permits a small current in the lines, that cuts down on energy losses through heating of the wires.

23. The bar magnet will slow down. From a magnetic force point of view, the moving magnet will induce current loops in the surrounding copper as it falls. The current loops produce a magnetic field that tends to repel the magnet as it approaches and attract it as it leaves, slowing it in its flight. From an energy point of view, the energy of the current that is induced in the loop is equal to the loss of kinetic energy of the magnet. The plastic pipe, on the other hand, is an insulator. So no current and therefore no magnetic field is induced to slow the motion of the falling magnet.

24. Such a scheme violates both the 1st and 2nd laws of thermodynamics. Because of inherent inefficiencies, the generator will produce less electricity than is used by the adjoining motor to power the generator. The transformers will step up voltage at the expense of current, or current at the expense of voltage, but it will not step up both simultaneously — that is, a transformer cannot step up energy or power. Like all practical systems, more energy is put in than is put out.

25. Electromagnetic waves depend on mutual field regeneration. If the induced electric fields did not in turn induce magnetic fields and pass energy to them, the energy would be localized rather than "waved" into space. Electromagnetic waves would not exist.

Chapter 24 Problem Solutions

1. If power losses can be ignored, in accord with energy conservation, the power provided by the secondary is also **100W**.

2. a. From the transformer relationship, $\dfrac{\text{Primary voltage}}{\text{primary turns}} = \dfrac{\text{secondary voltage}}{\text{secondary turns}}$,

secondary voltage $= \dfrac{\text{Primary voltage}}{\text{primary turns}} \times \text{secondary turns} = \dfrac{12V}{50} \times 250 = \mathbf{60V}$

   b. From Ohm's law, current $= \dfrac{V}{R} = \dfrac{60V}{10\Omega} = \mathbf{6A}$

   c. Power through primary is the same as the power through the secondary;

   Power = current x voltage = 6A x 60V = **360W**

3. From the transformer relationship, $\dfrac{\text{primary voltage}}{\text{primary turns}} = \dfrac{\text{secondary voltage}}{\text{secondary turns}}$,

$\dfrac{120V}{240 \text{ turns}} = \dfrac{6V}{x \text{ turns}}$

Solve for x: $x = \dfrac{6V}{240V} \times 240 \text{ turns} = \mathbf{12\ turns}$

4. From , $\dfrac{\text{primary voltage}}{\text{primary turns}} = \dfrac{\text{secondary voltage}}{\text{secondary turns}}$, simple rearrangement gives

$\dfrac{\text{primary voltage}}{\text{secondary voltage}} = \dfrac{\text{primary turns}}{\text{secondary turns}} = \dfrac{120V}{12000V} = \dfrac{1}{\mathbf{100}}$.

So there should be 100 times as many turns on the secondary as primary.

5. As in the preceding problem, the ratio of windings will be the ratio of voltages;

$\dfrac{\text{primary turns}}{\text{secondary turns}} = \dfrac{\text{primary voltage}}{\text{secondary voltage}} = \dfrac{12V}{24000V} = \dfrac{1}{\mathbf{2000}}$

So there must be 2000 times as many windings on the secondary coil as there are on the primary. (You can get quite a shock from that 12-volt battery under your car hood!)

Answers

1. Radio waves are longer than light waves, which are longer than the waves of x rays.

2. Between the sun, stars, and earth is the vacuum of interstellar and intersolar space. The fact that we can see the sun and stars from earth is convincing evidence that light travels through a vacuum.

3. The average speed of light will be less where it interacts with absorbing and re-emitting particles of matter, such as in the atmosphere as compared to in a vacuum. The greater the number of interactions along the light's path, the less the average speed.

4. The instantaneous speed of the bullet after penetrating the tree is less than its incident speed, but not so with light. The instantaneous speed of light before meeting the glass, while passing through it, and when emerging is a constant, c. The fundamental difference between a bullet fired through a tree and light passing through glass is that the *same* bullet strikes and later emerges. Not so for light. The "bullet of light" (photon) that is incident upon glass is absorbed by its interaction with an atom or molecule. The atom or molecule in turn then emits, with some time delay, a new "bullet of light" in the same direction. This process cascades through the glass with the result being that the "bullet of light" that emerges is not the same light that was first incident. Between all the interactions of light with matter, the instantaneous speed of light is c. Only its average speed, because of the time delay of the interactions, is less than c. That's why the light emerges with speed c.

5. Glass is opaque to frequencies of light that match its own natural frequencies. This is because the electrons in the absorbing medium are driven to vibrations of much larger amplitudes than occurs for non-resonant frequencies. These large amplitudes result in energy transfer to neighboring atoms and an increase in internal energy rather than a re-emission of light.

6. Transparency or opaqueness is determined by the match between incident light frequencies and the resonant frequency of the material. A substance that is transparent to a range of light frequencies will be opaque to those frequencies that match its own resonant frequency.

7. Clouds are transparent to ultraviolet light, which is why clouds offer no protection from sunburn. Glass, however, is opaque to ultraviolet light, and will therefore shield you from sunburn.

8. The frequency of ultraviolet light matches the natural frequency of atoms in the glass, so interaction produces resonance. This means the induction of large amplitude vibrations of electrons in the glass — so large, that energy is transferred to neighbors as heat.

9. The sunglasses will be warmer in sunlight than regular reading glasses. This is because the reading glasses transmit most of the light energy that is incident upon them, whereas the sunglasses absorb more light energy, which increases their internal energy.

10. Any shadow cast by a faraway object such as a high-flying plane is filled in mainly by light tapering in from the sun, which is not a point source. This tapering is responsible for the umbra and penumbra of solar eclipses (Figure 25.12). If the plane is low to the ground, however, the tapering of light around the airplane may be insufficient to fill in the shadow, part of which can be seen. This idea is shown in Figure 25.10.

11. A solar eclipse is a shadow of the moon that reaches a relatively small part of the earth, and only those people in the shadow or partial shadow experience it. But a lunar eclipse is the earth's shadow upon the moon, which is visible to all who can see the moon. So everyone who can see the sun won't see its eclipse unless they're in its shadow, but everyone who can see the moon will see its eclipse where there is one.

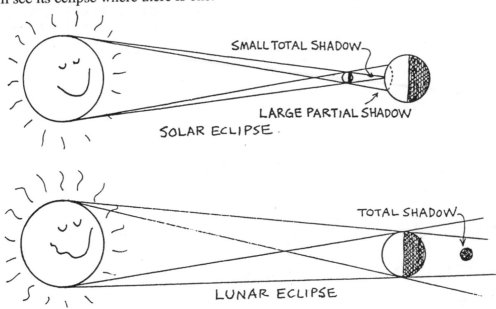

12. A lunar eclipse occurs when the earth, sun, and moon all fall on a straight line, with the earth in the middle. During perfect alignment the earth's shadow falls on the moon. Near-perfect alignment gives earth observers a full view of the moon. Moonlight is brightest and the moon is always fullest when the alignment is closest to perfect — on the night of a lunar eclipse. At the time of a half moon, however, lines from earth to moon and from earth to sun are at right angles to each other. This is as non-aligned as the earth, moon, and sun can be, with the moon nowhere near the earth's shadow — so no eclipse is possible. Similarly for the non-aligned times of a crescent moon.

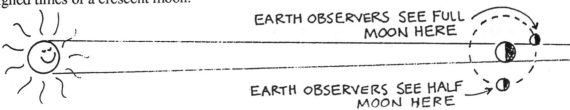

13. Rods, not cones, will fire in weak light, so you want to focus low-intensity light on a part of the retina that is composed of rods. That would be off to the side of the fovea. If you're looking at a weak star, look a bit off to the side of where you expect to see it. Then its image will fall on a part of your eye where rods may pick it up.

14. The light reflected by objects in the moonlight is most often too dim to fire the color-perceiving cones in the eye. So we see these objects primarily with our rods, which explains their lack of color.

15. We see no color at the periphery of our vision simply because there are no cones located on the outermost regions of the retina.

16. The blind spot is located on the side of the fovea away from your nose.

17. Unless light reaching her eyes has increased in intensity, her contracting pupils imply that she is displeased with what she sees, hears, tastes, smells, or how she feels. In short, she may be displeased with you!

18. We cannot infer that people with large pupils are generally happier than people with small pupils. The size of a person's pupils has to do with the sensitivity of the retina to light intensity. Your pupils tend to become smaller with age as well. But it is the *change* in pupil size that suggests one's psychological disposition.

Chapter 25 Problem Solutions

1. $\text{Speed} = \dfrac{\text{distance}}{\text{time}} = \dfrac{300\ 000\ 000\ \text{km}}{1000\ \text{s}} = 300\ 000\ \text{km/s.}$

2. From $v = \dfrac{d}{t}$, $\quad t = \dfrac{d}{v} = \dfrac{d}{c} = \dfrac{1.5 \times 10^{11}\text{m}}{3 \times 10^{8}\text{m/s}} = \textbf{500 s}$ (which equals 8.3 min).

   So it takes about 8 minutes for the sun's light to reach the earth.

3. As in the previous problem, $t = \dfrac{d}{v} = \dfrac{4.2 \times 10^{16}\ \text{m}}{3 \times 10^{8}\ \text{m/s}} = \textbf{1.4 x 10}^8\ \textbf{s.}$

   Converting to years by dimensional analysis,

   $1.4 \times 10^8\ \text{s} \times \dfrac{1\ \text{h}}{3600\ \text{s}} \times \dfrac{1\ \text{day}}{24\ \text{h}} \times \dfrac{1\ \text{yr}}{365\ \text{day}} = \textbf{4.4 yr.}$

4. From $c = f\lambda$, $\lambda = \dfrac{c}{f} = \dfrac{3 \times 10^8\text{m/s}}{6 \times 10^{14}\text{Hz}} = \textbf{5 x 10}^{\textbf{-7}}\ \textbf{m.}$

5. Light in water travels at $0.75c$ (page 455). $\lambda = \dfrac{c}{f}$ for light in a vacuum (or air), and $\lambda = \dfrac{0.75c}{f}$ for light in water. The ratio of λ_{air} to λ_{water} is therefore, whatever the frequency, **0.75**.

   So light waves in water are 3/4 their length in air. Wavelength changes while frequency remains the same.

Answers

1. The petals of a red rose will reflect red light while the green leaves absorb red light. The energy absorbed by the leaves tends to increase their temperature. White material reflects radiation and is therefore worn by those who do not wish to be warmed by absorbing radiant energy.

2. The customer is being reasonable in requesting to see the colors in the daylight. Under fluorescent lighting, with its predominant higher frequencies, the bluer colors rather than the redder colors will be accented. Colors will appear quite different in sunlight.

3. Either a white or green garment will reflect incident green light and be cooler. The complementary color, red, will absorb green light and be the best garment color to wear when the absorption of energy is desired.

4. Black is the absence of color. White is the result of an additive mixture of all the colors. Black and white, then, are not themselves colors.

5. The interior coating absorbs rather than reflects light, and therefore appears black. A black interior in an optical instrument will absorb any stray light rather than reflecting it and passing it around the interior of the instrument to interfere with the optical image.

6. Red cloth appears red in sunlight, and red by the illumination of the red light from a neon tube. But because the red cloth absorbs cyan light, it appears black when illuminated by cyan light.

7. A piece of paper that appears white in sunlight has the ability to reflect any color that is incident upon it.

8. The color that will emerge from a lamp coated to absorb yellow is blue, the complementary color. (White - yellow = blue.)

9. If the yellow clothes of stage performers are illuminated with a complementary blue light, they will appear black.

10. The overlapping blue and yellow beams will produce white light. When the two panes of glass are overlapped and placed in front of a single flashlight, however, no light will be transmitted.

11. Color television employs color addition. To produce yellow, green and red dots are illuminated; to produce magenta, red and blue dots are illuminated; to produce white, red, green, and blue dots are illuminated.

12. Yellow light + blue light = *white* light.
    Green light + *magenta* light = white light.
    Magenta light + yellow light + cyan light = *white* light.

13. Green + blue = cyan = white - *red*.

14. We cannot see stars in the daytime because their dim light is overwhelmed by the brighter skylight.

15. At higher altitudes, there are fewer molecules and therefore less scattering of sunlight. This results in a darker sky. The extreme, no molecules at all, results in a black sky, as on the moon.

16. As seen from the surface of the moon, both the sun and the stars are clearly visible. This is because there is no skylight to overwhelm the starlight.

17. From a space habitat above the earth's atmosphere, both the sun and the stars are visible at the same time. Like from the moon's surface, there is no skylight to overwhelm the starlight.

18. You know you are illuminated by visible light even in the shade, for your friends can easily see you. This is because even though direct sunlight is blocked, visible light is scattered by the atmosphere and you are illuminated by skylight. This is especially so for ultraviolet radiation, which is scattered even more by the atmosphere. So you can get a sunburn in the shade — by scattering and reflection as well. (The author was quite sunburned while sitting in the shade of a mangrove tree at a sandy beach brainstorming exercises for this book! I learned this one the hard way.)

19. The statement is true. A more positive tone would omit the word "just," for the sunset is not *just* the leftover colors, but *is* those colors that weren't scattered in other directions.

20. If the sky normally scattered orange light, then sunsets would be the complementary color of orange, a "sky blue." (White - sunset orange = sky blue.)

21. Clouds are composed of atoms, molecules, and particles of a variety of sizes. So not only are high-frequency colors scattered from clouds, but middle and low frequencies as well. A combination of all the scattered colors produces white.

22. Rain clouds are composed of relatively big particles that absorb much of the incident light. If the rain clouds were composed only of absorbing particles, then the cloud would appear black. But its mixture of particles includes tiny high-frequency scattering particles, so the cloud is not completely absorbing, and is simply dark instead of black.

23. If the atmosphere were about fifty times thicker, the sunlight to reach the earth would be predominantly low frequencies because most of the blue light would be scattered away. Snow would likely appear orange at noon, and a deep red when the sun is not directly overhead.

24. If we assume that Jupiter has an atmosphere which is similar to that of the earth in terms of transparency, then the sun would appear to be a deep reddish orange, just as it would when sunlight grazes 1000 kilometers of the earth's atmosphere for a sunset from an elevated position. Interestingly enough, there is a thick cloud cover in Jupiter's atmosphere that blocks all sunlight from reaching its "surface." And it doesn't even have a solid surface! Your children may visit one of Jupiter's moons, but will not "land" on Jupiter itself — not intentionally, anyway. (Incidentally, there are only 4 1/3 planets with "solid" surfaces: Mercury, Venus, Mars, Pluto, and 1/3 of earth!)

25. During a lunar eclipse the moon is not totally dark, even though it is in the earth's shadow. This is because the atmosphere of the world acts as a converging lens that refracts light into the earth's shadow. It is the low frequencies that pass more easily through the long grazing path through the earth's atmosphere to be refracted finally onto the moon. Hence its reddish color.

Answers

1. Fermat's principle for refraction is of least time, but for reflection it could be of least distance as well. This is because light does not go from one medium to another for reflection, so no change in speed occurs and least-time paths and least-distance paths are equivalent. But for refraction, light goes from a medium where it has a certain speed to another medium where its speed is different. When this happens the least-distance straight-line paths take a longer time to travel than the non-straight-line least-time paths. See, for example, the difference in the least-distance and least-time paths in Figure 27.12 on page 493.

2. Only light from card number 2 reaches her eye.

3. Cowboy Joe should simply aim at the mirrored image of his assailant, for the recoiling bullet will follow the same changes in direction when momentum changes (angle of incidence = angle of rebound) that light follows when reflecting from a plane surface.

4. The minimum length of a vertical mirror must be half your height in order for you to see a full-length view of yourself. This is because the light from your feet that reaches your eyes via the mirror meets the mirror halfway up. Then its angle of incidence (from your feet) equals the angle of reflection (to your eyes). Likewise, light from the top of your head meets the mirror halfway down to reflect at the same angle to reach your eyes. Halfway up and halfway down means you can see all of yourself with a mirror that is half your height (and half your width).

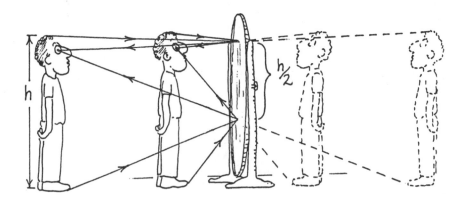

5. The half-height mirror works at any distance, as shown in the sketch above. This is because if you move closer, your image moves closer as well. If you move farther away, your image does the same. Many people must actually try this before they believe it. The confusion arises because people know that they can see whole distant buildings or even mountain ranges in a hand-held pocket mirror. Even then, the distance the object is from the mirror is the same as the distance of the virtual image on the other side of the mirror. You can see all of a distant person in your mirror, but the distant person cannot see all of herself in your mirror.

6. Note in your pocket mirror that the amount of your face you can see is twice the size of the mirror — whether you hold it close or at arm's length. Interesting information!

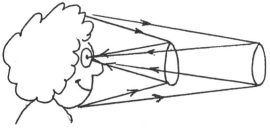

7. The smallest window will be half the height of the person or her twin. Note that this does not depend on distance, providing both subjects are the same distance from the wall. This illustrates Exercises 4 , 5, and 6 above.

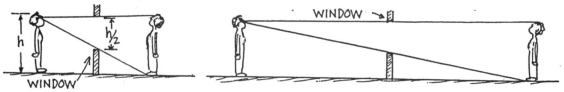

8. Relative to the mirror, you and your image walk at 1 m/s, but relative to each other your speed of approach is 2 m/s.

9. We would not see an image of the man in the mirror as shown. If he is viewing himself, then we wouldn't also be able to see his image unless we were in back (or in front) of him. If we are to stand to the side of the man and see him *and* an image of him in the mirror, then the mirror cannot be exactly in front of him. The mirror would have to be located to the man's right, as shown in the sketch. The man's view would miss the mirror completely. Such arrangements are made when staging an actor who is supposed to be viewing himself in a mirror. Actually, however, the actor pretends to be looking at himself. If he really were, his image in the mirror wouldn't be shared by the audience. That's Hollywood!

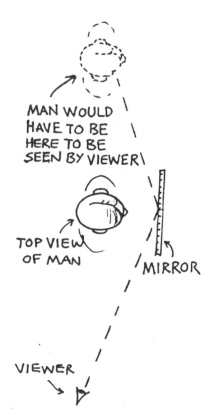

10. Such lettering is seen in proper form in the rear view mirrors of cars ahead.

11. A window is both transparent to light and a reflector of light. Whether it serves principally as a reflector or a transmitter depends on the relative intensities of light being reflected and transmitted. The person outside in the daylight who looks at the window of a room that is dark inside sees only outside light reflected from the window and almost no light transmitted from the room. The glass serves as a mirror. From the point of view of a person inside the dark room, only outside light is seen when looking at the window glass. The situation is reversed at nighttime when it is dark outside and the room is lit up. People in the room cannot see outside, and see only reflections of the room interior when they look at the window glass. The room or the outside does not have to be perfectly dark for this effect. A

23. A fish sees the sky when it looks upward at 45°, for the critical angle is 48° for water. If it looks at and beyond 48° it sees a reflection of the bottom beneath.

24. In sending a laser beam to a space station, make no corrections and simply aim at the station you see. This is like spearing the fish in Exercise 21. The path of refraction is the same in either direction.

25. The "nonwettable" leg of the water strider depresses and curves the surface of the water and effectively produces a lens that directs light away from the eye in the center of the depression which then appears as a shadow. Away from the center the circular lens concentrates a ring of light to your eye which appears as a bright ring. (Interestingly enough, the overall brightness of the shadow and bright ring averaged together is the same whether or not the water is depressed — "conservation of light" — Exercise 27.)

26. A magnifying lens used as a "burning glass" does nothing more than gather a certain amount of energy and concentrate it at some focal point. The important point is that the lens is considerably larger than the area over which the light is concentrated. But the solar heat sheet is not larger than the surface area of the swimming pool, and doesn't collect any more solar energy than the pool receives anyway. The sheet may help warm the pool by preventing evaporation, as would be the case with any cover, but in no way do the lenses direct additional solar energy to the water beneath. This fraudulent advertising plays on the ignorance of the public.

27. The average intensity of sunlight at the bottom is the same whether the water is moving or is still. Light that misses one part of the bottom of the pool reaches another part. Every dark region is balanced by a bright region — "conservation of light."

28. We cannot see a rainbow "off to the side," for a rainbow is not a tangible thing "out there." Colors are refracted in infinite directions and fill the sky. The only colors we see that aren't washed out by others are those that are along the conical angles between 40° and 42° to the sun-antisun axis. To understand this, consider a paper-cone cup with a hole cut at the bottom. You can view the circular rim of the cone as an ellipse when you look at it from a near side view. But if you view the rim only with your eye at the apex of the cone, through the hole, you can see it only as a circle. That's the way we view a rainbow. Our eye is at the apex of a cone, the axis of which is the sun-antisun axis, and the "rim" of which is the bow.

29. The fact that two observers standing apart from one another do not see the same rainbow can be understood by exaggerating the circumstance: Suppose the two observers are several kilometers apart. Obviously they are looking at different drops in the sky. Although they may both see a rainbow, they are looking at different rainbows. Likewise if they are closer together. Only if their eyes are at the very same location will they see exactly the same rainbow.

30. Seen from high enough, as from an airplane, the rainbow makes a complete circle. The shadow of the airplane will appear in the center of the circular bow. This is because the airplane is directly between the sun and the drops or rain cloud producing the bow.

31. Ice crystals floating in the upper atmosphere refract and disperse white moonlight into a spectrum. Whereas the colors that form a rainbow are from the part of the light *reflected* in the drops, *refracted* light forms the halos around the moon. Like the primary and secondary rainbow, the ice crystals disperse moonlight into two halos, the outer one being much fainter than the inner bow.

32. A projecting lens with chromatic aberration casts a rainbow-colored fringe around a spot of white light. The reason these colors don't appear inside the spot is because they overlap to form white. Only at the edges, which act as a ringed prism, do they not overlap.

33. A pinhole with two holes simply produces two images. If the holes are close together, the images overlap. Multiple holes produce multiple images. Overlapping can be prevented by placing a converging lens at the holes. Make the holes into one big hole with one big lens, and you have a conventional camera!

34. A converging lens will always produce a virtual image when the object is closer to the lens than the focal distance. Then it's a magnifier. When the object is beyond the focal point, the lens produces a real image (that which can be cast on a screen). A diverging lens used alone cannot produce a real image because under no conditions will the rays converge to a focus.

35. Your image is twice as far from the camera as the mirror frame. So although you can adjust the focus of your camera to clearly photograph your image in a mirror, and you can readjust the focus to clearly photograph the mirror frame, you cannot in the same photograph focus on both your image and the mirror frame. This is because they are at different distances from the camera.

36. For very distant objects, effectively at "infinity," light comes to focus at the focal plane of the lens. So your film is one focal length in back of the lens for very distant shots. For shorter distances, the film is farther from the lens.

37. Maps of the moon are upside down because images of the moon through the lenses of telescopes show an inverted image of the moon. The maps then match what the astronomy type sees.

38. The near point of vision recedes with advancing age. When you have to hold a book at arm's length to see it clearly, you're really ready for glasses!

39. The focal point for a lens under water will be longer than when it is in air. This is because the change in speed of light from water to glass, and then from glass to water again, is not so drastic. Less refraction occurs and light is not so quickly brought to focus. Nearsighted people see more clearly under water than in air!

40. The amount of light transmitted through two sheets of glass is 84.6%. To see this, consider an incident intensity of 100 units. Then 92 units are transmitted through the first pane. 92% of this amount are transmitted through the second pane (0.92 of 92 = 84.6).

28 | Light Waves

Answers

1. Diffraction is most pronounced for long-wavelength waves. The wavelength of sound waves is relatively long, and for light waves incredibly short. Hence it is the refraction of sound that is most evident in our everyday environment.

2. Both interference fringes of light and beats of sound are the result of the superposition of waves that interfere constructively and destructively.

3. Radio waves are much longer and therefore diffract more than the shorter waves of light.

4. The signals of lower channel numbers are broadcast at lower frequencies and longer wavelengths, which are diffracted into regions of poor reception more than higher-frequency signals.

5. The alternation of sound from loud to soft is evidence of interference. Where the sound is loud, the waves from each loudspeaker are interfering constructively; where it is soft, destructive interference from the speakers is taking place.

6. If the listener walks along the perpendicular to the midpoint of the line connecting the speakers, the listener will, at all points, be equidistant from both speakers. Tones from both speakers will be in phase all along this path. A bit of thought will show you there are other paths of non-interference as well.

7. The fringes will be spaced farther apart if the pattern is made of long-wavelength red light. The shorter wavelength blue light will produce closer fringes. (Investigation of Figure 28.19 should make this clear — note that if the wavelength were longer, the light and dark regions on the screen would be farther apart.)

8. Fringes become more numerous as the slits are moved farther apart. (Note Figure 28.15.)

9. Young's interference experiment produces a clearer fringe pattern with slits than with pinholes because the pattern is of parallel straight-line-shaped fringes rather than the fringes of overlapping circles. Circles overlap in relatively smaller segments than the broader overlap of parallel straight lines.

10. For complete cancellation, the amplitudes of each part of the wave must be identical. If the amplitudes are not the same, then partial cancellation results.

11. Multiple slits of identical spacings produce a wider and brighter interference pattern. Such an arrangement makes up a diffraction grating (Figure 28.21), which is a popular alternative to a prism for dispersing light into its component parts.

12. Diffraction is the principle by which peacocks and hummingbirds display their colors. The ridges in the surface layers of the feathers act as diffraction gratings.

13. Interference colors result from double reflections from the upper and lower surfaces of the thin transparent coating on the butterfly wings. Some other butterfly wings produce colors by diffraction, where ridges in the surface act as diffraction gratings.

14. The optical paths of light from upper and lower reflecting surfaces change with different viewing postions. Thus, different colors can be seen by holding the shell at different angles.

15. Interference of light from the upper and lower surfaces of the soap film is taking place.

16. A necessary condition for interference is that the out-of-phase parts of the wave coincide. If the film is thick, the part of the wave that reflects from one surface will be displaced from the part that reflects from the other surface. No interaction, no cancellation, no interference colors. For thin films, the two parts of the wave coincide as they recombine.

17. Light from a pair of stars will not produce an interference pattern because the waves of light from the two separate sources are incoherent with respect to one another; when combined they smudge. Interference occurs for monochromatic light or when light from a single source is split and recombined with a phase displacement.

18. In a loose sense, we can say that interference underlies the explanation of colors produced by light transmission with the aid of Polaroids, but in the strict sense this is not the case. With the Polaroids, a particular wavelength is allowed to pass through the system to the exclusion of other wavelengths, by virtue of the angle through which it has rotated. Note in the chapter that the colors produced by transmission do not involve "cancellations" of wavelengths as is the case for double reflection.

19. Glare is composed largely of polarized light in the plane of the reflecting surface. Most glaring surfaces are horizontal (roadways, water, etc.), so sunglasses with vertical polarization axes filter the glare of horizontally polarized light. Conventional non-polarizing sunglasses simply cut down on overall light transmission either by reflecting or absorbing incident light.

20. You can determine the polarization axis for a single sheet of Polaroid by viewing the glare from a flat surface. The glare is most intense when the polarization axis is parallel to the flat surface.

21. Since most glare is due to reflection from horizontal surfaces, the polarization axes of common sunglasses are vertical.

22. You can determine that the sky is partially polarized by rotating a single sheet of Polaroid in front of your eye while viewing the sky. You'll notice the sky darken where polarization is greatest.

23. To say that a Polaroid is ideal is to say that it will transmit 100% of the components of light that are parallel to its polarization axis, and absorb 100% of all components perpendicular to its polarization axis. Nonpolarized light has as many components along the polarization axis as it has perpendicular to the same axis. That's 50% along the axis, and 50% perpendicular to the axis. A perfect Polaroid transmits the 50% that is parallel to its polarization axis.

24. With polarization axes aligned, a pair of Polaroids will transmit all components of light along the axes. That's 50%, as explained in the preceding answer. With axes at right angles, no light will be transmitted.

25. When viewing a scene with both eyes, parallax is the principle means of perceiving depth — parallax tells you what is near and what is far. A painting is flat, and when viewed with both eyes, all parts are seen to be equidistant. Other cues, such as gradations of color, relative sizes, and brightnesses of objects, that the artist uses to simulate depth must contend with the absence of parallax. But if you view with one eye, parallax as a cue is eliminated. The brain's reliance on parallax is greatly diminished with a one-eyed view. Other cues of depth become more evident and the illusion of depth is enhanced.

26. Making holograms requires coherent light, exactly what a laser provides. Hence practical holography followed the advent of the laser. (Interestingly enough, the first holograms were made before the advent of the laser, and were crude by today's standards. They were made with monochromatic light from a sodium vapor lamp, through a tiny pinhole to provide a close approximation of coherent light, and required very long exposures.)

27. Magnification is accomplished by making the hologram with short wavelength light and viewing it with a longer wavelength light. This is similar to the wider spacings between fringes when long wavelength light illuminates thin slits.

28. You must use two eyes to perceive depth by parallax, whether in a hologram or otherwise. If depth is perceived by other cues, such as relative sizes and relative brightnesses of objects, then one eye is sufficient.

29 | Light Emission

1. The energy levels are different for the atoms and molecules of different materials, hence the different frequencies of radiation emitted when the atoms and molecules of these materials are excited. Different colors correspond to different frequencies.

2. Higher-frequency higher-energy blue light corresponds to a greater energy-level transition.

3. Electrons lose more energy when they stimulate atoms to emit higher-energy photons of blue light than lower-energy photons of red light. In accord with energy conservation, the energy the bombarding electron loses equals the energy of light that results (plus any heat formed).

4. More energy is associated with each photon of ultraviolet light than with photons that make up visible light. This extra energy per photon alters skin composition and produces sunburn.

5. Doubling the wavelength of light without changing its speed halves its frequency. Light of half frequency has half the energy per photon.

6. A neon tube doesn't "run out" of atoms to be excited because its atoms are re-excited over and over, without the need for "new" atoms.

7. If the slit in a spectroscope were replaced with a round hole, the "lines" would appear as round spots. This would be disadvantageous because the overlapping circles would provide very poor resolution.

8. Diffracted light from a neon tube produces many different colors, most of which are various shades of red. Light from a helium-neon laser is of one color, from only one of the "spectral lines" of neon.

9. When a spectrum of the sun is compared to the spectrum of iron, the iron lines overlap and match the Fraunhofer line pattern of solar radiation.

10. By comparing the absorption spectra of various sources through the earth's atmosphere, the lines due to the earth's atmosphere can be established. Then when viewing the spectra from the sun, extra lines and extra line intensities can be attributed to the atmosphere of the sun.

11. Atomic excitation occurs in solids, liquids, and gases. Radiation from a solid (and liquid) is smeared into a broad distribution to produce a continuous spectrum, whereas radiation from a gas is in discrete bunches that form "lines" when passed through a thin slit and diffracted.

12. When tungsten atoms are close-packed in a solid, the otherwise well-defined energy levels of outer electron shells are smeared by mutual interactions among neighboring atoms. The result of this close packing is an energy band composed of myriad separate levels very close together. Because there are about as many of these separate levels as there are atoms in the crystalline structure, the band cannot be distinguished from a continuous spread of energies.

13. Fluorescent materials produce bright colors because they both reflect and emit light. They literally glow when exposed to visible light, the higher frequencies of which excite molecules in the material (hence they are sometimes called "day-glow colors").

14. The different colors emitted by fluorescent minerals correspond to different molecules with different sets of energy states. Hence such minerals can therefore be visually distinguished.

15. Fluorescence is the process where high-frequency (high energy) ultraviolet radiation converts to low-frequency (lower energy) visible radiation with a bit of heat energy left over. If your friend is suggesting that low-energy infrared radiation can be converted to higher-energy visible light, that is clearly a violation of the conservation of energy — a no-no! Now if your friend is suggesting that infrared radiation can cause the fluorescence of still lower-frequency infrared radiation, which is not seen as light, then your friend's reasoning is well founded.

16. The acronym says it: *m*icrowave *a*mplification by *s*timulated *e*mission of *r*adiation.

17. The photons from the photoflash tube must have at least as much energy as the the photons they are intended to produce in the laser. Red photons have less energy than green photons, so wouldn't be energetic enough to stimulate the emission of green photons. Energetic green photons can produce less-energetic red photons, but not the other way around.

18. Light sources in decreasing order of efficiency are: fluorescent lamp (about 20%), incandescent lamp (about 5%), and a common laser (less than 1%).

19. Photons in the laser beam are coherent; photons in incandescant -lamp light are incoherent.

20. Your friend's assertion violates the law of energy conservation. A laser or any device cannot put out more energy than is put into it, as the next exercise begins.

21. No device can put out more energy than is put in.. But if a device takes in energy at a certain rate and emits it in a shorter time interval, then it is capable of putting out higher bursts of power than it takes in. (This is how Lawrence Livermore Lab's Nova laser emits short pulses with more power than is generated by all the power plants in the U.S. combined.)

22. A lamp filament of any object emits radiation at all temperatures greater than absolute zero. The peak frequency of this radiation is proportional to the absolute temperature of the object. At room temperature this frequency is in the infrared part of the spectrum and therefore can't normally be seen. When the temperature of the filament is increased, the radiation falls into the visible part of the spectrum and we have light.

23. We can't see objects at room temperature in the dark simply because our eyes are not sensitive to the radiation they emit. If the temperature of the objects is increased sufficiently, then we can see the radiation so emitted.

24. Star's relative temperatures — lowish for reddish; midish for whitish; and hotish for bluish.

25. For green light and only green light to be emitted by a star, all the atoms that emit light would have to be vibrating at nearly identical rates — highly unlikely. The radiation curve such as shown in Figure 29-7 would have to be extremely narrow and could not extend into the red and violet parts of the spectrum. A broader curve peaking at green is more likely, and would produce white light because of the overlapping of the other frequencies. Hence there are no green-hot stars.

26.

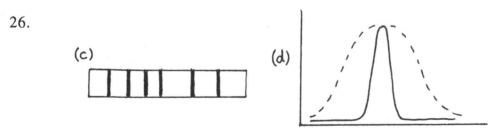

(c)

(d)

1. Classical physics is primarily the physics known before 1900 that involves the study of familiar things such as the forces, motions, momenta, and energy of massive particles that behave in a predictable manner in accord with Newton's laws; for this reason classical physics is often called Newtonian physics. After 1900 it was found that Newtonian rules simply don't apply in the domain of the very small — the submicroscopic. This is the domain of quantum physics, where everything is "grainy" and where values of energy, momentum, position, and perhaps even time occur in lumps, or quanta, all of which are governed by probabilities rather than certainties. The physics in this domain is different and we lack adequate words and visual pictures to describe it as we do classical physics. We nevertheless tend to impress our classical wave and particle models on our findings in an effort to visualize this subatomic world.

2. Electromagnetic waves are carriers of energy. To say that the energy is proportional to the frequency is to say that the more rapid the oscillations of the electric and magnetic fields that constitute the radiation, the greater is the energy. This is as reasonable as stating that the more rapidly you jerk a tight rope up and down to make a wave, the more energy is required and the more energetic the wave. We picture a photon as a pulsating packet of electromagnetic radiation; higher frequencies are more energetic than lower frequencies.

3. In accord with $E = hf$, the photon with the highest frequency — ultraviolet, of the three listed — has the greatest energy.

4. It makes no sense to talk of photons of white light, for white light is a mixture of photons of various frequencies. One photon of white light has no physical meaning.

5. Since red light carries less energy per photon, and both beams have the same energy, there must be more photons in the beam of red light.

6. Red is the first color to be seen as a solid is heated to incandescence because the higher-frequency end of its radiation curve (Figure 29.7 back on page 550) "sloshes over" into the lower-frequency portion of the visible spectrum. As the temperature rises, yellows, greens, and blues are activated and the solid appears white. Continued heating activates only the higher-frequencies and the material begins to look blue, but by this time it has vaporized. Hence we see only red, white, or blue incandescent stars.

7. The energy of red light is too low per photon to trigger the chemical reaction in the photographic crystals. Very bright light simply means more photons that are unable to trigger a reaction. Blue light, on the other hand, has sufficient energy per photon to trigger a reaction. Very dim blue light triggers fewer reactions only because there are fewer photons involved.

8. When a photon of ultraviolet light encounter a living cell, it transfers to the cell an amount of energy that can be damaging to the cell. When a photon of visible light encounters a living cell, the amount of energy it transfers to the cell is less, and less likely to be damaging. Hence skin exposure to ultraviolet radiation can be damaging to the skin while exposure to visible light generally is not.

9. The number of electrons ejected in the photoelectric effect is determined by the number of photons incident upon the metal. So the brightness of light determines the number of ejected electrons (the energy of the ejected electrons is determined by the frequency of the light).

10. Some automatic doors utilize a beam of light that continually shines on a photodetector. When you block the beam by walking through it, the generation of current in the photodetector ceases. This change of current then activates the opening of the door.

11. The photoelectric effect is discharging the ball. Some of the excess electrons are being "knocked off" the ball by the ultraviolet light. This discharges the ball. If the ball is positively charged, however, it already has a deficiency of electrons, and knocking off more tends to increase the charge rather than decrease it. (Fewer electrons are dislodged by ultraviolet light from the positive ball than from the negative ball. Do you know why?)

12. The energy of ultraviolet light goes into the lower energy of the emission of lower-frequency and lower-energy visible light plus internal energy of the dyed material. All energy is accounted for. But hardly so if the source is infrared light. There is not enough energy per photon for infrared light to do the same. Such would violate the conservation of energy.

13. There will likely be no current at all for red light, and some current for colors of higher frequency, depending on the photosensitive plate material. Once current is produced, the amount of current will increase with light frequency and for the visible colors will be greatest for violet. Greater current will be produced as the frequency range is extended into the ultraviolet. For a given frequency (color) the current will be proportional to the intensity (brightness) of the incident light.

14. *Electric eye*: A beam of light is directed to a photosensitive surface that completes the path of an electric circuit. When the beam is interrupted, the circuit is broken. The entire photoelectric circuit may be used as a switch for another circuit. *Light meter*: The variation of photoelectric current with variations in light intensity activates a galvanometer, or its equivalent, that is calibrated to show light intensity. *Sound track*: An optical sound track on motion picture film is a strip of emulsion of variable density that transmits light of variable intensity on to a photosensitive surface, which in turn produces an electric current of the desired variations. This current is amplified and then activates the loudspeaker.

15. The photoelectric effect doesn't prove that light is corpuscular, but rather supports the corpuscular model of light, which is compatible with the particle-like behavior observed. Likewise with interference experiments that support the wave model of light and are compatible with the wavelike behavior of light. We have models to help us conceptualize what something *is*; knowledge of the details of how something behaves helps us to refine the model. It is important that we keep in mind that our models for understanding nature are just that: models. (More about models in the answer to the next exercise.)

16. Young's explanation of the double-slit experiment is based on the wave model of the nature of light; Einstein's explanation of the photoelectric effect involves a model of light in which light is composed of particles. The effectiveness of one model or another doesn't invalidate the other model, particularly in this instance where the models are used to describe completely different phenomena. Models are not to be judged as being "true" or "mistaken"; models are useful or nonuseful. The particle model of light is useful in making sense of the details of the photoelectric effect, whereas the wave model of light is not useful in understanding these details. Likewise, the wave model of light is useful for understanding the details of interference, whereas the particle model is not useful. The effectiveness of one model over another means simply that: one model is more effective than another. This effectiveness doesn't mean that one model is correct and the other invalid. As we gather more data and gain new insights, we refine our models.

17. An explanation is the following: Light refracting through the lens system is understandable via the wave model of light, and its arrival spot by spot to form the image is understandable via

the particle model of light. How can this be? We don't exactly know; we find that various behaviors of light are suited to one or the other models, in accord with the complementarity principle. Another explanation is that in quantum physics we think of light waves as "guide waves" that tell photons where to go. These guide waves are probability waves that interfere constructively and destructively at different locations on the film to give the positions of photon impact. In this view, the image formed by a lens is actually a probability distribution for the arrival of photons.

18. If the frequency of a photon is related to its energy, then it follows that it is also related to its momentum. The wavelength of a wave is certainly related to its frequency, so it follows that the wavelength of a wave is related to its momentum. Likewise for matter waves, as described by de Broglie's formula. (The formula for wavelength in terms of momentum does not make sense in the domain of classical physics. But why should we suppose that our descriptions of the macroscopic everyday world should carry to the microworld? They don't; hence the invention of quantum physics.)

19. The twice-as-fast electron has twice the momentum. By de Broglie's formula, wavelength = h/momentum, twice the momentum means half the wavelength. The slower electron has the longer wavelength.

20. By de Broglie's formula, as velocity increases, momentum increases, so wavelength decreases.

21. The cannonball obviously has more momentum than the BB traveling at the same speed, which in accord with de Broglie's formula means it has the shorter wavelength.

22. The momenta of moving things in our everyday environment are huge compared to the momenta of submicroscopic particles even at speeds near the speed of light. This is because their masses are so huge in comparison. The large momenta, in accord with de Broglie's formula, correspond to incredibly short wavelengths. See the footnote on page 572.

23. The principal advantage of an electron microscope over an optical microscope is its ability to see things that are too small for viewing with an optical microscope. This is because an object cannot be discerned if it is smaller than the wavelength of the illuminating beam. An electron beam has a wavelength that is typically a thousand times shorter than the wavelength of visible light, which means it can discern particles a thousand times smaller than those barely seen with an optical microscope.

24. Diffraction increases with increasing wavelength (which is an asset for the long waves of radio and a liability for the short waves of light in an optical microscope). Protons of the same speed as electrons would have more momentum, and therefore smaller wavelengths, and therefore less diffraction. Why are there not proton microscopes? There are; we call them atomic accelerators. The high momenta of high-velocity protons enable detailed information of nuclear structure, which brings us to the smallest domain that we can imagine.

25. If h were zero, there would be no fundamental limit on the uncertainties we attribute to simultaneous measurements of momentum and position, and energy and time. Without a finite value of h, the uncertainty principle as we know it would not exist. If h were different than it is, nature as we know it would not exist!

26. In the best spirit of science, from our observations we develop a theory that gives meaning to those observations. However, it is often the case that belief in a theory precedes observations and influences our perception of those observations and the meaning we give them. We should be aware of this "human factor." Sometimes it is very beneficial and sometimes it is not.

27. If somebody looks at an electron on the tip of your nose with an electron beam or a light beam, then its motion as well as surrounding electrons will be altered. But simply passively looking at light after it has reflected from an object does not alter the electrons in the object. There is a difference between passive observation and probing. The uncertainty principle applies to probing, not to passive observation.

28. The way we phrase a question often influences the answer we get, so to various extents we alter that which we wish to measure in a public opinion survey. There are countless examples of altering circumstances by measuring them. My biologist friend, Jim Morgan, a few years ago noted with alarm many cases wherein the particular method of studying wild animals had more to do with adversely altering their circumstances than any other factors in their environment. (Jim's observation was not welcomed by the biologists whose livelihood depended on such studies.) The uncertainty principle, however, does not apply in these cases, but applies to events in the submicroscopic domain.

29. No, for there is a distinction between a determined system and a predictable system. To say that you understand a system's past and to understand how every mode of behavior was determined by the preceding mode is not to say that you can predict its future. Consider the old upright pinball machines. Take a slow-motion movie of a ball that makes its way down through the forest of metal pins to finally reach a position at the bottom. Running the moving backward allows you to account for every move at every pin, with no mystery along the way. the ball reached its landing place via a path determined by its motion and position with respect to the pins it encountered. You can see by hindsight (20/20 vision!) the results of classical physics in action. But this hindsight does not mean you can predict the determination of the final position of the next ball you drop through the maze of pins. If we cannot predict the future of a macroscopic system, then classical uncertainties, not quantum uncertainties, account for this inability.

30. This is perhaps the extreme in altering that which is being measured by the process of measuring itself, as well as an extreme case of criminal stupidity and academic arrogance. The bristlecone pine, Old Methuselah, was the oldest known living thing in the world.

1. The very dense nucleus of Rutherford's model of the atom accounts for the backscattering of alpha particles as they ricochet off the gold atoms of the thin foil. This backscattering would not occur if the mass of the atom was spread throughout the volume of the atom, just as a golf ball would not bounce backward when striking a piece of cake, or even when colliding with a tennis ball or especially another golf ball. A golf ball will bounce backward if it strikes a massive object such as a bowling ball. Similarly for alpha particles that bounce from the atomic nucleus.

2. Spectral lines are as characteristic of the elements as fingerprints are of people. Both help in identification.

3. Uranium has 92 protons in its nucleus, which is 92 times the positive charge as hydrogen. This greater charge pulls the surrounding electrons into tighter orbits. The result of this is that the heavier atoms are not appreciably larger in size than the lighter atoms (see Figure 31.6).

4. If like elements were of different shapes, for one thing, they would not combine to form crystals of symmetrical shapes. Bonding strengths would also differ, and the strength of the crystal, like the strength of a chain, would be no stronger than the weakest link. The world would be a very different place.

5. If we think of electrons as orbiting the nucleus in standing waves, then the circumference of these wave patterns must be a whole number of wavelengths. In this way the circumferences are discrete. This means that the radii of orbits are therefore discrete. Since energy depends upon this radial distance, the energy values are also discrete.

6. The one electron can be boosted to many energy levels, and therefore make many combinations of transitions to the ground level. Each transition is of a specific energy and accompanied by the emission of a photon of a specific frequency. Thus the variety of spectal lines.

7. Six transitions are possible. The transition from the 4th to the 1st level corresponds to the greatest ΔE and therefore highest frequency of light. The transition from the 4th to the 3rd level corresponds to the lowest ΔE and therefore lowest frequency of light.

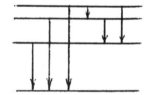

8. In accord with the conservation of energy, the combined energies equal the energy of the single transition. (Thus the sum of the frequencies of light emitted by the two steps will equal the frequency of light emitted with the one long step — the Ritz combination principle.)

9. The double charge of the helium nucleus, compared to the hydrogen nucleus, pulls the electron shell closer to the nucleus (see Figure 31.6).

10. Any odd-number of de Broglie wavelengths would interfere destructively and fail to form a standing wave. A standing wave, or a stable electron shell, must be composed of an integral number of complete waves (see Figure 31.8).

11. The wavelength of any wave is the distance a wave travels in one cycle. Likewise with a matter wave. Relatively long wavelengths have comparitively little momentum and undergo wider-angle diffraction than shorter matter waves. The amplitude of any wave is the maximum to and fro displacement in its vibratory mode. In the case of a matter wave, the amplitude is the

wave function   ("psi"), which represents all the possibilities that can occur in a system. When   is squared, it represents the probabilities of the possibilities occurring.

12. We can see this from de Broglie's equation (wavelength = h/momentum), where for a given momentum if h were larger, the wavelengths of the standing waves that comprise electron shells would be larger, and hence atoms would be larger.

13. The laws of probabilities applied to one or a few atoms gives poor predictability, but for hordes of atoms, the situation is entirely different. Although the certainty of predicting which electron will absorb a photon in the photoelectric effect is very crude, the certainty of predicting the current produced by a beam of light on photosensitive material is extremely accurate. We can't say where a given electron will hit a screen in double-slit diffraction, but we can predict with great accuracy the relative intensities of a wave-interference pattern for a bright beam of light. Predicting the kinetic energy of a particular atom as it bumbles about in an atomic lattice is highly inaccurate, but predicting the average kinetic energy of hordes of atoms in the same atomic lattice, the temperature of the substance, can be predicted with high precision. The indeterminacy at the quantum level can be discounted when large aggregates of atoms so well lend themselves to extremely accurate macroscopic prediction.

14. Light behavior such as interference and diffraction can only be satisfactorily explained in terms of waves; while the photoelectric effect can be satisfactorily explained only in terms of the particle model. Hence we say that light has both wave and particle properties.

15. Electrons have a definite mass and a definite charge, so we say they have particle properties; electrons also produce interference effects, so we say they have wave properties. There is a contradiction only if we insist the electron may have only particle OR only wave properties. Investigators find that electrons display both particle and wave properties.

16. We don't know if an electron *is* a particle or a wave; we know it *behaves* sometimes as a wave and sometimes as a particle. The unwarranted assumption is that an electron must be either a particle *or* a wave. It is common to hear some people say that something can only be either this or that, as if both were not possible (like those who say we must choose between biological evolution *or* in the existence of a supreme being).

17. The principle linking classical physics to quantum physics is the *correspondence principle*.

18. The correspondence principle simply states that a theory for one domain or set of circumstances, and another theory for another domain and another set of circumstances (like a theory for small things and a theory for big things, or a theory for slow things and a theory for fast things, or one for cold things and another for hot things) should correspond to each other in the region where the domains overlap. Unlike Heisenberg's uncertainty principle, the correspondence principle is relevant for all good theory in all fields of knowledge.

19. In accord with Newton's first law, in the absence of a net force, a body at rest will remain at rest; a body in motion will remain in motion. In accord with Newton's second law, the acceleration of a body will be equal to the net force per bodymass exerted on the body. So the second law reduces to the first when the net force goes to zero. Then the acceleration goes to zero, which is the nonchange of motion cited in the first law. Both laws correspond exactly when there is no net force. [This is not a particularly good example of Bohr's Correspondence principle, where we compare two facets of the same theory rather than of different theories.]

20. The philosopher was speaking of classical physics, the physics of the macroscopic world, where to a high degree of accuracy the same physical conditions do produce the same results. Feynman must have been speaking of the quantum domain where for small numbers of particles and events, the same conditions are not expected to produce the same results.

32 Atomic Nucleus and Radioactivity

Answers

1. X rays are high-frequency electromagnetic waves, and are therefore most similar to even higher-frequency electromagnetic waves — gamma rays. Alpha and beta rays, in contrast, are streams of particles.

2. A radioactive sample is always a little warmer than its surroundings because the radiating alpha or beta particles impart internal energy to the atoms of the sample. (Interestingly enough, the heat energy of the earth originates with radioactive decay of the earth's core and surrounding material.)

3. It is impossible for a hydrogen atom to eject an alpha particle, for an alpha particle is composed of a pair of hydrogen isotopes (deuterium). It is equally impossible for a one-kilogram melon to spontaneously break into four one-kilogram melons.

4. Alpha and beta rays are deflected in opposite directions in a magnetic field because they are oppositely charged — alpha are positive and beta negative. Gamma rays have no electric charge and are therefore undeflected.

5. The alpha particle has twice the charge, but almost 8000 times the inertia (since each of the four nucleons has nearly 2000 times the mass of an electron). Hence it bends very little compared to the much less massive electrons.

6. The paths of alpha, beta, and gamma radiation bend similarly in both electric and magnetic fields. In both fields, betas bend the most and in the opposite direction of the alphas, and gammas traverse undeflected.

7. Alpha radiation decreases the atomic number of the emitting element by 2 and the atomic mass number by 4. Beta radiation increases the atomic number of an element by 1 and does not affect the atomic mass number. Gamma radiation does not affect the atomic number or the atomic mass number. So alpha radiation results in the greatest change in atomic number, and hence charge, and mass number as well.

8. Gamma radiation produces not only the least change in mass and atomic numbers, but produces no change in mass number, atomic number, or electric charge. Both alpha and beta radiation do produce these changes, as discussed in the previous answer.

9. Because of the fact that like charges repel, and that protons have the same sign of charge (positive) as the target atomic nuclei, the protons must be driven into the target area with enormous energies if they are to bombard the nuclei. Lower-energy protons would be easily repelled by any nuclei they approach.

10. Alpha particles are first of all, much bigger in size than beta particles, which makes them less able to pass through the "pores" of materials. Second, alpha particles are enormously more massive than beta particles. So if beta particles have the same kinetic energy, they must be moving considerably faster. The faster moving and smaller beta particles are therefore more effective in penetrating materials.

11. Within the atomic nucleus, it is the strong nuclear force that tends to hold the nucleons together, and the electric force that tends to mutually repel the nucleons and push them apart.

12. The fact that atomic nuclei composed of many protons exist is evidence that something stronger than electric repulsion is occurring in the nucleus. If there were not a stronger attractive nuclear force to keep the repelling electrical force from driving protons apart from each other, the nucleus as we know it wouldn't exist.

13. At the end of the second year 1/4 of the original sample will be left; third year, 1/8 will be left; and at the end of the fourth year, 1/16 will be left.

14. The half life of the material will be two hours. A little thought will show that 160 halved 4 times equals 10. So there have been four half life periods in the 8 hours. And 8 hours/4 = 2 hours.

15. In accord with the inverse-square law, at 2 meters, double the distance, the count rate will be one-fourth 360, or 90 counts/minute; at 3 meters, the count rate will be one-ninth 360, or 40 counts/minute.

16. The spiral path of charged particles in a bubble chamber is the result of a slowdown of the particles due to collisions with the hydrogen atoms. The slower-moving charged particles bend less in the magnetic field of the chamber and their paths slow to spirals. If the charged particles moved without resistance, their paths would be circles or helixes.

17. Eight alpha particles and six beta particles are emitted in the decay of U-238 to Pb-206.

18. When radium (A = 88) emits an alpha particle, its atomic number reduces by 2 and becomes the new element radon (A = 86). The resulting atomic mass is reduced by 4. If the radium was of the most common isotope 226, then the radon isotope would have atomic mass number 222.

19. After beta emission from polonium, the atomic number increases by 1 and becomes 85, and the atomic mass is unchanged at 218. However, if an alpha particle is emitted, the atomic number decreases by 2 and becomes 82, and the atomic mass decreases by 4 and drops to 214.

20. Deuterium has 1 proton and 1 neutron; carbon has 6 protons and 6 neutrons; iron has 26 protons and 30 neutrons; gold has 79 protons and 118 neutrons; strontium has 38 protons and 52 neutrons; uranium has 92 protons and 146 neutrons.

21. An element can decay to elements of greater atomic number by emitting electrons (beta rays). When this happens, a neutron becomes a proton and the atomic number increases by one.

22. When phosphorus (A = 15) emits a positron (a "positively-charged electron") the charge of the atomic nucleus decreases by 1 and becomes the element silicon (A = 14).

23. If strontium-90 (A = 38) emits betas, it should become the element yttrium (A = 39); hence the physicist can test a sample of strontium for traces of yttrium by spectrographic means or other techniques.

24. The elements below uranium in atomic number with short half-lives exist as the product of the radioactive decay of uranium. As long as uranium is decaying, their existence is assured.

25. Your friend will most likely encounter more radioactivity from the granite outcroppings than he or she will living near a nuclear power plant. Furthermore, at high altitude your friend will be treated to increased cosmic radiation. But the radiations encountered in the vicinity of the plant, on the granite outcropping, or at high altitude are not appreciably different than the radiation one encounters in the "safest" of situations. Advise your friend to enjoy life anyway!

26. The earth's natural energy that heats the water in the hot spring is the energy of radioactive decay. Just as a piece of radioactive material is warmer than its surroundings due to thermal agitation from radioactive decay, the interior of the earth is similarly warmed. The great radioactivity in the earth's interior therefore heats the water, but doesn't make the water itself radioactive. The warmth of hot springs is one of the "nicer effects" of radioactive decay.

27. Although there is significantly more radioactivity in a nuclear power plant than in a coal-fired power plant, the absence of shielding for coal plants results in more radioactivity in the environment of a typical coal plant than in the environment of a typical nuclear plant. All nukes are shielded; coal plants are not.

28. You can tell your friend who is fearful of the radiation measured by the Geiger counter that his attempt to avoid the radiation by avoiding the instrument that measures it, is useless. He might as well avoid thermometers on a hot day in effort to escape the heat. If it will console your fearful friend, tell him that he and his ancestors from time zero have endured about the same level of radiation he receives whether or not he stands near the Geiger counter. They had, and he has, no better options. Make the best of the years available anyway!

29. Radioactive decay rates are statistical averages of large numbers of decaying atoms. Because of the relatively short half-life of carbon-14, only trace amounts would be left after 50 000 years — too little to be statistically accurate.

30. Stone tablets cannot be dated by the carbon dating technique. Nonliving stone does not in-gest carbon and transform that carbon by radioactive decay. Carbon dating pertains to organic material.

Answers

CONCEPTUAL **Physics** 7th EDITION

1. Uranium ore doesn't spontaneously explode because the uranium of which it is composed is primarily the isotope U-238, which doesn't undergo fission. U-235 atoms in the ore are too far apart for a chain reaction.

2. Nuclear fission is a poor prospect for powering automobiles primarily because of the massive shielding that would be required to protect the occupants and others from the radioactivity, and the problem of radioactive waste disposal.

3. Chemical burning and a nuclear chain reaction are similar in that both depend on the energy of one reaction to stimulate or trigger a neighboring reaction.

4. A neutron makes a better "bullet" for penetrating atomic nuclei because it has no electric charge and is therefore not deflected from its path by electrical interactions, nor is it electrically repelled by an atomic nucleus.

5. The greater the volume of the fissionable material, the less its surface area compared to the volume. Twice the volume, for example, is less than twice the increase in surface area (see the decreasing ratio of surface area per volume idea, Figure 11.16, page 204). Larger volumes of fissionable material have proportionally less area compared to their greater volumes, and therefore lose less neutrons.

6. Critical mass is the amount of fissionable mass that which will just sustain a chain reaction without exploding. This occurs when the production of neutrons in the material is balanced by neutrons escaping through the surface. The greater the escape of neutrons, the greater can be the mass. Now a spherical shape has the least surface area for any given volume, so for a given volume, a cube shape would have more area, and therefore more "leakage" of the neutron flux. So for critical mass, more mass can be assembled in a cube than in a sphere before exceeding the critical stage. (Look at it this way: a sphere of fissionable material that is critical will be subcritical if flattened into a pancake shape because of increased neutron leakage.)

7. (Another ratio of surface area to volume application:) Surface area for a given volume decreases when small pieces of material are assembled. (It's easier to see the opposite process where surface area for a given volume is increased when big pieces are broken up into little pieces; for example, you break a sugar cube into little pieces to increase the surface area exposed to tea for quick disolving.) In the case of uranium fuel, the process of assembling small pieces into a single big piece decreases the surface area, reduces neutron leakage, and increases the probability of a chain reaction and an explosion.

8. Because plutonium triggers more reactions per atom, a smaller mass will produce the same neutron flux as a somewhat larger mass of uranium. So plutonium has a smaller critical mass than a similar shape of uranium.

9. Plutonium will provide the faster chain reaction because more neutrons are released, than are released by the same number of uranium atoms.

10. Plutonium has a short half life (24 360 years), so any plutonium initially in the earth's crust has long since decayed. The same is true for any heavier elements with even shorter half lives from which plutonium might originate. Trace amounts of plutonium can occur naturally in U-238 concentrations, however, as a result of neutron capture, where U-238 becomes U-239 and

after beta emission becomes Np-239, and further beta emission to Pu-239. (There are elements in the earth's crust with half lives even shorter than plutonium's, but these are the products of uranium decay; between uranium and lead in the periodic table of elements.)

11. The lists can be very large. Foremost considerations are these: conventional fossil-fuel power plants consume our natural resources and convert them into poisonous contaminants that are discharged into the atmosphere, which produce among other things, acid rain. A lesser environmental problem exists with nuclear power plants that do not pollute the atmosphere. Pollution from nukes is concentrated in the radioactive waste products from the reactor core. Any rational discussion about the drawbacks of either of these power sources must acknowledge that *both* are polluters — so the argument is about which form of pollution we are more willing to accept in return for electrical power. (Before you say "No Nukes!", rational thinking suggests that you first be able to say that you "Know Nukes!")

12. A separate water cycle is used in nuclear reactors to restrict radioactive contamination of the reactor water to the reactor itself and to prevent interaction of the contaminants with the outside environment.

13. The mass of an atomic nucleus is less than the masses of the separate nucleons that compose it, which follows from the fact that the nucleons in the nucleus have less mass than outside. This can be understood by considering that work is required to pull a nucleon from the nucleus. The energy expended in this work is manifested in greater mass. Hence nucleons have greater mass outside the nucleus than inside. In this case, the mass of the nucleus is less than the sum of the masses of it parts.

14. If the difference in mass for changes in the atomic nucleus increased tenfold (from 0.1% to 1.0%), the energy release from such reactions would increase tenfold as well.

15. To predict the energy release of a nuclear reaction, simply find the difference in the mass of the beginning nucleus and the mass of its configuration after the reaction (either fission or fusion). This mass difference (called the "mass defect") can be found from the curve of Figure 33.15 or from a table of nuclear masses. Multiply this mass difference by the speed of light squared: $E_o = mc^2$. That's the energy release!

16. Energy would be released by the fissioning of gold and from the fusion of carbon, but by neither fission nor fusion for iron. Neither fission nor fusion will result in a decrease of mass for iron nucleons.

17. If uranium were split into three parts, the segments would be nuclei of smaller atomic numbers, more toward iron on the graph of Figure 33-15. The resulting mass per nucleon would be less, and there would be more mass converted to energy in such a fissioning.

18. If the masses of nucleons varied in accord with the shape of the curve of Figure 33-14 instead of the curve of Figure 33-15, then the fissioning of all elements would liberate energy and all fusion processes would absorb rather than liberate energy. This is because all fission reactions (decreasing atomic number) would result in nuclei with less mass per nucleon, and all fusion reactions (increasing atomic number) would result in the opposite; nuclei of more mass per nucleon.

19. Whereas a pair of hydrogen nuclei collectively weigh more when apart than when locked together, a pair of uranium nuclei would weigh more when fused together than when apart — assuming extrapolation of the curve of Figure 33-15 to "atomic number (2 x 92)."

20. Although more energy is released in the fissioning of a single uranium atom than in the fusing of a pair of deuterium atoms, the much greater number of lighter deuterium atoms in a gram of matter compared to the fewer heavier uranium atoms in a gram of matter, results in more energy liberated per gram for the fusion of deuterium.

21. If enough fission fuel is localized, it will ignite spontaneously by the triggering of a single neutron. Fusion fuel, on the other hand, is not ignited by the triggering of a chain reaction. It has no "critical mass," and can be stored in large or small amounts without undergoing spontaneous ignition.

22. The principal source of radioactive fallout from a hydrogen bomb is the fission bomb "trigger" that is used to provide the heat and pressure for the thermonuclear fusion reaction.

23. A major advantage of fusion power over fission power has to do with the fuel for each: fusion fuel (hydrogen) is the most plentiful in the universe; fission fuel (uranium and plutonium), on the other hand, are in short supply and scarce in the universe. A second advantage of fusion power has to do with the byproducts: whereas fission produces appreciable radioactive wastes, the chief byproduct of fusion is nonradioactive helium.

24. Energy from the sun is our chief source of energy, which itself is the energy of fusion.

25. Minerals which are now being mined can be recycled over and over again with the advent of a fusion-torch type operation. This recycling would tend to reduce the role of mining in providing raw materials.

26. Such speculation could fill volumes. The energy and material abundance that is the expected outcome of a fusion age will likely prompt several fundamental changes. Obvious changes would occur in the fields of economics and commerce which would be geared to relative abundance rather than scarcity. Already our present price system, which is geared to and in many ways dependent upon scarcity, often malfunctions in an environment of abundance. Hence we see instances where scarcity is created to keep the economic system functioning. Changes at the international level will likely be worldwide economic reform, and at the personal level in a re-evaluation of the idea that scarcity ought to be the basis of value. A fusion age will likely see changes that will touch every facet of our way of life.

34 | Special Theory of Relativity

Answers

1. The velocity of the bullet relative to the ground is equal to the gun's muzzle velocity when the freight car is at rest. When moving, the velocity relative to the ground is the muzzle velocity plus the velocity of the freight car. Relative to the freight car, however, the bullet's velocity is equal to the muzzle velocity of the gun, whether the car is at rest or uniformly moving.

2. In the case of a light beam shining from atop a moving freight car, the light beam has the same speed relative to the ground as it has relative to the train. The speed of light is the same in all reference frames.

3. The Michelson and Morley experiment was only a failure in the sense that it did not confirm the result that was expected. What was expected, that differences in the velocity of light would be encountered and measured, turned out to be impossible in nature. The experiment was successful in that it widened the doors to new insights in physics.

4. When you drive down the highway you are moving through space and also "through time."

5. The *average* speed of light in a transparent medium is less than *c*, but in the model of light discussed in Chapter 25, the photons that make up the beam travel at *c* in the void that lies between the atoms of the material. Hence the speed of individual photons is always *c*. In any event, Einstein's postulate is that the speed of light in *free* space is invariant.

6. Yes, events that occur in the same point in space that are simultaneous in one reference frame will be simultaneous in any reference frame because there can be no differences in the path and time that light takes between the source of the two events and receiver. A pair of events must be spacially separated if their occurrence with respect to each other is seen to be different from different frames of reference.

7. If you are closer enough to event B than to event A, you may witness event B before you witness event A, even though another observer closer to event A witnesses event A first. Still another observer could witness events A and B simultaneously. The order of events is relative.

8. More and more energy must be put into an object that is accelerated to higher and higher speeds. This energy is evidenced by increased momentum and by inference, increased mass. As the speed of light is approached, the momentum, and presumably mass, of the object approaches infinity — at the speed of light, the mass of an object is infinite. In this view there is infinite resistance to any further increase in speed. Hence the speed limit of *c* for material particles.

9. There is no upper limit on either the momentum or kinetic energy of a particle, since there is no upper limit on its mass.

10. When we say that light travels a certain distance in 20 000 years we are talking about distance relative to our time frame of reference. From the time frame of reference of a traveling astronaut, this distance may well correspond to that which she could cover in her time frame of 20 years. Hence future astronauts will likely travel to distances many light years away in a matter of months from their frame of reference.

11. If a person travels at relativistic speeds, distances as far as those that light takes thousands of years to travel (from our frame of reference) could be traversed well within an average

lifetime. This is because distance is relative to the frame of reference from which it is measured. Long distances from a rest frame may be quite short from a moving frame.

12. A twin who makes a long trip at relativistic speeds returns younger than his stay-at-home twin sister only in the sense that he has not aged as much as his sister during the duration of his trip. If they could watch each other during the trip, there would be no time where either would see a reversing of age, only a slowing or speeding of aging. A reversal would result only for speeds greater than the speed of light.

13. Yes, it is possible for a son or daughter to be biologically older than his or her parents. Suppose, for example, that a woman of any age gives birth to a baby and then departs in a high-speed rocket ship. She could theoretically return from a relativistic trip in a few years to find her baby 80 or so years older than when she left.

14. If you were in a high-speed (or no speed!) rocket ship, you would note no changes in your pulse, in your mass, or in your volume. This is because the velocity between the observer, that is, yourself, and the observed is zero. No relativistic effect occurs for the observer and the observed when both travel in the same reference frame.

15. In contrast to the previous exercise, if you were monitoring a person who is moving away from your frame of reference, you would note a decrease in his pulse, an increase in his mass, and a decrease in his volume. In this case, there is very definitely a velocity of the observed with respect to the observer.

16. Frequency and period are reciprocals of one another (Chapter 18). If the frequency is doubled, the period is halved. For uniform motion, one senses only half as much time between flashes that are doubled in frequency. For accelerated motion, the situation is different. If the source gains speed in approaching, then each successive flash has even less distance to travel and the frequency increases more, and the period decreases more as well with time.

17. $$V = \frac{U_1 + U_2}{1 + \frac{U_1 U_2}{c^2}} = \frac{0.5c + 0.5c}{1 + \frac{0.25c^2}{c^2}} = \frac{c}{1.25} = 0.8c$$

18. $$\frac{U_1 U_2}{c^2} \approx 0, \quad \therefore V = \frac{U_1 + U_2}{1 + 0} = U_1 + U_2$$

19. $$V = \frac{U_1 + U_2}{1 + \frac{U_1 U_2}{c^2}} = \frac{c + c}{1 + \frac{c^2}{c^2}} = \frac{2c}{2} = c$$

20. The density of a moving body is measured to increase because of a measured increase in mass and decrease in volume.

21. The stick must be oriented in a direction perpendicular to its motion, unlike that of a properly-thrown spear. This is because it is traveling at relativistic speed (actually $0.87c$) as evidenced by its increase in mass. The fact that its length is unaltered means that its long direction is not in the direction of motion. The thickness of the stick, not the length of the stick, will appear shrunken to half size.

22. The stick will appear to be one-half meter long when it moves with its length along the direction of motion. Why one half its length? Because it is moving fast enough for its mass to be doubled, which is $0.87c$.

23. Like the stick in the preceding exercise, the speed that will reduce its measurements by 1/2 will double its mass.

24. For the moving electron, length contraction reduces the apparent length of the 2-mile long tube. Because its speed is nearly the speed of light, the contraction is great.

25. The electrons gain mass relative to the frame of reference of the accelerator. The v in the mass-velocity equation is nearly c. But if you put yourself in the frame of reference of the moving electrons, the v in the mass-velocity equation would be zero, for there is no relative motion between the observed (the electrons) and the observer (you). You would measure no increase in their mass. But you would measure an increase in the masses of the target particles — as much as if you were at rest and the target was moving at the same speed. The effect of the collision is the same whether the electrons slam into the target or the target slams into the electrons.

26. The increased mass of the electrons that illuminate your TV picture tube result from extra energy supplied by your power utility. You pay the bill!

27. The correspondence principle is a guide to good sense. If a new idea is valid, then it ought to be in harmony with the areas it overlaps. If it doesn't, then either the areas themselves are suspect, or the new idea is suspect. If a new theory is valid, it must account for the verified results of the older theory, whether the theory is or is not in the field of science.

28. $E_o = mc^2$ means that energy and mass are equivalent to each other. The c^2 is the proportionality constant that links the units of energy and mass. In a practical sense, energy and mass are one and the same. When something gains energy, it gains mass. When something loses energy, it loses mass. Mass is simply congealed energy.

29. At $0.995c$ the muon has ten times as much time, or twenty-millionths of a second, to live. From the stationary earth frame of reference, the muon's "clock" is running ten times slower than earth clocks, allowing sufficient time to make the trip. (Interestingly enough, from the muon's frame of reference, the distance to earth is contracted by ten times, so it has sufficient time to get there.)

30. Just as time is required for knowledge of distant events to reach our eyes, a lesser yet finite time is required for nearby things to reach our eyes. So the answer is yes, there is always a finite interval between an event and our perception of that event. (There is even a time interval between touching your finger to a hot stove and feeling the pain!)

31. There are two enormous obstacles to the practice of "century hopping" at this time. First, although we have the means to easily accelerate atomic particles to speeds approaching the speed of light, we presently have no means of propelling a body as massive as an inhabited rocket to relativistic speeds. Second, if we did, we presently have no way of effectively shielding the occupants of such a rocket from the radiation that would result from the high-speed collisions with interstellar matter.

32. Kiekegaard's statement, "Life can only be understood backwards; but it must be lived forwards.", is consistent with special relativity. No matter how much time might be dilated as a result of high speeds, a space traveler can only effectively slow the passage of time relative to various frames of reference, but can never reverse it — the theory does not provide for one traveling backward in time. Time at whatever rate, flows only forward.

35 | General Theory of Relativity

Answers

1. In accord with the principle of equivalence, one cannot discern between accelerated motion and gravitation. The effects of each are identical. So unless she has other clues, she will not be able to tell the difference.

2. For the linear acceleration of a space ship, a net force must be produced which requires the use of fuel. But if the ship is set into rotation, it will spin of its own rotational inertia like a top, once it is set spinning. An astronaut in the ship experiences a centrifugal force that provides a simulated "gravity." No fuel is consumed to sustain this effect because the centrifugal (or centripetal) force is perpendicular to rotational motion and does no work on the astronaut.

3. Ole Jules called his shot wrong on this one. In a space ship that drifts through space, whether under the influence of moon, earth, or whatever gravitational field, the ship and its occupants are in a state of free fall — hence there is no sensation of up or down. Occupants of a spaceship would feel weight, or sense an up or down, only if the ship were made to accelerate against them — say, against their feet. Then they could stand and sense that down is toward their feet, and up away from their feet.

4. The separation distance of two people walking north from the earth's equator decreases, and if they continue to the north pole their separation distance will be zero. At the north pole, a step in any direction is a step south!

5. We don't notice the bending of light by gravity in our everyday environment because the gravity we experience is too weak for a noticeable effect. If there were stellar black holes in our vicinity, the bending of light near them would be quite noticeable.

6. We say that a tightened chalk line forms a straight line. It doesn't. We say the surface of a still lake is flat and that a line laid across it is straight. It isn't. But these approximate the straight lines in our practical world. A much better approximation, however, is a beam of light. For distances used by surveyors, a beam of light is the best approximation of a straight line known. In fact we say, practically speaking, that a laser beam of light *defines* a straight line.

7. A beam of light traveling horizontally for one second in a uniform gravitational field of strength 1 g will fall a vertical distance of 4.9 meters, just as a baseball would. This is providing it remains in a 1-g field for one second, for it would travel 300 000 kilometers during this second also, nearly 25 earth diameters away, and well away from the 1-g field strength of the earth's surface (unless it were confined to the 1-g region as shown in Figure 35.8, with mirrors). If light were to travel in a 1-g region for two seconds, then like a baseball, it would fall $1/2\ g\ 2^2 = 19.6$ meters in two seconds.

8. The change in energy for light is not evidenced by a change in speed, but by a change in frequency. If the energy of light is lowered, as in traveling against a strong gravitational field, its frequency is lowered, and the light is said to be gravitationally red shifted. If the energy of the light is increased, as when falling in a gravitational field, for example, then the frequency is increased and the the light is blue shifted.

9. If we are with a clock at the bottom of a very deep well, it will run a bit faster because the gravitational field is weaker than at the surface. (Interestingly enough, if we monitor the clock from the surface above, light signals from the clock lose energy and decrease in frequency as

they ascend against the earth's field to reach the surface. So depending on the depth of the well, from the surface the clock may appear slow.)

10. Events on the moon, as monitored from the earth, run a bit faster and are slightly blue shifted. And even though signals escaping the moon are red shifted in ascending the moon's gravitational field, they are blue shifted even more in descending to the earth's stronger g field, resulting in a net blue shift.

11. The gravitational field intensity will increase on the surface of a shrinking star because the matter that produces the field is becoming more compact and more localized. This is easiest to see by considering the force on a body of mass m at the surface of the star of mass M via Newton's equation, $F = GmM/d^2$, where the only term that changes is d, which diminishes and therefore results in an increasing F.

12. A clock at the equator is farther from the center of the earth, and therefore in a reduced gravitational field than a clock at one of the poles, and hence runs slightly faster. (Interestingly enough, a clock at the equator is in circular motion with a speed of about 1600 km/h and therefore runs slower because of time dilation. But this effect alters time only about half as much as the gravitational effect; so the net effect is a slightly faster running clock at the equator.)

13. The gravitational field is stronger at the bottom of a building than at the top. Time runs slightly slower in stronger gravitational fields, so a person living at the bottom of a building will age slower than a person who lives at the top. Strictly speaking, people who live in penthouses live faster lives!

14. Your friend views your light source in a stronger gravitational field than the gravitational field she is in at the top of the tower. She therefore sees the light red shifted, or lower in frequency than you perceive it to be.

15. At the surface of a massive star, gravitation is greater, which results in a gravitational red shift. Light emitted from the star is red shifted.

16. We would not see objects frozen in time about a black hole because the radiations reflected or emitted from them would be extremely shifted past the infrared and radio ranges of the electromagnetic spectrum. This is gravitational red shift in the extreme.

17. From the astronaut's view, the gravitational potential difference between his own locality and the drastically weaker gravitational fields of the normal universe result in blue-shifted signals from the normal universe.

18. Mercury follows an elliptical path in its orbit about the sun, with its perigee in a stronger part of the sun's gravitational field than its apogee. If Mercury followed a circular orbit, then there would be no variation of the sun's gravitational field in its orbit.

19. Binary stars that move about a common center of mass radiate gravitational waves, just as do all moving masses.

20. Einstein's theory of gravitation predicts the same results as Newton's theory of gravitation in weak gravitational fields such as those of the solar system. In weak fields, Einstein's theory overlaps, corresponds, and gives the same results as Newton's theory, and therefore obeys the correspondence principle.

Answers

1. If 30 days were required to fill the entire pond, and the doubling time was 1 day, then the pond was half covered on the 29th day, and one-quarter covered on the 28th day!

2. A dollar loses 1/2 its value in 1 doubling time of the inflationary economy; this is 70/7% = 10 years. It the dollar is loaned at 7% compound interest, it loses nothing.

3. At a steady inflation rate of 7%, the doubling time is 70/7% = 10 years; so every 10 years the prices of these items will double. This means the $10 theater ticket in 10 years will cost $20, in 20 years will cost $40, in 30 years will cost $80, in 40 years will cost $160, and in 50 years will cost $320. The $100 suit of clothes will similarly jump each decade to $200, $400, $800, $1,600, and $3,200. For a $10,000 car the decade jumps will be $20,000, $40,000, $80,000, $160,000, and $320,000. For a $100,000 home, the decade jumps in price are $200,000, $400,000, $800,000, $1,600,000, and $3,200,000! Inflation often increases earnings more than prices, so we'll be able to pay for these things — and more.

4. For a 5% growth rate, 42 years is three doubling times (70/5% = 14 years; 42/14 = 3). Three doubling times is an eightfold increase. So in 42 years the city would have to have 8 sewerage treatment plants to remain as presently loaded; more than 8 if load per plant is to be reduced while servicing 8 times as many people.

5. Doubling time for the United States, at the 1986 growth rate of 0.6% is 70/0.6% = 117 years; for Mexico at 2.6% growth rate, its doubling time is 70/2.6% = 27 years; for Kenya at 4.1%, doubling time is 70/4.1% = 17 years. (The unusually high growth rates for Mexico and Kenya are characteristic of underdeveloped countries — countries that are least economically capable of supporting growing populations.) Growth rates, however, rarely stay constant.

6. All things being equal, doubling of food for twice the number of people simply means that twice as many people will be eating, and twice as many will be starving as are starving now!

7. It is very doubtful that world population growth will continue to the point that population density reaches one person for each square meter of land surface. Before that time, by one means or another, world population growth will be reduced to zero. This eventuality is beyond debate. *How* this happens should be the subject of present and very serious debate.

8. Doubling one penny for 30 days yields a total of $10,737,418.23!

9. On the 30th day your wages will be $5,368,709.12, which is one penny more than the $5,368,709.11 total from all the preceding days.

10. The terms "scarce," "abundant," and "superabundant," usually refer to a certain amount of available resource. But the amount of resource diminishes according to the consumption rate. For example, an abundant quantity today that has a high consumption rate, may be quite scarce tomorrow. So the terms above are only meaningful when their consumption rates are also considered.

11. The argument that half of our oil deposits have served us for 120 years, and that the remaining half therefore ought to serve us for another 120 years, fails to take into account the growth in consumption. If consumption grows at a steady rate then the remaining oil is used in one doubling time, not 120 years.

12. When the bacteria in the bottle were at the 1/8 mark, there were 3 minutes left till noon.

13. Like the bacteria in the bottle that discovered a new bottle with as much new space as all they had ever known, their multiplying time was extended only to 12:01. Discovering oil reserves equal to those already consumed only extends the time of consumption by 1 doubling time if consumption rate is unchanged.

14. It doesn't make good sense to talk of abundant reserves and continued growth at the same time because those reserves are cut in half in a single doubling time. The notion of "abundance" is a temporary state if there is a growth in consumption.

15. One can extrapolate the consumption curve, such as that shown in Figure 4, to estimate the lifetime of the reserve. In this way one can obtain a fairly reliable estimate of the time that a resource will last in terms of its consumption rate.

16. It is generally acknowledged that if the human race is to survive, even from an overheating of the world standpoint, while alleviating even part of the misery that afflicts so much of humankind, the present rates of energy consumption and population growth must be reduced. The chances of achieving reduced growth rates are greater in a climate of scarce energy than in a climate of abundant energy. It is hoped that by the time we have fusion under control, that we will have learned to optimize our numbers and to use energy more wisely.